Eureka Math
Grade 6
Module 5

Special thanks go to the Gordon A. Cain Center and to the Department of Mathematics at Louisiana State University for their support in the development of *Eureka Math*.

Published by the non-profit Great Minds

Copyright © 2015 Great Minds. No part of this work may be reproduced, sold, or commercialized, in whole or in part, without written permission from Great Minds. Non-commercial use is licensed pursuant to a Creative Commons Attribution-NonCommercial-ShareAlike 4.0 license; for more information, go to http://greatminds.net/maps/math/copyright. "Great Minds" and "Eureka Math" are registered trademarks of Great Minds.

Printed in the U.S.A.

This book may be purchased from the publisher at eureka-math.org

10 9 8 7 6 5 4 3 2

ISBN 978-1-63255-389-8

Eureka Math: A Story of Ratios **Contributors**

Michael Allwood, Curriculum Writer
Tiah Alphonso, Program Manager—Curriculum Production
Catriona Anderson, Program Manager—Implementation Support
Beau Bailey, Curriculum Writer
Scott Baldridge, Lead Mathematician and Lead Curriculum Writer
Bonnie Bergstresser, Math Auditor
Gail Burrill, Curriculum Writer
Beth Chance, Statistician
Joanne Choi, Curriculum Writer
Jill Diniz, Program Director
Lori Fanning, Curriculum Writer
Ellen Fort, Math Auditor
Kathy Fritz, Curriculum Writer
Glenn Gebhard, Curriculum Writer
Krysta Gibbs, Curriculum Writer
Winnie Gilbert, Lead Writer / Editor, Grade 8
Pam Goodner, Math Auditor
Debby Grawn, Curriculum Writer
Bonnie Hart, Curriculum Writer
Stefanie Hassan, Lead Writer / Editor, Grade 8
Sherri Hernandez, Math Auditor
Bob Hollister, Math Auditor
Patrick Hopfensperger, Curriculum Writer
Sunil Koswatta, Mathematician, Grade 8
Brian Kotz, Curriculum Writer
Henry Kranendonk, Lead Writer / Editor, Statistics
Connie Laughlin, Math Auditor
Jennifer Loftin, Program Manager—Professional Development
Nell McAnelly, Project Director
Ben McCarty, Mathematician
Stacie McClintock, Document Production Manager
Saki Milton, Curriculum Writer
Pia Mohsen, Curriculum Writer
Jerry Moreno, Statistician
Ann Netter, Lead Writer / Editor, Grades 6–7
Sarah Oyler, Document Coordinator
Roxy Peck, Statistician, Lead Writer / Editor, Statistics
Terrie Poehl, Math Auditor
Kristen Riedel, Math Audit Team Lead
Spencer Roby, Math Auditor
Kathleen Scholand, Math Auditor
Erika Silva, Lead Writer / Editor, Grade 6–7
Robyn Sorenson, Math Auditor
Hester Sutton, Advisor / Reviewer Grades 6–7
Shannon Vinson, Lead Writer / Editor, Statistics
Allison Witcraft, Math Auditor

Julie Wortmann, Lead Writer / Editor, Grade 7
David Wright, Mathematician, Lead Writer / Editor, Grades 6–7

This page intentionally left blank

Mathematics Curriculum

6
GRADE

Table of Contents[1]

Area, Surface Area, and Volume Problems

---

[1]Each lesson is ONE day, and ONE day is considered a 45-minute period.

©2015 Great Minds. eureka-math.org
G6-M5-TE-B5-1.3.1-01.2016

Topics C through D (assessment 1 day, return 1 day, remediation or further applications 1 day)

Grade 6 • Module 5

Area, Surface Area, and Volume Problems

OVERVIEW

Starting in Grade 1, students compose and decompose plane and solid figures (**1.G.A.2**). They move to spatial structuring of rectangular arrays in Grade 2 (**2.G.A.2**) and continually build upon their understanding of arrays to ultimately apply their knowledge to two- and three-dimensional figures in Grade 4 (**4.MD.A.3**) and Grade 5 (**5.MD.C.3**, **5.MD.C.5**). Students move from building arrays to using arrays to find area and eventually move to decomposing three-dimensional shapes into layers that are arrays of cubes. In this module, students utilize their previous experiences in shape composition and decomposition in order to understand and develop formulas for area, volume, and surface area.

In Topic A, students use composition and decomposition to determine the area of triangles, quadrilaterals, and other polygons. They determine that area is additive. Students learn through exploration that the area of a triangle is exactly half of the area of its corresponding rectangle. In Lesson 1, students discover through composition that the area of a parallelogram is the same as a rectangle. In Lesson 2, students compose rectangles using two copies of a right triangle. They extend their previous knowledge about the area formula for rectangles (**4.MD.A.3**) to evaluate the area of the rectangle using $A = bh$ and discover through manipulation that the area of a right triangle is exactly half that of its corresponding rectangle. In Lesson 3, students discover that any triangle may be decomposed into right triangles, and in Lesson 4, students further explore all triangles and discover through manipulation that the area of all triangles is exactly half the area of its corresponding rectangle. During this discovery process, students become aware that triangles have a notion of *height*, which is the length of a chosen altitude. The altitude is the perpendicular segment from a vertex of a triangle to the line containing the opposite side. The opposite side is called the base. Students understand that any side of the triangle can be a base, but the altitude always determines the base. They move from recognizing right triangles as categories (**4.G.A.2**) to determining that right triangles are constructed when altitudes are perpendicular and meet the base at one endpoint. Acute triangles are constructed when the altitude is perpendicular and meets within the length of the base, and obtuse triangles are constructed when the altitude is perpendicular and lies outside the length of the base. Students use this information to cut triangular pieces and rearrange them to fit exactly within one half of the corresponding rectangle to determine that the area formula for any triangle can be determined using $A = \frac{1}{2}bh$.

  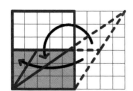

In Lesson 5, students apply their knowledge of the area of a triangular region, where they deconstruct parallelograms, trapezoids, and other quadrilaterals and polygons into triangles or rectangles in order to determine area. They intuitively decompose rectangles to determine the area of polygons. Topic A closes with Lesson 6, where students apply their learning from the topic to find areas of composite figures in real-life contexts, as well as to determine the area of missing regions (**6.G.A.1**).

In Module 3, students used coordinates and absolute value to find distances between points on a coordinate plane (**6.NS.C.8**). In Topic B, students extend this learning to Lessons 7 and 8, where they find edge lengths of polygons (the distance between two vertices using absolute value) and draw polygons given coordinates (**6.G.A.3**). From these drawings, students determine the area of polygons on the coordinate plane by composing and decomposing into polygons with known area formulas. In Lesson 9, students further investigate and calculate the area of polygons on the coordinate plane and also calculate the perimeter. They note that finding perimeter is simply finding the sum of the polygon's edge lengths (or finding the sum of the distances between vertices). Topic B concludes with students determining distance, perimeter, and area on the coordinate plane in real-world contexts.

In Grade 5, students recognized volume as an attribute of solid figures. They measured volume by packing right rectangular prisms with unit cubes and found that determining volume was the same as multiplying the edge lengths of the prism (**5.MD.C.3**, **5.MD.C.4**). Students extend this knowledge to Topic C, where they continue packing right rectangular prisms with unit cubes; however, this time the right rectangular prism has fractional lengths (**6.G.A.2**). In Lesson 11, students decompose a one cubic unit prism in order to conceptualize finding the volume of a right rectangular prism with fractional edge lengths using unit cubes. They connect those findings to apply the formula $V = lwh$ and multiply fractional edge lengths (**5.NF.B.4**). In Lessons 12 and 13, students extend and apply the volume formula to $V =$ the area of the base × height or simply $V = bh$, where b represents the area of the base. In Lesson 12, students explore the bases of right rectangular prisms and find the area of the base first and then multiply by the height. They determine that two formulas can be used to find the volume of a right rectangular prism. In Lesson 13, students apply both formulas to application problems. Topic C concludes with real-life application of the volume formula, where students extend the notion that volume is additive (**5.MD.C.5c**) and find the volume of composite solid figures. They apply volume formulas and use their previous experience with solving equations (**6.EE.B.7**) to find missing volumes and missing dimensions.

Module 5 concludes with deconstructing the faces of solid figures to determine surface area. Students note the difference between finding the volume of right rectangular prisms and finding the surface area of such prisms. In Lesson 15, students build solid figures using nets. They note which nets compose specific solid figures and also understand when nets cannot compose a solid figure. From this knowledge, students deconstruct solid figures into nets to identify the measurement of the solids' face edges. With this knowledge from Lesson 16, students are prepared to use nets to determine the surface area of solid figures in Lesson 17. They find that adding the areas of each face of the solid results in a combined surface area. In Lesson 18, students find that each right rectangular prism has a front, a back, a top, a bottom, and two sides. They determine that surface area is obtained by adding the areas of all the faces. They understand that the front and back of the prism have the same surface area, the top and bottom have the same surface area, and the sides have the same surface area. Thus, students develop the formula $SA = 2lw + 2lh + 2wh$ (**6.G.A.4**). To wrap up the module, students apply the surface area formula to real-life contexts and distinguish between the need to find surface area or volume within contextual situations.

©2015 Great Minds. eureka-math.org
G6-M5-TE-B5-1.3.1-01.2016

Focus Standards

Solve real-world and mathematical problems involving area, surface area, and volume.

6.G.A.1   Find the area of right triangles, other triangles, special quadrilaterals, and polygons by composing into rectangles or decomposing into triangles and other shapes; apply these techniques in the context of solving real-world and mathematical problems.

6.G.A.2   Find the volume of a right rectangular prism with fractional edge lengths by packing it with unit cubes of the appropriate unit fraction edge lengths, and show that the volume is the same as would be found by multiplying the edge lengths of the prism. Apply the formulas $V = lwh$ and $V = bh$ to find volumes of right rectangular prisms with fractional edge lengths in the context of solving real-world and mathematical problems.

6.G.A.3   Draw polygons in the coordinate plane given coordinates for the vertices; use coordinates to find the length of a side joining points with the same first coordinate or the same second coordinate. Apply these techniques in the context of solving real-world and mathematical problems.

6.G.A.4   Represent three-dimensional figures using nets made up of rectangles and triangles, and use the nets to find the surface area of these figures. Apply these techniques in the context of solving real-world and mathematical problems.

Foundational Standards

Reason with shapes and their attributes.

1.G.A.2   Compose two-dimensional shapes (rectangles, squares, trapezoids, triangles, half-circles, and quarter circles) or three-dimensional shapes (cubes, right rectangular prisms, right circular cones, and right circular cylinders) to create a composite shape, and compose new shapes from the composite shape.[2]

2.G.A.2   Partition a rectangle into rows and columns of same-size squares and count to find the total number of them.

3.G.A.2   Partition shapes into parts with equal areas. Express the area of each part as a unit fraction of the whole. *For example, partition a shape into 4 parts with equal area, and describe the area of each part as 1/4 of the area of the shape.*

Solve problems involving measurement and conversion of measurements from a larger unit to a smaller unit.

4.MD.A.3   Apply the area and perimeter formulas for rectangles in real world and mathematical problems. *For example, find the width of a rectangular room given the area of the flooring and the length, by viewing the area formula as a multiplication equation with an unknown factor.*

---

[2]Students do not need to learn formal names such as "right rectangular prism."

Draw and identify lines and angles, and classify shapes by properties of their lines and angles.

4.G.A.2   Classify two-dimensional figures based on the presence or absence of parallel or perpendicular lines, or the presence or absence of angles of a specified size. Recognize right triangles as a category, and identify right triangles.

Apply and extend previous understandings of multiplication and division to multiply and divide fractions.

5.NF.B.4   Apply and extend previous understandings of multiplication to multiply a fraction or whole number by a fraction.

   a.   Interpret the product $(a/b) \times q$ as a parts of a partition of q into b equal parts; equivalently, as the result of a sequence of operations $a \times q \div b$. *For example, use a visual fraction model to show* $(2/3) \times 4 = 8/3$, *and create a story context for this equation. Do the same with* $(2/3) \times (4/5) = 8/15$. *(In general, $(a/b) \times (c/d) = ac/bd$.)*

5.NF.B.7   Apply and extend previous understandings of division to divide unit fractions by whole numbers and whole numbers by unit fractions.[3]

Geometric measurement: understand conceptual concepts of volume and relate volume to multiplication and to addition.

5.MD.C.3   Recognize volume as an attribute of solid figures and understand concepts of volume measurement.

   a.   A cube with side length 1 unit, called a "unit cube," is said to have "one cubic unit" of volume, and can be used to measure volume.

   b.   A solid figure which can be packed without gaps or overlaps using n unit cubes is said to have a volume of n cubic units.

5.MD.C.4   Measure volumes by counting unit cubes, using cubic cm, cubic in, cubic ft, and improvised units.

5.MD.C.5   Relate volume to the operations of multiplication and addition and solve real-world and mathematical problems involving volume.

   a.   Find the volume of a right rectangular prism with whole-number side lengths by packing it with unit cubes, and show that the volume is the same as would be found by multiplying the edge lengths, equivalently by multiplying the height by the area of the base. Represent threefold whole-number products as volumes, e.g., to represent the associative property of multiplication.

---

[3]Students able to multiply fractions in general can develop strategies to divide fractions in general by reasoning about the relationship between multiplication and division. But division of a fraction by a fraction is not a requirement at this grade.

©2015 Great Minds. eureka-math.org
G6-M5-TE-B5-1.3.1-01.2016

b. Apply the formulas $V = l \times w \times h$ and $V = b \times h$ for rectangular prisms to find volumes of right rectangular prisms with whole-number edge lengths in the context of solving real world and mathematical problems.

c. Recognize volume as additive. Find volumes of solid figures composed of two non-overlapping right rectangular prisms by adding the volumes of the non-overlapping parts, applying this technique to solve real world problems.

Graph points on a coordinate plane to solve real-world and mathematical problems.

5.G.A.1   Use a pair of perpendicular number lines, called axes, to define a coordinate system, with the intersection of the lines (the origin) arranged to coincide with the 0 on each line and a given point in the plane located by using an ordered pair of numbers, called its coordinates. Understand that the first number indicates how far to travel from the origin in the direction of one axis, and the second number indicates how far to travel in the direction of the second axis, with the convention that the names of the two axes and the coordinates correspond (e.g., x-axis and x-coordinate, y-axis and y-coordinate).

5.G.A.2   Represent real world and mathematical problems by graphing points in the first quadrant of the coordinate plane, and interpret coordinate values of points in the context of the situation.

Classify two-dimensional figures into categories based on their properties.

5.G.B.3   Understand that attributes belonging to a category of two-dimensional figures also belong to all subcategories of that category. *For example, all rectangles have four right angles and squares are rectangles, so all squares have four right angles.*

Apply and extend previous understandings of numbers to the system of rational numbers.

6.NS.C.8   Solve real-world and mathematical problems by graphing points in all four quadrants of the coordinate plane. Include use of coordinates and absolute value to find distances between points with the same first coordinate or the same second coordinate.

Reason about and solve one-variable equations and inequalities.

6.EE.B.7   Solve real-world and mathematical problems by writing and solving equations of the form $x + p = q$ and $px = q$ for cases in which p, q and x are all nonnegative rational numbers.

Focus Standards for Mathematical Practice

MP.1   **Make sense of problems and persevere in solving them.** Students make sense of real-world problems that involve area, volume, and surface area. One problem involves multiple steps without breaking the problem into smaller, simpler questions. To solve surface area problems, students have to find the area of different parts of the polygon before calculating the total area.

Module 5:   Area, Surface Area, and Volume Problems   7

MP.3   **Construct viable arguments and critique the reasoning of others**. Students develop different arguments as to why area formulas work for different polygons. Through this development, students may discuss and question their peers' thinking processes. When students draw nets to represent right rectangular prisms, their representations may be different from their peers'. Although more than one answer may be correct, students have an opportunity to defend their answers as well as question their peers. Students may also solve real-world problems using different methods; therefore, they may have to explain their thinking and critique their peers.

MP.4   **Model with mathematics.** Models are used to demonstrate why the area formulas for different quadrilaterals are accurate. Students use unit cubes to build right rectangular prisms and use these to calculate volume. The unit cubes are used to model that $V = lwh$ and $V = bh$, where b represents the area of the base, and that both are accurate formulas to calculate the volume of a right rectangular prism. Students will use nets to model the process of calculating the surface area of a right rectangular prism.

MP.6   **Attend to precision.** Students understand and use labels correctly throughout the module. For example, when calculating the area of a triangle, the answer will be labeled $units^2$ because the area is the product of two dimensions. When two different units are given within a problem, students know to use previous knowledge of conversions to make the units match before solving the problem. In multi-step problems, students solve each part of the problem separately and know when to round in order to calculate the most precise answer. Students attend to precision of language when describing exactly how a region may be composed or decomposed to determine its area.

Terminology

New or Recently Introduced Terms

- **Altitude and Base of a Triangle** (An *altitude* of a triangle is a perpendicular segment from a vertex of a triangle to the line containing the opposite side. The opposite side is called the *base*. For every triangle, there are three choices for the altitude, and hence there are three base-altitude pairs. The *height* of a triangle is the length of the altitude. The length of the base is called either the *base length* or, more commonly, the *base*. Usually, context makes it clear whether the *base* refers to a number or a segment. These terms can mislead students: base suggests the bottom, while *height* usually refers to vertical distances. Do not reinforce these impressions by consistently displaying all triangles with horizontal bases.)
- **Cube** (A *cube* is a right rectangular prism all of whose edges are of equal length.)

©2015 Great Minds. eureka-math.org
G6-M5-TE-B5-1.3.1-01.2016

- **Hexagon** (Given 6 different points A, B, C, D, E, F in the plane, a 6-*sided polygon*, or *hexagon,* is the union of 6 segments $\overline{AB}, \overline{BC}, \overline{CD}, \overline{DE}, \overline{EF}, \overline{FA}$ such that (1) the segments intersect only at their endpoints, and (2) no two adjacent segments are collinear.

  For both pentagons and hexagons, the segments are called the *sides*, and their endpoints are called the *vertices*. Like quadrilaterals, pentagons and hexagons can be denoted by the order of vertices defining the segments. For example, the pentagon $ABCDE$ has vertices A, B, C, D, E that define the 5 segments in the definition above. Similar to quadrilaterals, pentagons and hexagons also have *interiors*, which can be described using pictures in elementary school.)

- **Line Perpendicular to a Plane** (A line L in space that intersects a plane E at a point P is said to be *perpendicular to the plane E* if L is perpendicular to every line that (1) lies in E and (2) passes through the point P. A segment is said to be perpendicular to a plane if the line that contains the segment is perpendicular to the plane. In Grade 6, a line perpendicular to a plane can be described using a picture.)

- **Net** (If the surface of a 3-dimensional solid can be cut along sufficiently many edges so that the faces can be placed in one plane to form a connected figure, then the resulting system of faces is called a *net of the solid*.)

- **Parallel Planes** (Two planes in space are *parallel* if they do not intersect.

  In Euclidean geometry, a useful test for checking whether two planes are parallel is if the planes are different and if there is a line that is perpendicular to both planes.)

- **Pentagon** (Given 5 different points A, B, C, D, E in the plane, a 5-*sided polygon,* or *pentagon*, is the union of 5 segments $\overline{AB}, \overline{BC}, \overline{CD}, \overline{DE}, \overline{EA}$ such that (1) the segments intersect only at their endpoints, and (2) no two adjacent segments are collinear.)

- **Right Rectangular Prism** (Let E and E' be two parallel planes. Let B be a rectangular region[4] in the plane E. At each point P of B, consider the segment PP' perpendicular to E, joining P to a point P' of the plane E'. The union of all these segments is called a *right rectangular prism.*

  It can be shown that the region B' in E' corresponding to the region B is also a rectangular region whose sides are equal in length to the corresponding sides of B. The regions B and B' are called the *base faces* (or just *bases*) of the prism. It can also be shown that the planar region between two corresponding sides of the bases is also a rectangular region called the *lateral face* of the prism. In all, the boundary of a right rectangular prism has 6 *faces*: the 2 base faces and 4 lateral faces. All adjacent faces intersect along segments called *edges*—base edges and lateral edges.)

- **Surface of a Prism** (The *surface of a prism* is the union of all of its faces—the base faces and lateral faces.)

- **Triangular Region** (A *triangular region* is the union of the triangle and its interior.)

---

[4]A rectangular region is the union of a rectangle and its interior.

Familiar Terms and Symbols[5]

- Angle
- Area
- Length of a Segment
- Parallel
- Parallelogram
- Perimeter
- Perpendicular
- Quadrilateral
- Rectangle
- Segment
- Square
- Trapezoid
- Triangle
- Volume

Suggested Tools and Representations

- Coordinate Planes
- Nets
- Prisms
- Rulers

Assessment Summary

Assessment Type	Administered	Format	Standards Addressed
Mid-Module Assessment Task	After Topic B	Constructed response with rubric	6.G.A.1, 6.G.A.3
End-of-Module Assessment Task	After Topic D	Constructed response with rubric	6.G.A.1, 6.G.A.2, 6.G.A.3, 6.G.A.4

---

[5]These are terms and symbols students have seen previously.

EUREKA MATH™

Mathematics Curriculum

6
GRADE

Topic A

Area of Triangles, Quadrilaterals, and Polygons

6.G.A.1

Focus Standard:	6.G.A.1	Find the area of right triangles, other triangles, special quadrilaterals, and polygons by composing into rectangles or decomposing into triangles and other shapes; apply these techniques in the context of solving real-world and mathematical problems.
Instructional Days:	6	
	Lesson 1:	The Area of Parallelograms Through Rectangle Facts (S)[1]
	Lesson 2:	The Area of Right Triangles (E)
	Lesson 3:	The Area of Acute Triangles Using Height and Base (M)
	Lesson 4:	The Area of All Triangles Using Height and Base (E)
	Lesson 5:	The Area of Polygons Through Composition and Decomposition (S)
	Lesson 6:	Area in the Real World (E)

In Topic A, students discover the area of triangles, quadrilaterals, and other polygons through composition and decomposition. In Lesson 1, students discover through composition that the area of a parallelogram is the same as the area of a rectangle with the same base and height measurements. Students show the area formula for the region bound by a parallelogram by composing it into rectangles and determining that the area formula for rectangles and parallelograms is $A = bh$. In Lesson 2, students justify the area formula for a right triangle by viewing the right triangle as part of a rectangle composed of two right triangles. They discover that a right triangle is exactly half of a rectangle, thus proving that the area of a triangle is $\frac{1}{2}bh$.

Students further explore the area formula for all triangles in Lessons 3 and 4. They decompose triangles into right triangles and deconstruct triangles to discover that the area of a triangle is exactly one half the area of a parallelogram. Using known area formulas for rectangles, triangles, and parallelograms, students find area

---

[1]Lesson Structure Key: **P**-Problem Set Lesson, **M**-Modeling Cycle Lesson, **E**-Exploration Lesson, **S**-Socratic Lesson

formulas for polygons by decomposing the regions into triangles, rectangles, and parallelograms. Specifically, students use right triangles to develop an understanding of the area of all triangles. They decompose the region of a trapezoid into two triangles and determine the area. The topic closes with Lesson 6, where students determine the area of composite figures in real-life contextual situations using composition and decomposition of polygons. They determine the area of a missing region using composition and decomposition of polygons.

**EUREKA
MATH**

Lesson 1: The Area of Parallelograms Through Rectangle Facts

Student Outcomes

- Students show the area formula for the region bounded by a parallelogram by composing it into rectangles. They understand that the area of a parallelogram is the area of the region bounded by the parallelogram.

Lesson Notes

In order to participate in the discussions, each student needs the parallelogram templates attached to this lesson, along with the following: scissors, glue, ruler, and paper on which to glue their shapes.

Classwork

Fluency Exercise (5 minutes): Multiplication of Fractions

Sprint: Refer to the Sprints and the Sprint Delivery Script sections in the Module 4 Module Overview for directions to administer a Sprint.

Opening Exercise (4 minutes)

Students name the given shapes.

> **Scaffolding:**
> Some students may not know this vocabulary yet, so creating a poster or chart for student desks may help students to remember these terms.

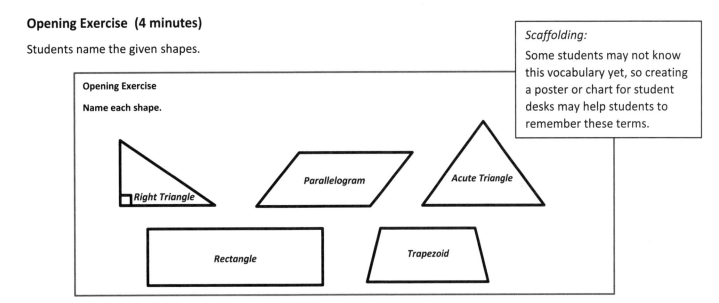

- Identify the shape that is commonly referred to as a parallelogram. How do you know it is a parallelogram?

Note: A rectangle is considered a parallelogram but is commonly called a rectangle because it is a more specific name.

  □ *The shape located in the top middle position is commonly referred to as a parallelogram. The shape is a quadrilateral (4-sided) and has two sets of parallel lines.*

- What are some quadrilaterals that you know?
  - *Answers will vary but could include quadrilaterals such as square, rectangle, parallelogram, rhombus, or trapezoid.*
- Today, we are going to find the area of one of these quadrilaterals: the parallelogram. We are going to use our knowledge of the area of rectangles to help us. Who can remind us what we mean by area?
  - *Answers may vary. One answer might be: The number of square units that make up the inside of the shape.*

Note: English language learners would benefit from a further discussion of area that relates to things to which they have personal connections.

- Talk to your neighbor about how to calculate the area of a rectangle.

Pick someone who can clearly explain how to find the area of a rectangle.

  - *Count the number of square units inside the shape (if that is given), or multiply the base by the height.*

Discussion (10 minutes)

Provide each student with the picture of a parallelogram provided as an attachment to this lesson.

- What shape do you have in front of you?
  - *A parallelogram*
- Work with a partner to make a prediction of how we would calculate the area of the shape.
  - *Answers will vary.*
- Cut out the parallelogram.
- Since we know how to find the area of a rectangle, how can we change the parallelogram into a rectangle?
  - *Cut off a right triangle on one side of the parallelogram, and glue it to the other side.*
- Draw a dotted line, perpendicular to the base, to show the triangle you will cut. Fold your paper along this line.

  -

Check to make sure all students have drawn the dotted line in the correct place before instructing them to cut. Explain that the fold on the line shows that the two right angles form a 180° angle.

- Could the dotted line be drawn in a different location? If so, where?
  - *The dotted line can be drawn in a different location. It could be drawn on the other side of the parallelogram, as shown below.*

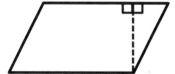

EUREKA MATH

©2015 Great Minds. eureka-math.org
G6-M5-TE-B5-1.3.1-01.2016

MP.7

- The base and height of a parallelogram form a right angle.
- Measure, in inches, the base and height of the parallelogram using the correct mathematical tools.
  - *The base is 7 inches, and the height is 3 inches.*
- Cut along the dotted line.
- Glue both parts of the parallelogram onto a piece of paper to make a rectangle.

- Why is the new shape classified as a rectangle?
  - *The new shape is a rectangle because it is a quadrilateral that has four right angles.*
- Use the correct mathematical tool to measure, in inches, and label each side of the rectangle created from the original parallelogram.

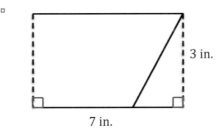

- How do these measurements compare to the base and height of the parallelogram?
  - *They are the same.*
- When we moved the right triangle, did the area inside the shape change? Explain.
  - *The area did not change because both shapes are the same size. The original quadrilateral just looks different.*
- What is the area of the rectangle?
  - *21 square inches or 21 inches squared or 21 in²*

Note: English language learners would benefit from a discussion on why all three of these answers represent the same value.

- If the area of the rectangle is 21 square inches, what is the area of the original parallelogram? Why?
  - *The area of the original parallelogram is also 21 square inches because both shapes have the same amount of space inside.*
- We know the formula for the area of a rectangle is Area = base × height, or $A = bh$. What is the formula to calculate the area of a parallelogram?
  - *The formula to calculate the area of a parallelogram would be the same as the formula used to calculate the area of a rectangle, $A = bh$.*

- Examine the given parallelogram, and label the base and height.

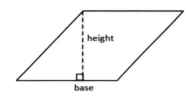

MP.7

- Why is the height the vertical line and not the slanted edge?

Note: English language learners may need a further explanation of the meaning of the slanted edge.

- *If we look back to the rectangle we created, the base and height of both the rectangle and the original parallelogram are perpendicular to each other. Therefore, the height of a parallelogram is the perpendicular line segment drawn from the top base to the bottom base.*

Exercise 1 (5 minutes)

Students work individually to complete the following problems.

Exercises

1. Find the area of each parallelogram below. Note that the figures are not drawn to scale.

a.
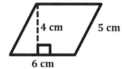

$A = bh$
$\quad = (6\ \text{cm})(4\ \text{cm})$
$\quad = 24\ \text{cm}^2$

Scaffolding:

English language learners may need some clarification about what it means to not be drawn to scale and why this may be the case.

b.

$A = bh$
$\quad = (25\ \text{m})(8\ \text{m})$
$\quad = 200\ \text{m}^2$

c.
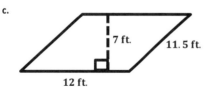

$A = bh$
$\quad = (12\ \text{ft.})(7\ \text{ft.})$
$\quad = 84\ \text{ft}^2$

Discussion (8 minutes)

Give each student a copy of the slanted parallelogram shown on the following page.

- How could we construct a rectangle from this parallelogram?

- *Answers will vary.*

EUREKA
MATH™

- Why can't we use the same method we used previously?
    - *The vertical dotted line does not go through the entire parallelogram.*

Students may struggle drawing the height because they may not be sure whether part of the height can be outside of the parallelogram.

- Cut out the shape.
- To solve this problem, we are actually going to cut the parallelogram horizontally into four equal pieces. Use the appropriate measurement tool to determine where to make the cuts.

Allow time for students to think about how to approach this problem. If time allows, have students share their thoughts before the teacher demonstrates how to move forward.

Demonstrate these cuts before allowing students to make the cuts.

- We have four parallelograms. How can we use them to calculate the area of the original parallelogram?
    - *Turn each of the parallelograms into rectangles.*
- How can we make these parallelograms into rectangles?
    - *Cut a right triangle off of every parallelogram, and move the right triangle to the other side of the parallelogram.*

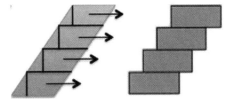

- How can we show that the original parallelogram forms a rectangle?
    - *If we push all the rectangles together, they form one rectangle.*

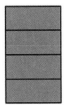

©2015 Great Minds. eureka-math.org
G6-M5-TE-B5-1.3.1-01.2016

- Therefore, it does not matter how tilted a parallelogram is. The formula to calculate the area is always the same as the area formula of a rectangle.
- Draw and label the height of the parallelogram below.

- Connect the two dotted lines as shown below to show that the height can be shown outside of the parallelogram.

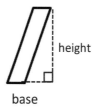

Exercise 2 (5 minutes)

Students complete the exercises individually.

2. Draw and label the height of each parallelogram. Use the correct mathematical tool to measure (in inches) the base and height, and calculate the area of each parallelogram.

a.

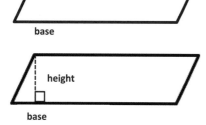

$$A = bh = (0.5 \text{ in.})(2 \text{ in.}) = 1 \text{ in}^2$$

b.

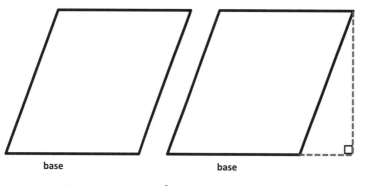

$$A = bh = (1.5 \text{ in.})(2 \text{ in.}) = 3 \text{ in}^2$$

EUREKA
MATH™

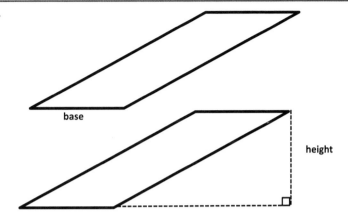

c.

base

height

$$A = bh = (1 \text{ in.})(1 \text{ in.}) = 1 \text{ in}^2$$

3. If the area of a parallelogram is $\frac{35}{42}$ cm^2 and the height is $\frac{1}{7}$ cm, write an equation that relates the height, base, and area of the parallelogram. Solve the equation.

$$\frac{35}{42} = b\left(\frac{1}{7}\right)$$

$$\frac{35}{42} \div \frac{1}{7} = b\left(\frac{1}{7}\right) \div \frac{1}{7}$$

$$\frac{35}{6} = b$$

$$5\frac{5}{6} = b$$

Therefore, the base is $5\frac{5}{6}$ cm.

> **Scaffolding:**
> English language learners may benefit from a sentence starter such as "The formulas are the same because …."

Closing (3 minutes)

- Why are the area formulas for rectangles and parallelograms the same?
  - *The area formulas for rectangles and parallelograms are the same because a parallelogram can be changed to a rectangle. By cutting a right triangle from one side of the parallelogram and connecting it to the other side of the parallelogram, a rectangle is formed.*

Lesson Summary

The formula to calculate the area of a parallelogram is $A = bh$, where b represents the base and h represents the height of the parallelogram.

The height of a parallelogram is the line segment perpendicular to the base. The height is usually drawn from a vertex that is opposite the base.

Exit Ticket (5 minutes)

Name _____   Date _____

Lesson 1: The Area of Parallelograms Through Rectangle Facts

Exit Ticket

Calculate the area of each parallelogram. Note that the figures are not drawn to scale.

1.

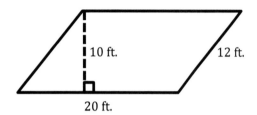

2.

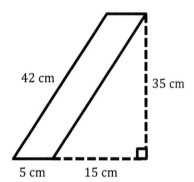

3.

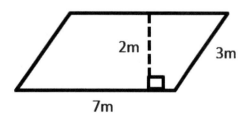

©2015 Great Minds. eureka-math.org
G6-M5-TE-B5-1.3.1-01.2016

EUREKA
MATH

Exit Ticket Sample Solutions

Calculate the area of each parallelogram. Note that the figures are not drawn to scale.

1.

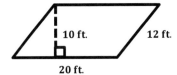

$A = bh = (20 \text{ ft.})(10 \text{ ft.}) = 200 \text{ ft}^2$

2.

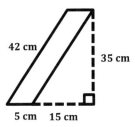

$A = bh = (5 \text{ cm})(35 \text{ cm}) = 175 \text{ cm}^2$

3.

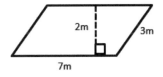

$A = bh = (7 \text{ m})(2 \text{ m}) = 14 \text{ m}^2$

Problem Set Sample Solutions

Draw and label the height of each parallelogram.

1.

2.

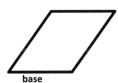

Calculate the area of each parallelogram. The figures are not drawn to scale.

3.

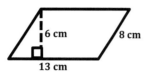

$A = bh$
$$= (13 \text{ cm})(6 \text{ cm})$$
$$= 78 \text{ cm}^2$$

4.

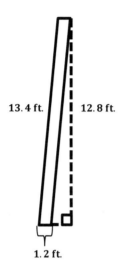

$A = bh$
$$= (1.2 \text{ ft.})(12.8 \text{ ft.})$$
$$= 15.36 \text{ ft}^2$$

5.

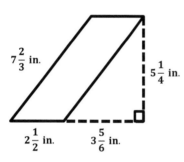

$A = bh$
$$= \left(2\frac{1}{2} \text{ in.}\right)\left(5\frac{1}{4} \text{ in.}\right)$$
$$= \left(\frac{5}{2} \text{ in.}\right)\left(\frac{21}{4} \text{ in.}\right)$$
$$= \frac{105}{8} \text{ in}^2$$
$$= 13\frac{1}{8} \text{ in}^2$$

6.

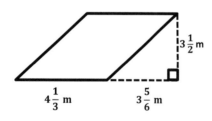

$A = bh$
$$= \left(4\frac{1}{3} \text{ m}\right)\left(3\frac{1}{2} \text{ m}\right)$$
$$= \left(\frac{13}{3} \text{ m}\right)\left(\frac{7}{2} \text{ m}\right)$$
$$= \frac{91}{6} \text{ m}^2$$
$$= 15\frac{1}{6} \text{ m}^2$$

EUREKA
MATH™

7. Brittany and Sid were both asked to draw the height of a parallelogram. Their answers are below.

Brittany   Sid

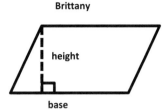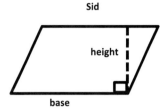

Are both Brittany and Sid correct? If not, who is correct? Explain your answer.

Both Brittany and Sid are correct because both of their heights represent a line segment that is perpendicular to the base and whose endpoint is on the opposite side of the parallelogram.

8. Do the rectangle and parallelogram below have the same area? Explain why or why not.

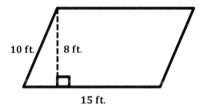

Yes, the rectangle and parallelogram have the same area because if we cut off the right triangle on the left side of the parallelogram, we can move it over to the right side and make the parallelogram into a rectangle. After transforming the parallelogram into a rectangle, both rectangles would have the same dimensions; therefore, their areas would be the same.

9. A parallelogram has an area of 20.3 cm^2 and a base of 2.5 cm. Write an equation that relates the area to the base and height, h. Solve the equation to determine the height of the parallelogram.

$$20.3 = (2.5)(h)$$
$$20.3 \div 2.5 = (2.5)(h) \div 2.5$$
$$8.12 = h$$

Therefore, the height of the parallelogram is 8.12 cm.

Number Correct: _____

Multiplication of Fractions I—Round 1

Directions: Determine the product of the fractions and simplify.

1.	$\frac{1}{2} \times \frac{3}{4}$		16.	$\frac{8}{9} \times \frac{3}{4}$	
2.	$\frac{5}{6} \times \frac{5}{7}$		17.	$\frac{3}{4} \times \frac{4}{7}$	
3.	$\frac{3}{4} \times \frac{7}{8}$		18.	$\frac{1}{4} \times \frac{8}{9}$	
4.	$\frac{4}{5} \times \frac{8}{9}$		19.	$\frac{3}{5} \times \frac{10}{11}$	
5.	$\frac{1}{4} \times \frac{3}{7}$		20.	$\frac{8}{13} \times \frac{7}{24}$	
6.	$\frac{5}{7} \times \frac{4}{9}$		21.	$2\frac{1}{2} \times 3\frac{3}{4}$	
7.	$\frac{3}{5} \times \frac{1}{8}$		22.	$1\frac{4}{5} \times 6\frac{1}{3}$	
8.	$\frac{2}{9} \times \frac{7}{9}$		23.	$8\frac{2}{7} \times 4\frac{5}{6}$	
9.	$\frac{1}{3} \times \frac{2}{5}$		24.	$5\frac{2}{5} \times 2\frac{1}{8}$	
10.	$\frac{3}{7} \times \frac{5}{8}$		25.	$4\frac{6}{7} \times 1\frac{1}{4}$	
11.	$\frac{2}{3} \times \frac{9}{10}$		26.	$2\frac{2}{3} \times 4\frac{2}{5}$	
12.	$\frac{3}{5} \times \frac{1}{6}$		27.	$6\frac{9}{10} \times 7\frac{1}{3}$	
13.	$\frac{2}{7} \times \frac{3}{4}$		28.	$1\frac{3}{8} \times 4\frac{2}{5}$	
14.	$\frac{5}{8} \times \frac{3}{10}$		29.	$3\frac{5}{6} \times 2\frac{4}{15}$	
15.	$\frac{4}{5} \times \frac{7}{8}$		30.	$4\frac{1}{3} \times 5$	

EUREKA MATH

Multiplication of Fractions I—Round 1 [KEY]

Directions: Determine the product of the fractions and simplify.

1.	$\dfrac{1}{2} \times \dfrac{3}{4}$	$\dfrac{3}{8}$	16.	$\dfrac{8}{9} \times \dfrac{3}{4}$	$\dfrac{24}{36} = \dfrac{2}{3}$
2.	$\dfrac{5}{6} \times \dfrac{5}{7}$	$\dfrac{25}{42}$	17.	$\dfrac{3}{4} \times \dfrac{4}{7}$	$\dfrac{12}{28} = \dfrac{3}{7}$
3.	$\dfrac{3}{4} \times \dfrac{7}{8}$	$\dfrac{21}{32}$	18.	$\dfrac{1}{4} \times \dfrac{8}{9}$	$\dfrac{8}{36} = \dfrac{2}{9}$
4.	$\dfrac{4}{5} \times \dfrac{8}{9}$	$\dfrac{32}{45}$	19.	$\dfrac{3}{5} \times \dfrac{10}{11}$	$\dfrac{30}{55} = \dfrac{6}{11}$
5.	$\dfrac{1}{4} \times \dfrac{3}{7}$	$\dfrac{3}{28}$	20.	$\dfrac{8}{13} \times \dfrac{7}{24}$	$\dfrac{56}{312} = \dfrac{7}{39}$
6.	$\dfrac{5}{7} \times \dfrac{4}{9}$	$\dfrac{20}{63}$	21.	$2\dfrac{1}{2} \times 3\dfrac{3}{4}$	$\dfrac{75}{8} = 9\dfrac{3}{8}$
7.	$\dfrac{3}{5} \times \dfrac{1}{8}$	$\dfrac{3}{40}$	22.	$1\dfrac{4}{5} \times 6\dfrac{1}{3}$	$\dfrac{171}{15} = 11\dfrac{2}{5}$
8.	$\dfrac{2}{9} \times \dfrac{7}{9}$	$\dfrac{14}{81}$	23.	$8\dfrac{2}{7} \times 4\dfrac{5}{6}$	$\dfrac{1,682}{42} = 40\dfrac{1}{21}$
9.	$\dfrac{1}{3} \times \dfrac{2}{5}$	$\dfrac{2}{15}$	24.	$5\dfrac{2}{5} \times 2\dfrac{1}{8}$	$\dfrac{459}{40} = 11\dfrac{19}{40}$
10.	$\dfrac{3}{7} \times \dfrac{5}{8}$	$\dfrac{15}{56}$	25.	$4\dfrac{6}{7} \times 1\dfrac{1}{4}$	$\dfrac{170}{28} = 6\dfrac{1}{14}$
11.	$\dfrac{2}{3} \times \dfrac{9}{10}$	$\dfrac{18}{30} = \dfrac{3}{5}$	26.	$2\dfrac{2}{3} \times 4\dfrac{2}{5}$	$\dfrac{176}{15} = 11\dfrac{11}{15}$
12.	$\dfrac{3}{5} \times \dfrac{1}{6}$	$\dfrac{3}{30} = \dfrac{1}{10}$	27.	$6\dfrac{9}{10} \times 7\dfrac{1}{3}$	$\dfrac{1,518}{30} = 50\dfrac{3}{5}$
13.	$\dfrac{2}{7} \times \dfrac{3}{4}$	$\dfrac{6}{28} = \dfrac{3}{14}$	28.	$1\dfrac{3}{8} \times 4\dfrac{2}{5}$	$\dfrac{242}{40} = 6\dfrac{1}{20}$
14.	$\dfrac{5}{8} \times \dfrac{3}{10}$	$\dfrac{15}{80} = \dfrac{3}{16}$	29.	$3\dfrac{5}{6} \times 2\dfrac{4}{15}$	$\dfrac{782}{90} = 8\dfrac{31}{45}$
15.	$\dfrac{4}{5} \times \dfrac{7}{8}$	$\dfrac{28}{40} = \dfrac{7}{10}$	30.	$4\dfrac{1}{3} \times 5$	$\dfrac{65}{3} = 21\dfrac{2}{3}$

Multiplication of Fractions I—Round 2

Number Correct: _____

Improvement: _____

Directions: Determine the product of the fractions and simplify.

1.	$\dfrac{5}{6} \times \dfrac{1}{4}$		16.	$\dfrac{3}{7} \times \dfrac{2}{9}$	
2.	$\dfrac{2}{3} \times \dfrac{5}{7}$		17.	$\dfrac{4}{5} \times \dfrac{10}{13}$	
3.	$\dfrac{1}{3} \times \dfrac{2}{5}$		18.	$\dfrac{2}{9} \times \dfrac{3}{8}$	
4.	$\dfrac{5}{7} \times \dfrac{5}{8}$		19.	$\dfrac{1}{8} \times \dfrac{4}{5}$	
5.	$\dfrac{3}{8} \times \dfrac{7}{9}$		20.	$\dfrac{3}{7} \times \dfrac{2}{15}$	
6.	$\dfrac{3}{4} \times \dfrac{5}{6}$		21.	$1\dfrac{1}{2} \times 4\dfrac{3}{4}$	
7.	$\dfrac{2}{7} \times \dfrac{3}{8}$		22.	$2\dfrac{5}{6} \times 3\dfrac{3}{8}$	
8.	$\dfrac{1}{4} \times \dfrac{3}{4}$		23.	$1\dfrac{7}{8} \times 5\dfrac{1}{5}$	
9.	$\dfrac{5}{8} \times \dfrac{3}{10}$		24.	$6\dfrac{2}{3} \times 2\dfrac{3}{8}$	
10.	$\dfrac{6}{11} \times \dfrac{1}{2}$		25.	$7\dfrac{1}{2} \times 3\dfrac{6}{7}$	
11.	$\dfrac{6}{7} \times \dfrac{5}{8}$		26.	$3 \times 4\dfrac{1}{3}$	
12.	$\dfrac{1}{6} \times \dfrac{9}{10}$		27.	$2\dfrac{3}{5} \times 5\dfrac{1}{6}$	
13.	$\dfrac{3}{4} \times \dfrac{8}{9}$		28.	$4\dfrac{2}{5} \times 7$	
14.	$\dfrac{5}{6} \times \dfrac{2}{3}$		29.	$1\dfrac{4}{7} \times 2\dfrac{1}{2}$	
15.	$\dfrac{1}{4} \times \dfrac{8}{11}$		30.	$3\dfrac{5}{6} \times \dfrac{3}{10}$	

EUREKA MATH

©2015 Great Minds. eureka-math.org
G6-M5-TE-B5-1.3.1-01.2016

Multiplication of Fractions I—Round 2 [KEY]

Directions: Determine the product of the fractions and simplify.

1.	$\frac{5}{6} \times \frac{1}{4}$	$\frac{5}{24}$	16.	$\frac{3}{7} \times \frac{2}{9}$	$\frac{6}{63} = \frac{2}{21}$
2.	$\frac{2}{3} \times \frac{5}{7}$	$\frac{10}{21}$	17.	$\frac{4}{5} \times \frac{10}{13}$	$\frac{40}{65} = \frac{8}{13}$
3.	$\frac{1}{3} \times \frac{2}{5}$	$\frac{2}{15}$	18.	$\frac{2}{9} \times \frac{3}{8}$	$\frac{6}{72} = \frac{1}{12}$
4.	$\frac{5}{7} \times \frac{5}{8}$	$\frac{25}{56}$	19.	$\frac{1}{8} \times \frac{4}{5}$	$\frac{4}{40} = \frac{1}{10}$
5.	$\frac{3}{8} \times \frac{7}{9}$	$\frac{21}{72} = \frac{7}{24}$	20.	$\frac{3}{7} \times \frac{2}{15}$	$\frac{6}{105} = \frac{2}{35}$
6.	$\frac{3}{4} \times \frac{5}{6}$	$\frac{15}{24} = \frac{5}{8}$	21.	$1\frac{1}{2} \times 4\frac{3}{4}$	$\frac{57}{8} = 7\frac{1}{8}$
7.	$\frac{2}{7} \times \frac{3}{8}$	$\frac{6}{56} = \frac{3}{28}$	22.	$2\frac{5}{6} \times 3\frac{3}{8}$	$\frac{459}{48} = 9\frac{9}{16}$
8.	$\frac{1}{4} \times \frac{3}{4}$	$\frac{3}{16}$	23.	$1\frac{7}{8} \times 5\frac{1}{5}$	$\frac{390}{40} = 9\frac{3}{4}$
9.	$\frac{5}{8} \times \frac{3}{10}$	$\frac{15}{80} = \frac{3}{16}$	24.	$6\frac{2}{3} \times 2\frac{3}{8}$	$\frac{380}{24} = 15\frac{5}{6}$
10.	$\frac{6}{11} \times \frac{1}{2}$	$\frac{6}{22} = \frac{3}{11}$	25.	$7\frac{1}{2} \times 3\frac{6}{7}$	$\frac{405}{14} = 28\frac{13}{14}$
11.	$\frac{6}{7} \times \frac{5}{8}$	$\frac{30}{56} = \frac{15}{28}$	26.	$3 \times 4\frac{1}{3}$	$\frac{39}{3} = 13$
12.	$\frac{1}{6} \times \frac{9}{10}$	$\frac{9}{60} = \frac{3}{20}$	27.	$2\frac{3}{5} \times 5\frac{1}{6}$	$\frac{403}{30} = 13\frac{13}{30}$
13.	$\frac{3}{4} \times \frac{8}{9}$	$\frac{24}{36} = \frac{2}{3}$	28.	$4\frac{2}{5} \times 7$	$\frac{154}{5} = 30\frac{4}{5}$
14.	$\frac{5}{6} \times \frac{2}{3}$	$\frac{10}{18} = \frac{5}{9}$	29.	$1\frac{4}{7} \times 2\frac{1}{2}$	$\frac{55}{14} = 3\frac{13}{14}$
15.	$\frac{1}{4} \times \frac{8}{11}$	$\frac{8}{44} = \frac{2}{11}$	30.	$3\frac{5}{6} \times \frac{3}{10}$	$\frac{69}{60} = 1\frac{3}{20}$

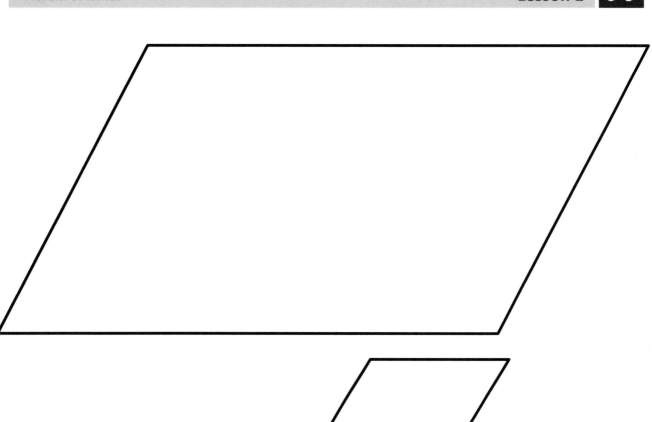

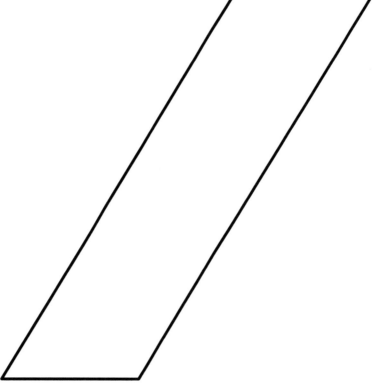

EUREKA
MATH

©2015 Great Minds. eureka-math.org
G6-M5-TE-B5-1.3.1-01.2016

Lesson 2: The Area of Right Triangles

Student Outcomes

- Students justify the area formula for a right triangle by viewing the right triangle as part of a rectangle composed of two right triangles.

Lesson Notes

For students to complete the Exploratory Challenge, they need the attached templates to this lesson, as well as scissors, a ruler, and glue. Students may need more than one copy of each triangle.

Students use the attached template to develop the formula necessary to calculate the area of a right triangle. The templates also allow students to visualize why the area of a right triangle is exactly half of the area of a rectangle with the same dimensions. They calculate the area of two different right triangles to see that the formula works for more than just the first triangle given. Once students develop the formula, they can use substitution and the given dimensions to calculate the area.

Classwork

Discussion (1 minute)

- What are some properties of a right triangle?
  - *Three-sided polygon*
  - *One interior angle must measure exactly* 90°.

Exploratory Challenge (14 minutes)

Students work in groups of 2 or 3 to discover the formula that can be used to calculate the area of a right triangle. Each group will need the templates attached to this lesson, glue, a ruler, and scissors.

MP.1

Exploratory Challenge

a. **Use the shapes labeled with an X to predict the formula needed to calculate the area of a right triangle. Explain your prediction.**

Formula for the area of right triangles:

$A = \frac{1}{2} \times \text{base} \times \text{height} \ or \ A = \frac{\text{base} \times \text{height}}{2}$

Area of the given triangle:

$A = \frac{1}{2} \times 3 \text{ in.} \times 2 \text{ in.} = 3 \text{ in}^2$

Scaffolding:

It students are struggling, use some guiding questions:

- What do you know about the area of a rectangle?
- How are the area of a triangle and rectangle related?
- Can you fit the triangle inside the rectangle?

MP.1

> b.   Use the shapes labeled with a Y to determine if the formula you discovered in part (a) is correct.
>
>   Does your area formula for triangle Y match the formula you got for triangle X?
>
>   *Answers will vary; however, the area formulas should be the same if students discovered the correct area formula.*
>
>   If so, do you believe you have the correct formula needed to calculate the area of a right triangle? Why or why not?
>
>   *Answers will vary.*
>
>   If not, which formula do you think is correct? Why?
>
>   *Answers will vary.*
>
>   Area of the given triangle:
>
> $A = \frac{1}{2} \times 3 \text{ in.} \times 3 \text{ in.} = 4.5 \text{ in}^2$

Discussion (5 minutes)

- What is the area formula for right triangles?
  - *The area formula of a right triangle is $A = \frac{1}{2}bh$, or $A = \frac{bh}{2}$.*
- How do we know this formula is correct?
  - *Each right triangle represents half of a rectangle. The area formula of a rectangle is $A = bh$, but since a right triangle only covers half the area of a rectangle, we take the area of the rectangle and multiply it by half, or divide by 2.*
- How can we determine which side of a right triangle is the base and which side is the height?
  - *Similar to a parallelogram, the base and the height of a right triangle are perpendicular to each other, so they form the right angle of the triangle. However, it does not matter which of these two sides is labeled the base and which is labeled the height. The commutative property of multiplication allows us to calculate the formula in any order.*

Exercises (15 minutes)

Students complete each exercise independently. Students may use a calculator.

> **Exercises**
>
> Calculate the area of each right triangle below. Each figure is not drawn to scale.
>
> 1.
>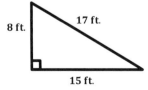
> 8 ft.   17 ft.   15 ft.
>
> $A = \frac{1}{2}bh$
>
> $= \frac{1}{2}(8 \text{ ft.})(15 \text{ ft.})$
>
> $= 60 \text{ ft}^2$

©2015 Great Minds. eureka-math.org
G6-M5-TE-B5-1.3.1-01.2016

2.

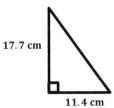

17.7 cm

11.4 cm

$A = \frac{1}{2}bh$

$= \frac{1}{2}(11.4 \text{ cm})(17.7 \text{ cm})$

$= 100.89 \text{ cm}^2$

3.

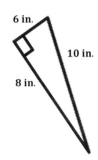

6 in.

10 in.

8 in.

$A = \frac{1}{2}bh$

$= \frac{1}{2}(6 \text{ in.})(8 \text{ in.})$

$= 24 \text{ in}^2$

4.

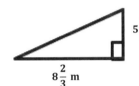

$5\frac{3}{5}$ m

$8\frac{2}{3}$ m

$A = \frac{1}{2}bh$

$= \frac{1}{2}\left(8\frac{2}{3} \text{ m}\right)\left(5\frac{3}{5} \text{ m}\right)$

$= \frac{1}{2}\left(\frac{26}{3} \text{ m}\right)\left(\frac{28}{5} \text{ m}\right)$

$= \frac{728}{30} \text{ m}^2$

$= 24\frac{8}{30} \text{ m}^2 \text{ or } 24\frac{4}{15} \text{ m}^2$

5.

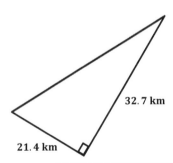

32.7 km

21.4 km

$A = \frac{1}{2}bh$

$= \frac{1}{2}(32.7 \text{ km})(21.4 \text{ km})$

$= 349.89 \text{ km}^2$

©2015 Great Minds. eureka-math.org
G6-M5-TE-B5-1.3.1-01.2016

6. Mr. Jones told his students they each need half of a piece of paper. Calvin cut his piece of paper horizontally, and Matthew cut his piece of paper diagonally. Which student has the larger area on his half piece of paper? Explain.

Calvin's Paper      Matthew's Paper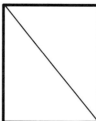

After cutting the paper, both Calvin and Matthew have the same area. Calvin cut his into two rectangles that are each half the area of the original piece of paper. Matthew cut his paper into two equivalent right triangles that are also half the area of the original piece of paper.

7. Ben requested that the rectangular stage be split into two equal sections for the upcoming school play. The only instruction he gave was that he needed the area of each section to be half of the original size. If Ben wants the stage to be split into two right triangles, did he provide enough information? Why or why not?

Ben did not provide enough information because the stage may be split horizontally or vertically through the middle of the rectangle. This would result in two equal pieces, but they would not be right triangles.

8. If the area of a right triangle is 6.22 sq. in. and its base is 3.11 in., write an equation that relates the area to the height, h, and the base. Solve the equation to determine the height.

$$6.22 = \frac{1}{2}(3.11)h$$
$$6.22 = (1.555)h$$
$$6.22 \div 1.555 = (1.555)h \div 1.555$$
$$4 = h$$

Therefore, the height of the right triangle is 4 in.

Closing (5 minutes)

- How are the area formulas of rectangles and right triangles related?

  - *When the two sides that form the right angle are the same length in both a rectangle and a right triangle, the area of the right triangle is exactly half of the area of the rectangle. Therefore, the area formula of the rectangle divided by 2 (or multiplied by a half) is equal to the area formula of the right triangle.*

Exit Ticket (5 minutes)

EUREKA
MATH™

©2015 Great Minds. eureka-math.org
G6-M5-TE-B5-1.3.1-01.2016

Name _____   Date _____

Lesson 2: The Area of Right Triangles

Exit Ticket

1. Calculate the area of the right triangle. Each figure is not drawn to scale.

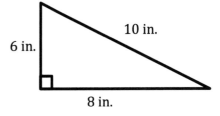

2. Dan and Joe are responsible for cutting the grass on the local high school soccer field. Joe cuts a diagonal line through the field, as shown in the diagram below, and says that each person is responsible for cutting the grass on one side of the line. Dan says that this is not fair because he will have to cut more grass than Joe. Is Dan correct? Why or why not?

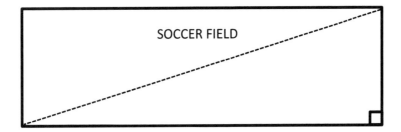

©2015 Great Minds. eureka-math.org
G6-M5-TE-B5-1.3.1-01.2016

Exit Ticket Sample Solutions

1. Calculate the area of the right triangle. Each figure is not drawn to scale.

$$A = \frac{1}{2}\,bh = \frac{1}{2}(8 \text{ in.})(6 \text{ in.}) = 24 \text{ in}^2$$

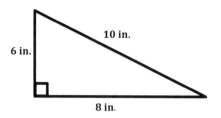

6 in.

10 in.

8 in.

2. Dan and Joe are responsible for cutting the grass on the local high school soccer field. Joe cuts a diagonal line through the field, as shown in the diagram below, and says that each person is responsible for cutting the grass on one side of the line. Dan says that this is not fair because he will have to cut more grass than Joe. Is Dan correct? Why or why not?

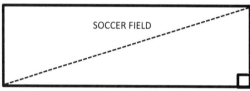

SOCCER FIELD

Dan is not correct. The diagonal line Joe cut in the grass would split the field into two right triangles. The area of each triangle is exactly half the area of the entire field because the area formula for a right triangle is
$$A = \frac{1}{2} \times \textbf{base} \times \textbf{height}.$$

Problem Set Sample Solutions

Calculate the area of each right triangle below. Note that the figures are not drawn to scale.

1.

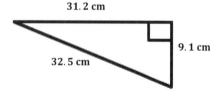

31. 2 cm

9. 1 cm

32. 5 cm

$$A = \frac{1}{2}\,bh = \frac{1}{2}(31.2 \text{ cm})(9.1 \text{ cm}) = 141.96 \text{ cm}^2$$

2.

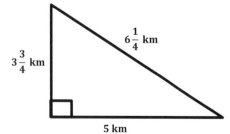

$6\frac{1}{4}$ km

$3\frac{3}{4}$ km

5 km

$$A = \frac{1}{2}\,bh = \frac{1}{2}(5 \text{ km})\left(3\frac{3}{4} \text{ km}\right) = \frac{1}{2}\left(\frac{5}{1} \text{ km}\right)\left(\frac{15}{4} \text{ km}\right) = \frac{75}{8} \text{ km}^2 = 9\frac{3}{8} \text{ km}^2$$

EUREKA
MATH™

©2015 Great Minds. eureka-math.org
G6-M5-TE-B5-1.3.1-01.2016

3.

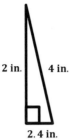

3.2 in.   4 in.

2.4 in.

$$A = \frac{1}{2}bh = \frac{1}{2}(2.4 \text{ in.})(3.2 \text{ in.}) = 3.84 \text{ in}^2$$

4.

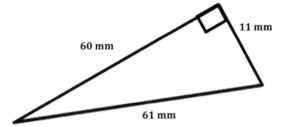

11 mm

60 mm

61 mm

$$A = \frac{1}{2}bh = \frac{1}{2}(11 \text{ mm})(60 \text{ mm}) = 330 \text{ mm}^2$$

5.

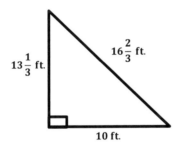

$16\frac{2}{3}$ ft.

$13\frac{1}{3}$ ft.

10 ft.

$$A = \frac{1}{2}bh = \frac{1}{2}\left(13\frac{1}{3} \text{ ft.}\right)(10 \text{ ft.}) = \frac{1}{2}\left(\frac{40}{3} \text{ ft.}\right)\left(\frac{10}{1} \text{ ft.}\right) = \frac{400}{6} \text{ ft}^2 = 66\frac{2}{3} \text{ ft}^2$$

6. Elania has two congruent rugs at her house. She cut one vertically down the middle, and she cut diagonally through the other one.

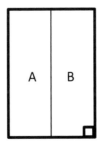

A   B

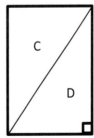

C

D

After making the cuts, which rug (labeled A, B, C, or D) has the larger area? Explain.

All of the rugs are the same size after making the cuts. The vertical line goes down the center of the rectangle, making two congruent parts. The diagonal line also splits the rectangle into two congruent parts because the area of a right triangle is exactly half the area of the rectangle.

7. Give the dimensions of a right triangle and a parallelogram with the same area. Explain how you know.

    Answers will vary.

8. If the area of a right triangle is $\frac{9}{16}$ sq. ft. and the height is $\frac{3}{4}$ ft., write an equation that relates the area to the base, *b,* and the height. Solve the equation to determine the base.

$$\frac{9}{16} = \frac{1}{2} b \left(\frac{3}{4} \right)$$

$$\frac{9}{16} = \left(\frac{3}{8} \right) b$$

$$\frac{9}{16} \div \frac{3}{8} = \left(\frac{3}{8} \right) b \div \frac{3}{8}$$

$$\frac{3}{2} = b$$

$$1\frac{1}{2} = b$$

Therefore, the base of the right triangle is $1\frac{1}{2}$ ft.

©2015 Great Minds. eureka-math.org
G6-M5-TE-B5-1.3.1-01.2016

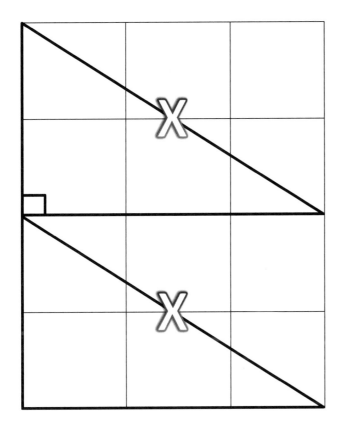

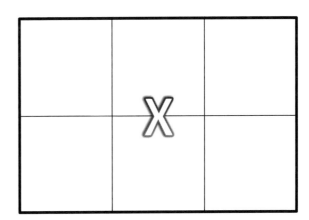

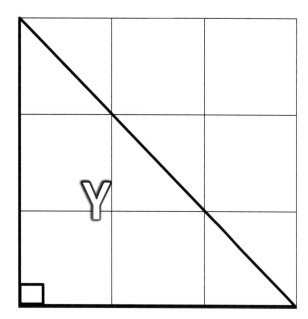

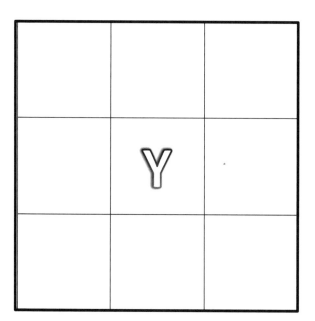

EUREKA
MATH™

Lesson 3: The Area of Acute Triangles Using Height and Base

Student Outcomes

- Students show the area formula for a triangular region by decomposing a triangle into right triangles. For a given triangle, the height of the triangle is the length of the altitude. The length of the base is called either the length base or, more commonly, the base.
- Students understand that the height of the triangle is the perpendicular segment from a vertex of a triangle to the line containing the opposite side. The opposite side is called the base. Students understand that any side of a triangle can be considered a base and that the choice of base determines the height.

Lesson Notes

For this lesson, students need the triangle template attached to this lesson and a ruler.

Throughout the lesson, students determine if the area formula for right triangles is the same as the formula used to calculate the area of acute triangles.

Classwork

Fluency Exercise (5 minutes): Multiplication of Decimals

Sprint: Refer to the Sprints and the Sprint Delivery Script sections of the Module 4 Module Overview for directions to administer a Sprint.

Discussion (5 minutes)

- What is different between the two triangles below?

  - *One triangle is a right triangle because it has one right angle; the other does not have a right angle, so it is not a right triangle.*
- How do we find the area of the right triangle?
  - $A = \frac{1}{2} \times \text{base} \times \text{height}$

- How do we know which side of the right triangle is the base and which is the height?
    - *If we choose one of the two shorter sides to be the base, then the side that is perpendicular to this side is the height.*
- How do we calculate the area of the other triangle?
    - *We do not know how to calculate the area of the other triangle because we do not know its height.*

Mathematical Modeling Exercise (10 minutes)

Students need the triangle template found at the end of the lesson and a ruler to complete this example. To save class time, cut out the triangles ahead of time.

- The height of a triangle does not always have to be a side of the triangle. The height of a triangle is also called the altitude, which is a line segment from a vertex of the triangle and perpendicular to the opposite side.

Note: English language learners may benefit from a poster showing each part of a right triangle and acute triangle (and eventually an obtuse triangle) labeled, so they can see the height (or altitude) and develop a better understanding of the new vocabulary words.

Model how to draw the altitude of the given triangle.

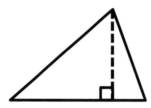

- Fold the paper to show where the altitude would be located, and then draw the altitude, or the height, of the triangle.

MP.3
- Notice that by drawing the altitude we have created two right triangles. Using the knowledge we gained yesterday, can we calculate the area of the entire triangle?
    - *We can calculate the area of the entire triangle by calculating the area of the two right triangles and then adding these areas together.*

- Measure and label each base and height. Round your measurements to the nearest half inch.
    -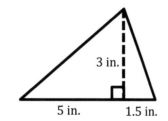

> Scaffolding:
> Outline or shade each right triangle with a different color to help students see the two different triangles.

- Calculate the area of each right triangle.
    - $A = \frac{1}{2}bh = \frac{1}{2}(5 \text{ in.})(3 \text{ in.}) = 7.5 \text{ in}^2$
    - $A = \frac{1}{2}bh = \frac{1}{2}(1.5 \text{ in.})(3 \text{ in.}) = 2.25 \text{ in}^2$
- Now that we know the area of each right triangle, how can we calculate the area of the entire triangle?
    - *To calculate the area of the entire triangle, we can add the two areas together.*

©2015 Great Minds. eureka-math.org
G6-M5-TE-B5-1.3.1-01.2016

- Calculate the area of the entire triangle.
  - $A = 7.5 \text{ in}^2 + 2.25 \text{ in}^2 = 9.75 \text{ in}^2$
- Talk to your neighbor, and try to determine a more efficient way to calculate the area of the entire triangle.

Allow students some time to discuss their thoughts.

  - *Answers will vary. Allow a few students to share their thoughts.*

Test a few of the students' predictions on how to find the area of the entire triangle. The last prediction you should try is the correct one shown below.

- In the previous lesson, we said that the area of right triangles can be calculated using the formula $A = \frac{1}{2} \times$ base $\times$ height. Some of you believe we can still use this same formula for the given triangle.
- Draw a rectangle around the given triangle.
  -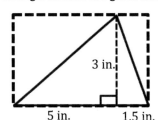

- Does the triangle represent half of the area of the rectangle? Why or why not?
  - *The triangle does represent half of the area of the rectangle. If the altitude of the triangle splits the rectangle into two separate rectangles, then the slanted sides of the triangle split these rectangles into two equal parts.*
- What is the length of the base?
  - *The length of the base is 6.5 inches because we have to add the two parts together.*
- What is the length of the altitude (the height)?
  - *The height is 3 inches because that is the length of the line segment that is perpendicular to the base.*
- Calculate the area of the triangle using the formula we discovered yesterday, $A = \frac{1}{2} \times$ base $\times$ height.
  - $A = \frac{1}{2}bh = \frac{1}{2}(6.5 \text{ in.})(3 \text{ in.}) = 9.75 \text{ in}^2$
- Is this the same area we got when we split the triangle into two right triangles?
  - *Yes*
- It is important to determine if this is true for more than just this one example.

Exercises (15 minutes)

Students work with partners on the exercises below. The purpose of the first exercise is to determine if the area formula, $A = \frac{1}{2}bh$, is always correct. One partner calculates the area of the given triangle by calculating the area of two right triangles, and the other partner calculates the area just as one triangle. Partners should switch who finds each area in order to provide every student with a chance to practice both methods. Students may use a calculator as long as they record their work on their paper as well.

Exercises

1. Work with a partner on the exercises below. Determine if the area formula $A = \frac{1}{2}bh$ is always correct. You may use a calculator, but be sure to record your work on your paper as well. Figures are not drawn to scale.

	Area of Two Right Triangles	Area of Entire Triangle
	$A = \frac{1}{2}(9 \text{ cm})(12 \text{ cm})$ $A = 54 \text{ cm}^2$ $A = \frac{1}{2}(12.6 \text{ cm})(12 \text{ cm})$ $A = 75.6 \text{ cm}^2$ $A = 54 \text{ cm}^2 + 75.6 \text{ cm}^2 = 129.6 \text{ cm}^2$	base $= 9 \text{ cm} + 12.6 \text{ cm} = 21.6 \text{ cm}$ $A = \frac{1}{2}(21.6 \text{ cm})(12 \text{ cm})$ $A = 129.6 \text{ cm}^2$
	$A = \frac{1}{2}(3.9 \text{ ft.})(5.2 \text{ ft.})$ $A = 10.14 \text{ ft}^2$ $A = \frac{1}{2}(8 \text{ ft.})(5.2 \text{ ft.})$ $A = 20.8 \text{ ft}^2$ $A = 10.14 \text{ ft}^2 + 20.8 \text{ ft}^2 = 30.94 \text{ ft}^2$	base $= 8 \text{ ft.} + 3.9 \text{ ft.} = 11.9 \text{ ft.}$ $A = \frac{1}{2}(11.9 \text{ ft.})(5.2 \text{ ft.})$ $A = 30.94 \text{ ft}^2$
	$A = \frac{1}{2}(2 \text{ in.})\left(2\frac{5}{6} \text{ in.}\right)$ $A = \frac{1}{2}\left(\frac{2}{1} \text{ in.}\right)\left(\frac{17}{6} \text{ in.}\right)$ $A = \frac{34}{12} = 2\frac{5}{6} \text{ in}^2$ $A = \frac{1}{2}\left(\frac{5}{6} \text{ in.}\right)\left(2\frac{5}{6} \text{ in.}\right)$ $A = \frac{1}{2}\left(\frac{5}{6} \text{ in.}\right)\left(\frac{17}{6} \text{ in.}\right)$ $A = \frac{85}{72} \text{ in}^2 = 1\frac{13}{72} \text{ in}^2$ $A = 2\frac{5}{6} \text{ in}^2 + 1\frac{13}{72} \text{ in}^2$ $A = 2\frac{60}{72} \text{ in}^2 + 1\frac{13}{72} \text{ in}^2$ $A = 4\frac{1}{72} \text{ in}^2$	base $= 2 \text{ in.} + \frac{5}{6} \text{ in.} = 2\frac{5}{6} \text{ in.}$ $A = \frac{1}{2}\left(2\frac{5}{6} \text{ in.}\right)\left(2\frac{5}{6} \text{ in.}\right)$ $A = \frac{1}{2}\left(\frac{17}{6} \text{ in.}\right)\left(\frac{17}{6} \text{ in.}\right)$ $A = \frac{289}{72} \text{ in}^2 = 4\frac{1}{72} \text{ in}^2$
	$A = \frac{1}{2}(34 \text{ m})(32 \text{ m})$ $A = 544 \text{ m}^2$ $A = \frac{1}{2}(12 \text{ m})(32 \text{ m})$ $A = 192 \text{ m}^2$ $A = 544 \text{ m}^2 + 192 \text{ m}^2 = 736 \text{ m}^2$	base $= 12 \text{ m} + 34 \text{ m} = 46 \text{ m}$ $A = \frac{1}{2}(46 \text{ m})(32 \text{ m})$ $A = 736 \text{ m}^2$

EUREKA
MATH™

©2015 Great Minds. eureka-math.org
G6-M5-TE-B5-1.3.1-01.2016

MP.2

2. Can we use the formula $A = \frac{1}{2} \times$ base $\times$ height to calculate the area of triangles that are not right triangles? Explain your thinking.

    Yes, the formula $A = \frac{1}{2} \times$ base $\times$ height can be used for more than just right triangles. We just need to be able to determine the height when it is not necessarily the length of one of the sides.

3. Examine the given triangle and expression.

    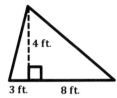

    $$\frac{1}{2}(11 \text{ ft.})(4 \text{ ft.})$$

    Explain what each part of the expression represents according to the triangle.

    11 ft. *represents the base of the triangle because* **8 ft.** $+$ **3 ft.** $=$ **11 ft.**

    4 ft. *represents the altitude of the triangle because this length is perpendicular to the base.*

4. Joe found the area of a triangle by writing $A = \frac{1}{2}(11 \text{ in.})(4 \text{ in.})$, while Kaitlyn found the area by writing $A = \frac{1}{2}(3 \text{ in.})(4 \text{ in.}) + \frac{1}{2}(8 \text{ in.})(4 \text{ in.})$. Explain how each student approached the problem.

    Joe combined the two bases of the triangle first and then calculated the area of the entire triangle, whereas Kaitlyn calculated the area of two smaller right triangles and then added these areas together.

5. The triangle below has an area of 4.76 sq. in. If the base is 3.4 in., let h be the height in inches.

    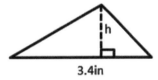

    3.4in

    a. Explain how the equation $4.76 \text{ in}^2 = \frac{1}{2}(3.4 \text{ in.})h$ represents the situation.

        The equation shows the area, 4.76 in^2, is one half the base, 3.4 in., times the height, in inches, h.

    b. Solve the equation.

        $$4.76 \text{ in}^2 = \frac{1}{2}(3.4 \text{ in.})h$$
        $$4.76 \text{ in}^2 = (1.7 \text{ in.})h$$
        $$4.76 \text{ in}^2 \div 1.7 \text{ in.} = (1.7 \text{ in.})h \div 1.7 \text{ in.}$$
        $$2.8 \text{ in.} = h$$

Closing (5 minutes)

- When a triangle is not a right triangle, how can you determine its base and height?

  □ *The height of a triangle is the length of the altitude. The altitude is the perpendicular line segment from a vertex of a triangle to the line containing the opposite side (or the base).*

- How can you use your knowledge of area to calculate the area of more complex shapes?

Show students the shape to the right.

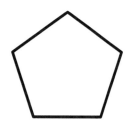

  □ *I can decompose the shape into smaller shapes for which I know how to calculate the area and then add all the areas together.*

Exit Ticket (5 minutes)

Lesson 3:   The Area of Acute Triangles Using Height and Base

EUREKA MATH

Name _____   Date _____

Lesson 3: The Area of Acute Triangles Using Height and Base

Exit Ticket

Calculate the area of each triangle using two different methods. Figures are not drawn to scale.

1.

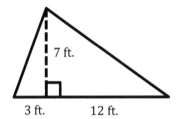

3 ft.   12 ft.

7 ft.

2.

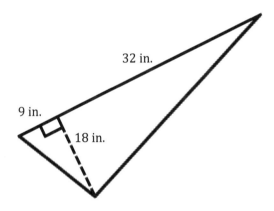

32 in.

9 in.

18 in.

Exit Ticket Sample Solutions

Calculate the area of each triangle using two different methods. Figures are not drawn to scale.

1.

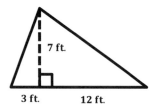

$A = \dfrac{1}{2}(3\text{ ft.})(7\text{ ft.}) = 10.5\text{ ft}^2$

$A = \dfrac{1}{2}(12\text{ ft.})(7\text{ ft.}) = 42\text{ ft}^2$

$A = 10.5\text{ ft}^2 + 42\text{ ft}^2 = 52.5\text{ ft}^2$

OR

$A = \dfrac{1}{2}(15\text{ ft.})(7\text{ ft.}) = 52.5\text{ ft}^2$

2.

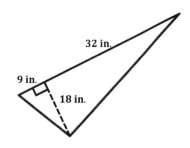

$A = \dfrac{1}{2}(9\text{ in.})(18\text{ in.}) = 81\text{ in}^2$

$A = \dfrac{1}{2}(32\text{ in.})(18\text{ in.}) = 288\text{ in}^2$

$A = 81\text{ in}^2 + 288\text{ in}^2 = 369\text{ in}^2$

OR

$A = \dfrac{1}{2}(41\text{ in.})(18\text{ in.}) = 369\text{ in}^2$

Problem Set Sample Solutions

Calculate the area of each shape below. Figures are not drawn to scale.

1.

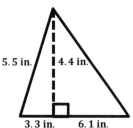

$A = \dfrac{1}{2}(3.3\text{ in.})(4.4\text{ in.}) = 7.26\text{ in}^2$

$A = \dfrac{1}{2}(6.1\text{ in.})(4.4\text{ in.}) = 13.42\text{ in}^s$

$A = 7.26\text{ in}^2 + 13.42\text{ in}^2 = 20.68\text{ in}^2$

OR

$A = \dfrac{1}{2}(9.4\text{ in.})(4.4\text{ in.}) = 20.68\text{ in}^2$

EUREKA
MATH

©2015 Great Minds. eureka-math.org
G6-M5-TE-B5-1.3.1-01.2016

2.

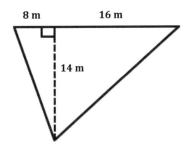

$A = \frac{1}{2}(8\text{ m})(14\text{ m}) = 56\text{ m}^2$

$A = \frac{1}{2}(16\text{ m})(14\text{ m}) = 112\text{ m}^2$

$A = 56\text{ m}^2 + 112\text{ m}^2 = 168\text{ m}^2$

OR

$A = \frac{1}{2}(24\text{ m})(14\text{ m}) = 168\text{ m}^2$

3.

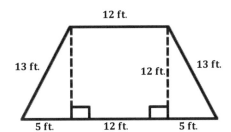

$A = \frac{1}{2}(5\text{ ft.})(12\text{ ft.}) = 30\text{ ft}^2$

$A = (12\text{ ft.})(12\text{ ft.}) = 144\text{ ft}^2$

$A = \frac{1}{2}(5\text{ ft.})(12\text{ ft.}) = 30\text{ ft}^2$

$A = 30\text{ ft}^2 + 144\text{ ft}^2 + 30\text{ ft}^2 = 204\text{ ft}^2$

4.

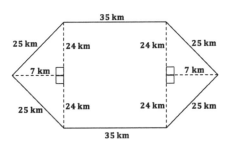

$A = \frac{1}{2}(48\text{ km})(7\text{ km}) = 168\text{ km}^2$

$A = (35\text{ km})(48\text{ km}) = 1{,}680\text{ km}^2$

$A = \frac{1}{2}(48\text{ km})(7\text{ km}) = 168\text{ km}^2$

$A = 168\text{ km}^2 + 1{,}680\text{ km}^2 + 168\text{ km}^2 = 2{,}016\text{ km}^2$

5. Immanuel is building a fence to make an enclosed play area for his dog. The enclosed area will be in the shape of a triangle with a base of 48 m and an altitude of 32 m. How much space does the dog have to play?

$A = \frac{1}{2}bh = \frac{1}{2}(48\text{ m})(32\text{ m}) = 768\text{ m}^2$

The dog has 768 m^2 in which to play.

6. Chauncey is building a storage bench for his son's playroom. The storage bench will fit into the corner and against two walls to form a triangle. Chauncey wants to buy a triangular shaped cover for the bench.

If the storage bench is $2\frac{1}{2}$ ft. along one wall and $4\frac{1}{4}$ ft. along the other wall, how big will the cover have to be to cover the entire bench?

$A = \frac{1}{2}\left(2\frac{1}{2}\text{ ft.}\right)\left(4\frac{1}{4}\text{ ft.}\right) = \frac{1}{2}\left(\frac{5}{2}\text{ ft.}\right)\left(\frac{17}{4}\text{ ft.}\right) = \frac{85}{16}\text{ ft}^2 = 5\frac{5}{16}\text{ ft}^2$

Chauncey would have to buy a cover that has an area of $5\frac{5}{16}$ ft^2 to cover the entire bench.

Note: Figure is not to scale.

7. Examine the triangle to the right.

   a.   Write an expression to show how you would calculate the area.

$$\frac{1}{2}\left(7\text{ in.}\right)\left(4\text{ in.}\right)+\frac{1}{2}\left(3\text{ in.}\right)\left(4\text{ in.}\right)\ or\ \frac{1}{2}\left(10\text{ in.}\right)\left(4\text{ in.}\right)$$

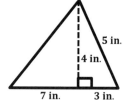

5 in.

4 in.

7 in.   3 in.

   b.   Identify each part of your expression as it relates to the triangle.

If students wrote the first expression, then 7 in. *and* 3 in. *represent the two parts of the base, and* 4 in. *is the height, or the altitude, of the triangle.*

If students wrote the second expression, then 10 in. *represents the base because* 7 in. + 3 in. = 10 in., *and* 4 in. *represents the height, or the altitude, of the triangle.*

8. The floor of a triangular room has an area of $32\frac{1}{2}$ sq. m. If the triangle's altitude is $7\frac{1}{2}$ m, write an equation to determine the length of the base, b, in meters. Then solve the equation.

$$32\frac{1}{2}=\frac{1}{2}b\left(7\frac{1}{2}\right)$$

$$32\frac{1}{2}\text{ m}^2=\left(\frac{15}{4}\right)b$$

$$32\frac{1}{2}\div\frac{15}{4}=\left(\frac{15}{4}\right)b\div\frac{15}{4}$$

$$\frac{26}{3}=b$$

$$8\frac{2}{3}=b$$

Therefore, the base is $8\frac{2}{3}$ m.

EUREKA
MATH™

©2015 Great Minds. eureka-math.org
G6-M5-TE-B5-1.3.1-01.2016

©2015 Great Minds. eureka-math.org
G6-M5-TE-B5-1.3.1-01.2016

Number Correct: _____

Multiplication of Decimals – Round 1

Directions: Evaluate each expression.

1.	5×1		23.	5×3	
2.	5×0.1		24.	5×0.3	
3.	5×0.01		25.	0.5×3	
4.	5×0.001		26.	0.3×0.5	
5.	2×4		27.	9×2	
6.	0.2×4		28.	0.2×9	
7.	0.02×4		29.	0.9×2	
8.	0.002×4		30.	0.2×0.9	
9.	3×3		31.	4×0.4	
10.	3×0.3		32.	0.4×0.4	
11.	3×0.03		33.	0.04×0.4	
12.	0.1×0.8		34.	0.8×0.6	
13.	0.01×0.8		35.	0.8×0.06	
14.	0.1×0.08		36.	0.006×0.8	
15.	0.01×0.08		37.	0.006×0.08	
16.	0.3×0.2		38.	0.7×0.9	
17.	0.03×0.2		39.	0.07×0.9	
18.	0.02×0.3		40.	0.9×0.007	
19.	0.02×0.03		41.	0.09×0.007	
20.	0.2×0.2		42.	1.2×0.7	
21.	0.02×0.2		43.	1.2×0.07	
22.	0.2×0.02		44.	0.007×0.12	

Multiplication of Decimals – Round 1 [KEY]

Directions: Evaluate each expression.

1.	5×1	5	23.	5×3	15
2.	5×0.1	0.5	24.	5×0.3	1.5
3.	5×0.01	0.05	25.	0.5×3	1.5
4.	5×0.001	0.005	26.	0.3×0.5	0.15
5.	2×4	8	27.	9×2	18
6.	0.2×4	0.8	28.	0.2×9	1.8
7.	0.02×4	0.08	29.	0.9×2	1.8
8.	0.002×4	0.008	30.	0.2×0.9	0.18
9.	3×3	9	31.	4×0.4	1.6
10.	3×0.3	0.9	32.	0.4×0.4	0.16
11.	3×0.03	0.09	33.	0.04×0.4	0.016
12.	0.1×0.8	0.08	34.	0.8×0.6	0.48
13.	0.01×0.8	0.008	35.	0.8×0.06	0.048
14.	0.1×0.08	0.008	36.	0.006×0.8	0.0048
15.	0.01×0.08	0.0008	37.	0.006×0.08	0.00048
16.	0.3×0.2	0.06	38.	0.7×0.9	0.63
17.	0.03×0.2	0.006	39.	0.07×0.9	0.063
18.	0.02×0.3	0.006	40.	0.9×0.007	0.0063
19.	0.02×0.03	0.0006	41.	0.09×0.007	0.00063
20.	0.2×0.2	0.04	42.	1.2×0.7	0.84
21.	0.02×0.2	0.004	43.	1.2×0.07	0.084
22.	0.2×0.02	0.004	44.	0.007×0.12	0.00084

Lesson 3:   The Area of Acute Triangles Using Height and Base

EUREKA
MATH™

©2015 Great Minds. eureka-math.org
G6-M5-TE-B5-1.3.1-01.2016

Multiplication of Decimals – Round 2

Directions: Evaluate each expression.

1.	9×1	
2.	0.9×1	
3.	0.09×1	
4.	0.009×1	
5.	2×2	
6.	2×0.2	
7.	2×0.02	
8.	2×0.002	
9.	3×2	
10.	0.3×2	
11.	2×0.03	
12.	0.7×0.1	
13.	0.07×0.1	
14.	0.01×0.7	
15.	0.01×0.07	
16.	0.2×0.4	
17.	0.02×0.4	
18.	0.4×0.02	
19.	0.04×0.02	
20.	0.1×0.1	
21.	0.01×0.1	
22.	0.1×0.01	

23.	3×4	
24.	3×0.4	
25.	0.3×4	
26.	0.4×0.3	
27.	7×7	
28.	7×0.7	
29.	0.7×7	
30.	0.7×0.7	
31.	2×0.8	
32.	0.2×0.8	
33.	0.02×0.8	
34.	0.6×0.5	
35.	0.6×0.05	
36.	0.005×0.6	
37.	0.005×0.06	
38.	0.9×0.9	
39.	0.09×0.9	
40.	0.009×0.9	
41.	0.009×0.09	
42.	1.3×0.6	
43.	1.3×0.06	
44.	0.006×1.3	

Multiplication of Decimals – Round 2 [KEY]

Directions: Evaluate each expression.

1.	9×1	9	23.	3×4	12
2.	0.9×1	0.9	24.	3×0.4	1.2
3.	0.09×1	0.09	25.	0.3×4	1.2
4.	0.009×1	0.009	26.	0.4×0.3	0.12
5.	2×2	4	27.	7×7	49
6.	2×0.2	0.4	28.	7×0.7	4.9
7.	2×0.02	0.04	29.	0.7×7	4.9
8.	2×0.002	0.004	30.	0.7×0.7	0.49
9.	3×2	6	31.	2×0.8	1.6
10.	0.3×2	0.6	32.	0.2×0.8	0.16
11.	2×0.03	0.06	33.	0.02×0.8	0.016
12.	0.7×0.1	0.07	34.	0.6×0.5	0.3
13.	0.07×0.1	0.007	35.	0.6×0.05	0.03
14.	0.01×0.7	0.007	36.	0.005×0.6	0.003
15.	0.01×0.07	0.0007	37.	0.005×0.06	0.0003
16.	0.2×0.4	0.08	38.	0.9×0.9	0.81
17.	0.02×0.4	0.008	39.	0.09×0.9	0.081
18.	0.4×0.02	0.008	40.	0.009×0.9	0.0081
19.	0.04×0.02	0.0008	41.	0.009×0.09	0.00081
20.	0.1×0.1	0.01	42.	1.3×0.6	0.78
21.	0.01×0.1	0.001	43.	1.3×0.06	0.078
22.	0.1×0.01	0.001	44.	0.006×1.3	0.0078

EUREKA MATH™

©2015 Great Minds. eureka-math.org
G6-M5-TE-B5-1.3.1-01.2016

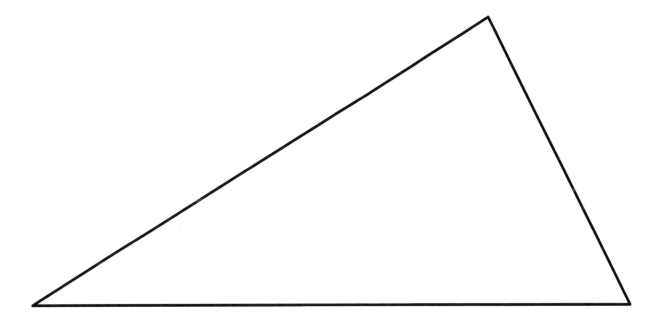

Lesson 4: The Area of All Triangles Using Height and Base

Student Outcomes

- Students construct the altitude for three different cases: an altitude that is a side of a right angle, an altitude that lies over the base, and an altitude that is outside the triangle.
- Students deconstruct triangles to justify that the area of a triangle is exactly one half the area of a parallelogram.

Lesson Notes

Students need the attached templates, scissors, a ruler, and glue to complete the Exploratory Challenge.

Classwork

Opening Exercise (5 minutes)

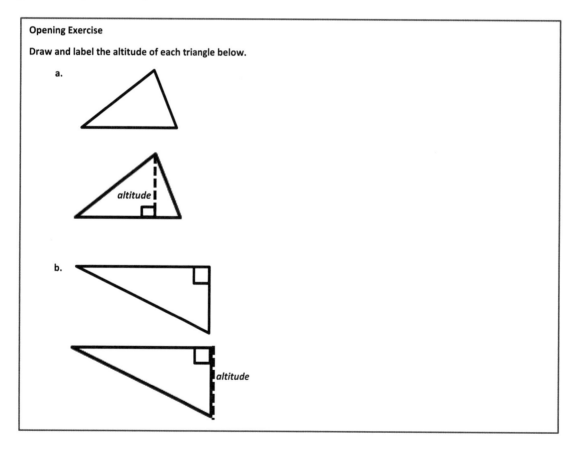

EUREKA
MATH™

©2015 Great Minds. eureka-math.org
G6-M5-TE-B5-1.3.1-01.2016

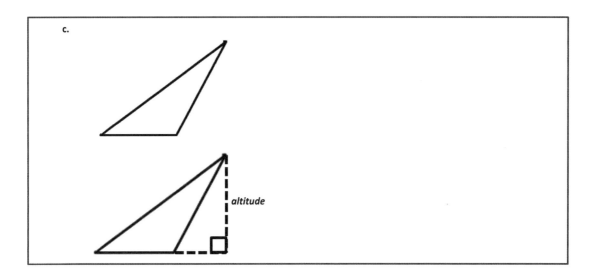

Discussion (3 minutes)

- The last few lessons showed that the area formula for triangles is $A = \frac{1}{2} \times$ base $\times$ height. Today we are going to show that the formula works for three different types of triangles.

- Examine the triangles in the Opening Exercise. What is different about them?

  - *The height, or altitude, is in a different location for each triangle. The first triangle has an altitude inside the triangle. The second triangle has a side length that is the altitude, and the third triangle has an altitude outside of the triangle.*

- If we wanted to calculate the area of these triangles, what formula do you think we would use? Explain.

  - *We would use $A = \frac{1}{2} \times$ base $\times$ height because that is the area formula we have used for both right triangles and acute triangles.*

Exploratory Challenge/Exercises 1–5 (22 minutes)

Students work in small groups to show that the area formula is the same for all three types of triangles shown in the Opening Exercise. Each group needs the attached templates, scissors, a ruler, and glue. Each exercise comes with steps that might be useful to provide for students who work better with such scaffolds.

MP.1

> **Exploratory Challenge/Exercises 1–5**
>
> 1. Use rectangle X and the triangle with the altitude inside (triangle X) to show that the area formula for the triangle is $A = \frac{1}{2} \times$ **base** $\times$ **height.**
>
>   a. **Step One: Find the area of rectangle X.**
>
> $A = 3$ in. $\times 2.5$ in. $= 7.5$ in^2
>
>   b. **Step Two: What is half the area of rectangle X?**
>
>   *Half of the area of the rectangle is 7.5 in$^2 \div 2 = 3.75$ in^2.*

> c.   Step Three: Prove, by decomposing triangle X, that it is the same as half of rectangle X. Please glue your decomposed triangle onto a separate sheet of paper. Glue it into rectangle X. What conclusions can you make about the triangle's area compared to the rectangle's area?

Students should cut their triangle and glue it into half of the rectangle. This may take more than one try, so extra copies of the triangles may be necessary.

> *Because the triangle fits inside half of the rectangle, we know the triangle's area is half of the rectangle's area.*
>
> 2.   Use rectangle Y and the triangle with a side that is the altitude (triangle Y) to show the area formula for the triangle is $A = \frac{1}{2} \times$ base $\times$ height.
>
>   a.   Step One: Find the area of rectangle Y.
>
> $A = 3 \text{ in.} \times 3 \text{ in.} = 9 \text{ in}^2$
>
>   b.   Step Two: What is half the area of rectangle Y?
>
>   *Half the area of the rectangle is* $9 \text{ in}^2 \div 2 = 4.5 \text{ in}^2$.
>
>   c.   Step Three: Prove, by decomposing triangle Y, that it is the same as half of rectangle Y. Please glue your decomposed triangle onto a separate sheet of paper. Glue it into rectangle Y. What conclusions can you make about the triangle's area compared to the rectangle's area?

MP.1

Students should cut triangle Y and glue it into the rectangle. This may take more than one try, so extra copies of the triangles may be necessary.

> *The right triangle also fits in exactly half of the rectangle, so the triangle's area is once again half the size of the rectangle's area.*
>
> 3.   Use rectangle Z and the triangle with the altitude outside (triangle Z) to show that the area formula for the triangle is $A = \frac{1}{2} \times$ base $\times$ height.
>
>   a.   Step One: Find the area of rectangle Z.
>
> $A = 3 \text{ in.} \times 2.5 \text{ in.} = 7.5 \text{ in}^2$
>
>   b.   Step Two: What is half the area of rectangle Z?
>
>   *Half of the area of the rectangle is* $7.5 \text{ in}^2 \div 2 = 3.75 \text{ in}^2$.
>
>   c.   Step Three: Prove, by decomposing triangle Z, that it is the same as half of rectangle Z. Please glue your decomposed triangle onto a separate sheet of paper. Glue it into rectangle Z. What conclusions can you make about the triangle's area compared to the rectangle's area?

Scaffolding:

- Students may struggle with this step since they have yet to see an obtuse angle. Consider modeling this step to help students who may become confused.
- After watching the teacher model this step, students can then try this step on their own.

Students should cut their triangle and glue it into the rectangle to show that an obtuse triangle also has an area that is half the size of a rectangle that has the same dimensions. This may take more than one try, so extra copies of the triangles may be necessary.

©2015 Great Minds. eureka-math.org
G6-M5-TE-B5-1.3.1-01.2016

Note: In order for students to fit an obtuse triangle into half of a rectangle, they need to cut the triangle into three separate triangles.

MP.1

> *Similar to the other two triangles, when the altitude is outside the triangle, the area of the triangle is exactly half of the area of the rectangle.*
>
> 4. **When finding the area of a triangle, does it matter where the altitude is located?**
>
>   *It does not matter where the altitude is located. To find the area of a triangle, the formula is always* $A = \frac{1}{2} \times \textbf{base} \times \textbf{height}.$
>
> 5. **How can you determine which part of the triangle is the base and which is the height?**
>
>   *The base and the height of any triangle form a right angle because the altitude is always perpendicular to the base.*

Take time to show how other groups may have calculated the area of the triangle using a different side for the base and how this still results in the same area.

After discussing how any side of a triangle can be labeled the base, students write a summary to explain the outcomes of the Exploratory Challenge.

Exercises 6–8 (5 minutes)

Exercises 6–8

Calculate the area of each triangle. Figures are not drawn to scale.

6.

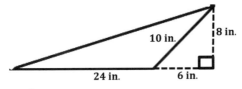

$$A = \frac{1}{2}(24 \text{ in.})(8 \text{ in.}) = 96 \text{ in}^2$$

7.

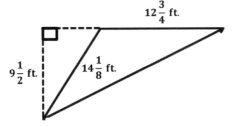

$$A = \frac{1}{2}\left(12\frac{3}{4} \text{ ft.}\right)\left(9\frac{1}{2} \text{ ft.}\right) = \frac{1}{2}\left(\frac{51}{4} \text{ ft.}\right)\left(\frac{19}{2} \text{ ft.}\right) = \frac{969}{16} \text{ ft}^2 = 60\frac{9}{16} \text{ ft}^2$$

8. **Draw three triangles (acute, right, and obtuse) that have the same area. Explain how you know they have the same area.**

   Answers will vary.

Lesson 4:   The Area of All Triangles Using Height and Base   **57**

Closing (5 minutes)

- Different groups share their Exploratory Challenge and discuss the outcomes.
- Why does the area formula for a triangle work for every triangle?
  - *Every type of triangle fits inside exactly half of a rectangle that has the same base and height lengths.*

Exit Ticket (5 minutes)

©2015 Great Minds. eureka-math.org
G6-M5-TE-B5-1.3.1-01.2016

Name _____   Date _____

Lesson 4: The Area of All Triangles Using Height and Base

Exit Ticket

Find the area of each triangle. Figures are not drawn to scale.

1.

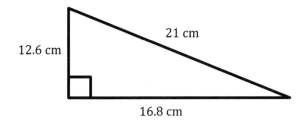

2.

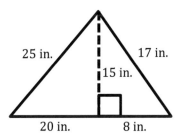

3.

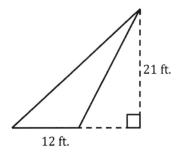

Exit Ticket Sample Solutions

Find the area of each triangle. Figures are not drawn to scale.

1.
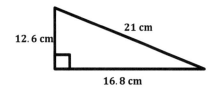

$$A = \frac{1}{2}(12.6 \text{ cm})(16.8 \text{ cm}) = 105.84 \text{ cm}^2$$

2.
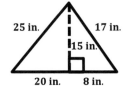

$$A = \frac{1}{2}(28 \text{ in.})(15 \text{ in.}) = 210 \text{ in}^2$$

3.
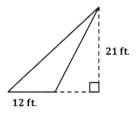

$$A = \frac{1}{2}(12 \text{ ft.})(21 \text{ ft.}) = 126 \text{ ft}^2$$

Problem Set Sample Solutions

Calculate the area of each figure below. Figures are not drawn to scale.

1.
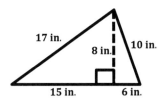

$$A = \frac{1}{2}(21 \text{ in.})(8 \text{ in.}) = 84 \text{ in}^2$$

EUREKA MATH

2.

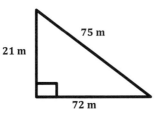

$$A = \frac{1}{2}(72 \text{ m})(21 \text{ m}) = 756 \text{ m}^2$$

3.

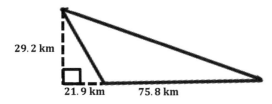

$$A = \frac{1}{2}(75.8 \text{ km})(29.2 \text{ km}) = 1,106.68 \text{ km}^2$$

4.

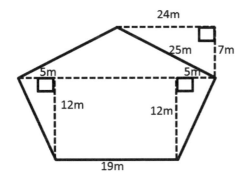

$$A = \frac{1}{2}(5 \text{ m})(12 \text{ m}) = 30 \text{ m}^2$$

$$A = \frac{1}{2}(7 \text{ m})(29 \text{ m}) = 101.5 \text{ m}^2$$

$$A = (12 \text{ m})(19 \text{ m}) = 228 \text{ m}^2$$

$$A = 30 \text{ m}^2 + 30 \text{ m}^2 + 101.5 \text{ m}^2 + 228 \text{ m}^2$$
$$A = 389.5 \text{ m}^2$$

5. The Andersons are going on a long sailing trip during the summer. However, one of the sails on their sailboat ripped, and they have to replace it. The sail is pictured below.

    If the sailboat sails are on sale for $2 per square foot, how much will the new sail cost?

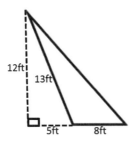

$$A = \frac{1}{2}bh$$
$$= \frac{1}{2}(8 \text{ ft.})(12 \text{ ft.})$$
$$= 48 \text{ ft}^2$$

$$\frac{2 \text{ dollars}}{\text{ft}^2} \times 48 \text{ ft}^2 = 96 \text{ dollars } (\textit{or } \$96)$$

The cost of the new sail is $96.

6. Darnell and Donovan are both trying to calculate the area of an obtuse triangle. Examine their calculations below.

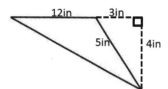

Darnell's Work	Donovan's Work
$A = \dfrac{1}{2} \times 3 \text{ in.} \times 4 \text{ in.}$	$A = \dfrac{1}{2} \times 12 \text{ in.} \times 4 \text{ in.}$
$A = 6 \text{ in}^2$	$A = 24 \text{ in}^2$

Which student calculated the area correctly? Explain why the other student is not correct.

Donovan calculated the area correctly. Although Darnell did use the altitude of the triangle, he used the length between the altitude and the base rather than the length of the actual base.

7. Russell calculated the area of the triangle below. His work is shown.

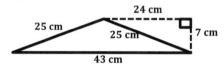

$$A = \frac{1}{2} \times 43 \text{ cm} \times 7 \text{ cm}$$
$$A = 150.5 \text{ cm}^2$$

Although Russell was told his work is correct, he had a hard time explaining why it is correct. Help Russell explain why his calculations are correct.

The formula for the area of a triangle is $A = \frac{1}{2}bh$. Russell followed this formula because 7 cm is the height of the triangle, and 43 cm is the base of the triangle.

8. The larger triangle below has a base of 10.14 m; the gray triangle has an area of 40.325 m^2.

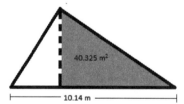

a. Determine the area of the larger triangle if it has a height of 12.2 m.

$$A = \frac{1}{2}(10.14 \text{ m})(12.2 \text{ m})$$
$$= 61.854 \text{ m}^2$$

b. Let A be the area of the unshaded (white) triangle in square meters. Write and solve an equation to determine the value of A, using the areas of the larger triangle and the gray triangle.

$$40.325 \text{ m}^2 + A = 61.854 \text{ m}^2$$
$$40.325 \text{ m}^2 + A - 40.325 \text{ m}^2 = 61.854 \text{ m}^2 - 40.325 \text{ m}^2$$
$$A = 21.529 \text{ m}^2$$

EUREKA
MATH

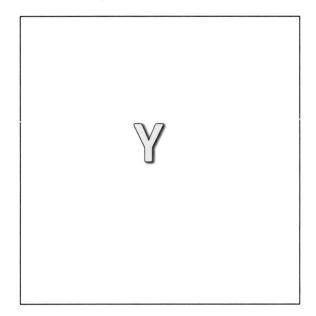

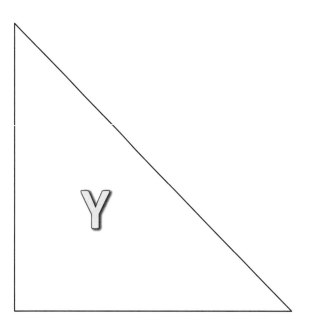

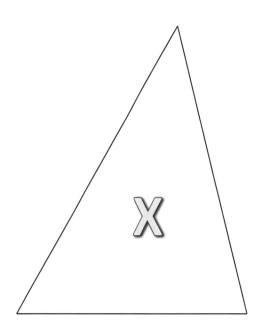

EUREKA
MATH™

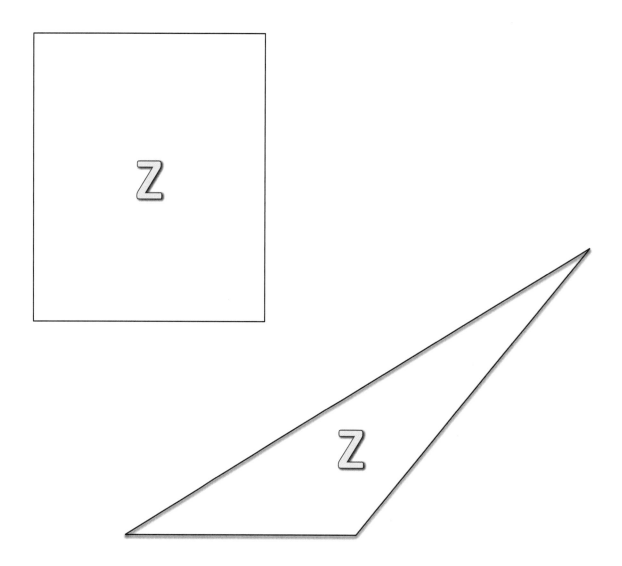

EUREKA
MATH™

Lesson 5: The Area of Polygons Through Composition and Decomposition

Student Outcomes

- Students show the area formula for the region bounded by a polygon by decomposing the region into triangles and other polygons. They understand that the area of a polygon is actually the area of the region bounded by the polygon.
- Students find the area for the region bounded by a trapezoid by decomposing the region into two triangles. They understand that the area of a trapezoid is actually the area of the region bounded by the trapezoid. Students decompose rectangles to determine the area of other quadrilaterals.

Lesson Notes

This graphic can be displayed for students to make sense of the second part of each Student Outcome.

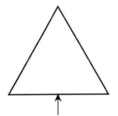

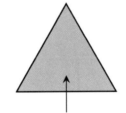

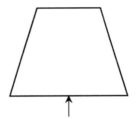

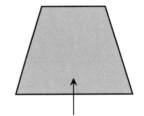

The triangle consists of only the three lines.

The triangular region is the triangle and its interior points.

The trapezoid consists of only the four lines.

The trapezoidal region is the trapezoid and its interior points.

MP.2 & MP.7

Decomposing irregularly shaped polygons into rectangles involves making a choice of where to separate the figure. This very often involves calculating the length of unknown sides of the new figures. This may be more intuitive for some students than others. Mastering missing length problems makes the objectives of this lesson more easily achieved.

When decomposing irregularly shaped polygons into triangles and other polygons, identifying the base and height of the triangle also sometimes requires missing length skills.

> **Scaffolding:**
> The words *composition* and *decomposition* are likely new words. The base word, *compose*, is a verb that means the act of joining or putting together. Decompose means the opposite, to take apart. In this lesson, the words composition and decomposition are used to describe how irregular figures can be separated into triangles and other polygons. The area of these parts can then be added together to calculate the area of the whole figure.

Classwork

Opening Exercise (5 minutes): Missing Length Problems

There are extra copies of this figure at the end of this lesson. Project this image with a document camera or interactive white board, if desired. Specify the length of two horizontal lengths and two vertical lengths, and have students find the missing side lengths. Highlighting vertical sides in one color and horizontal sides in another color is valuable for many students.

©2015 Great Minds. eureka-math.org
G6-M5-TE-B5-1.3.1-01.2016

Opening Exercise

Here is an aerial view of a woodlot.

If $AB = 10$ units, $FE = 8$ units, $AF = 6$ units, and $DE = 7$ units, find the lengths of the other two sides.

$DC = 2$ *units*

$BC = 13$ *units*

If $DC = 10$ units, $FE = 30$ units, $AF = 28$ units, and $BC = 54$ units, find the lengths of the other two sides.

$AB = 40$ *units*

$DE = 26$ *units*

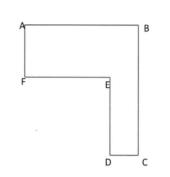

Scaffolding:

If students have difficulty seeing these relationships, it can be helpful to show progressions of figures, such as those below, which move gradually from the sides of a rectangle to an irregular rectilinear figure. Consistent use of visuals, as well as manipulatives, such as cutouts of these figures, should aid in understanding.

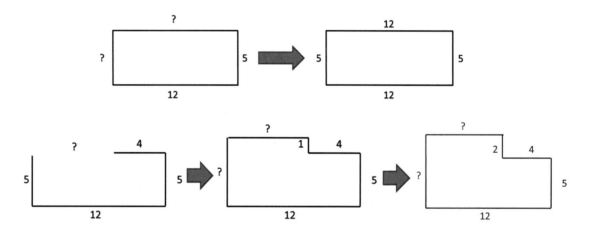

Discussion (5 minutes)

If students are struggling to see this relationship, it might be helpful for them to complete the rectangle that encloses the figure:

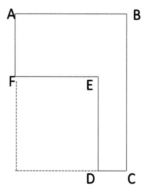

©2015 Great Minds. eureka-math.org
G6-M5-TE-B5-1.3.1-01.2016

- How do we know which operation to use when finding missing side lengths?
  - *If we know two short sides (vertical or horizontal), we add to find the longer side.*
  - *If we know the long side and one short side (vertical or horizontal), we subtract.*
- These examples used whole numbers for the lengths of the sides. What would we do if there were decimal lengths?
  - *We would add or subtract the decimal numbers.*

- Would the process be the same for deciding whether to add or subtract?
  - *Yes*
- When adding or subtracting decimals, what is one step that is critical to arriving at the correct answer?
  - *One critical step is making sure we add and subtract numbers that have the same place value by lining up the decimal points.*
- What if the lengths were given as fractions or mixed numbers?
  - *We would add or subtract the fractions or the mixed numbers.*
- Would the process be the same for deciding whether to add or subtract?
  - *Yes*

Ask students to find the next diagram on their classwork page. Work through the scenario with them. The area of this figure can be found in at least three ways: using two horizontal cuts, using two vertical cuts, or subtracting the missing area from the larger rectangle (using overall length and width). There is a drawing included at the end of this lesson that has the grid line inserted.

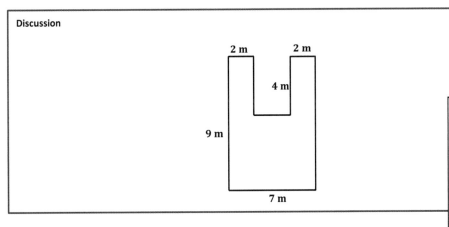

Discussion

2 m   2 m

4 m

9 m

7 m

Scaffolding:
Some students may benefit from actually cutting the irregularly shaped polygons before marking the dimensions on the student pages. If needed, there are reproducible copies included at the end of the lesson.

MP.1

- How could we determine the total area?
  - *Using two horizontal lines, two vertical lines, or one of each*
- Let's divide the figure using two horizontal lines. Does that make any rectangles with two known sides?
  - *Yes, it makes two 2 m by 4 m rectangles.*
- Can we then use this 9 m measure directly? Why or why not?
  - *No. The 9 m includes the top part of the figure, but we have already found the dimensions of this part.*
- What is the height of that third rectangle, and how do you find it?
  - *The entire 9 m side cannot be used. Part has been removed, 4 m, leaving only 5 m. We use subtraction.*

- What are the dimensions of the three resulting rectangles?
  - *2 m by 4 m, 2 m by 4 m, and 7 m by 5 m*
- Calculate and mark each of these areas.
  - $2 \text{ m} \times 4 \text{ m} = 8 \text{ m}^2$, $2 \text{ m} \times 4 \text{ m} = 8 \text{ m}^2$, $7 \text{ m} \times 5 \text{ m} = 35 \text{ m}^2$
- What is the total area of the figure?
  - 51 m^2
- Divide the next figure using two vertical lines. Does that make any rectangles with two known sides?
  - *Yes, it makes two 2 m by 9 m rectangles.*
- Can we then use this 7 m measure directly? Why or why not?
  - *No, the entire 7 m side cannot be used. Part has been removed, two 2 m segments, leaving only 3 m.*
- What are the dimensions of the three resulting rectangles?
  - *2 m by 9 m, 2 m by 9 m, and 3 m by 5 m*
- Calculate and mark each of these areas.
  - $2 \text{ m} \times 9 \text{ m} = 18 \text{ m}^2$, $2 \text{ m} \times 9 \text{ m} = 18 \text{ m}^2$, $3 \text{ m} \times 5 \text{ m} = 15 \text{ m}^2$
- What is the total area of the figure?
  - 51 m^2
- Divide the last figure using one vertical line and one horizontal line. Are there missing sides to calculate?
  - *Yes, both sides of the 5 m by 5 m rectangle have to be found by decomposing the other measures.*
- What are the dimensions of the three resulting rectangles?
  - *2 m by 9 m, 2 m by 4 m, and 5 m by 5 m*
- Calculate and mark each of these areas.
  - $2 \text{ m} \times 9 \text{ m} = 18 \text{ m}^2$, $2 \text{ m} \times 4 \text{ m} = 8 \text{ m}^2$, $5 \text{ m} \times 5 \text{ m} = 25 \text{ m}^2$
- What is the total area of the figure?
  - 51 m^2
- Finally, if we look at this as a large rectangle with a piece removed, what are the dimensions of the large rectangle?
  - *9 m by 7 m*
- What are the dimensions of the missing piece that looks like it was cut out?
  - *3 m by 4 m*
- Calculate these two areas.
  - $9 \text{ m} \times 7 \text{ m} = 63 \text{ m}^2$, $3 \text{ m} \times 4 \text{ m} = 12 \text{ m}^2$
- How can we use these two areas to find the area of the original figure?
  - *Subtract the smaller area from the larger one.*
- What is the difference between 63 m^2 and 12 m^2?
  - $63 \text{ m}^2 - 12 \text{ m}^2 = 51 \text{ m}^2$
- Is there an advantage to one of these methods over the others?
  - *Answers will vary. In this example, either one or two calculations are necessary when decomposing the figure.*
- Consider the two expressions: $18 \text{ m}^2 + 8 \text{ m}^2 + 25 \text{ m}^2$ and $63 \text{ m}^2 - 12 \text{ m}^2$.

Lesson 5 **6•5**

- What do the terms in these expressions represent in this problem?
    □ *The first is a "sum of the parts" expression, and the second is a "whole minus part" expression. More specifically, the first expression shows that the total area is the sum of the areas of three rectangles; the second expression shows that the total area is the area of a large rectangle minus the area of a small one.*

MP.2

Allow some time for discussion before moving on.

Example 1 (10 minutes): Decomposing Polygons into Rectangles

Example 1: Decomposing Polygons into Rectangles

The Intermediate School is producing a play that needs a special stage built. A diagram of the stage is shown below (not drawn to scale).

a. On the first diagram, divide the stage into three rectangles using two horizontal lines. Find the dimensions of these rectangles, and calculate the area of each. Then, find the total area of the stage.

Dimensions: 2 m *by* 4 m, 2 m *by* 4 m, *and* 7 m *by* 5 m

Area: 2 m × 4 m = 8 m², 2 m × 4 m = 8 m², 7 m × 5 m = 35 m²

Total: 8 m² + 8 m² + 35 m² = 51 m²

b. On the second diagram, divide the stage into three rectangles using two vertical lines. Find the dimensions of these rectangles, and calculate the area of each. Then, find the total area of the stage.

Dimensions: 2 m *by* 9 m, 2 m *by* 9 m, *and* 3 m *by* 5 m

Area: 2 m × 9 m = 18 m², 2 m × 9 m = 18 m², 3 m × 5 m = 15 m²

Total: 51 m²

c. On the third diagram, divide the stage into three rectangles using one horizontal line and one vertical line. Find the dimensions of these rectangles, and calculate the area of each. Then, find the total area of the stage.

Dimensions: 2 m *by* 9 m, 2 m *by* 4 m, *and* 5 m *by* 5 m

Area: 2 m × 9 m = 18 m², 2 m × 4 m = 8 m², 5 m × 5 m = 25 m²

Total: 51 m²

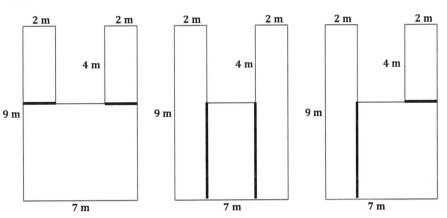

©2015 Great Minds. eureka-math.org
G6-M5-TE-B5-1.3.1-01.2016

d. **Think of this as a large rectangle with a piece removed.**

i. **What are the dimensions of the large rectangle and the small rectangle?**

   Dimensions: 9 m *by* 7 m *and* 3 m *by* 4 m

ii. **What are the areas of the two rectangles?**

   Area: $9 \text{ m} \times 7 \text{ m} = 63 \text{ m}^2$, $3 \text{ m} \times 4 \text{ m} = 12 \text{ m}^2$

iii. **What operation is needed to find the area of the original figure?**

   Subtraction

iv. **What is the difference in area between the two rectangles?**

   $63 \text{ m}^2 - 12 \text{ m}^2 = 51 \text{ m}^2$

v. **What do you notice about your answers to (a), (b), (c), and (d)?**

   The area is the same.

vi. **Why do you think this is true?**

   No matter how we decompose the figure, the total area is the sum of its parts. Even if we take the area around the figure and subtract the part that is not included, the area of the figure remains the same, 51 m^2.

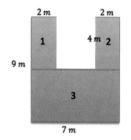

Area of Rectangle 1: $b \cdot h$
$\qquad 2 \text{ m} \cdot 4 \text{ m} = 8 \text{ m}^2$
Area of Rectangle 2: $b \cdot h$
$\qquad 2 \text{ m} \cdot 4 m = 8 \text{ m}^2$
Area of Rectangle 3: $b \cdot h$
$\qquad 7 \text{ m} \cdot 5 \text{ m} = 35 \text{ m}^2$

Area of Polygon: $8 \text{ m}^2 + 8 \text{ m}^2 + 35 \text{ m}^2 = 51 \text{ m}^2$

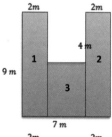

Area of Rectangle 1: $b \cdot h$
$\qquad 9 \text{ m} \cdot 2 \text{ m} = 18 \text{ m}^2$
Area of Rectangle 2: $b \cdot h$
$\qquad 9 \text{ m} \cdot 2 m = 18 \text{ m}^2$
Area of Rectangle 3: $b \cdot h$
$\qquad 3 \text{ m} \cdot 5 \text{ m} = 15 \text{ m}^2$

Area of Polygon: $18 \text{ m}^2 + 18 \text{ m}^2 + 15 \text{ m}^2 = 51 \text{ m}^2$

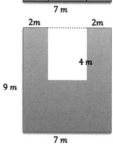

Area of Rectangle: $b \cdot h$
$\qquad 9 \text{ m} \cdot 7 \text{ m} = 63 \text{ m}^2$
Area of Missing Rectangle 2: $b \cdot h$
$\qquad 3 \text{ m} \cdot 4 \text{ m} = 12 \text{ m}^2$

Area of Polygon: $63 \text{ m}^2 - 12 \text{ m}^2 = 51 \text{ m}^2$

Scaffolding:

As an extension, ask students to manipulate the un-simplified numerical expressions on either side of the equal sign(s) to demonstrate equivalence of areas (MP.2).

For example, using the factors of the area, showing that
$$2 \times 4 + 2 \times 4 + 7 \times 5 =$$
$$2 \times 9 + 2 \times 9 + 3 \times 5$$
by applying the distributive property and using decomposition of whole numbers.

Using the products (areas), the equivalence should be made clear.
$$8 + 8 + 35 = 18 + 18 + 15$$
$$= 63 - 12$$

EUREKA MATH™

Example 2 (10 minutes): Decomposing Polygons into Rectangles and Triangles

In this example, a parallelogram is bisected along a diagonal. The resulting triangles are congruent, with the same base and height of the parallelogram. Students should see that the area for a parallelogram is equal to the base times the height, regardless of how much the bases are skewed. Ask how we could find the area using only triangles.

Example 2: Decomposing Polygons into Rectangles and Triangles

Parallelogram $ABCD$ is part of a large solar power collector. The base measures 6 m and the height is 4 m.

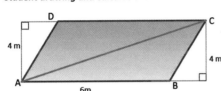

a.   Draw a diagonal from A to C. Find the area of both triangles ABC and ACD.

Student drawing and calculations are shown here.

Triangle ABC	Triangle ACD
$A = \frac{1}{2}bh$	$A = \frac{1}{2}bh$
$A = \frac{1}{2}(6\text{ m})(4\text{ m})$	$A = \frac{1}{2}(6\text{ m})(4\text{ m})$
$A = 12\text{ m}^2$	$A = 12\text{ m}^2$

Scaffolding:

Some students may benefit from actually cutting the parallelograms from paper to prove their congruency. There are reproducible copies included at the end of the lesson.

- What is the area of each triangle?
  - 12 m^2
- What is the area of the parallelogram?
  - 24 m^2

---

b.   Draw in the other diagonal, from B to D. Find the area of both triangles ABD and BCD.

Student drawing and calculations are shown here.

Triangle ABD	Triangle BCD
$A = \frac{1}{2}bh$	$A = \frac{1}{2}bh$
$A = \frac{1}{2}(6\text{ m})(4\text{ m})$	$A = \frac{1}{2}(6\text{ m})(4\text{ m})$
$A = 12\text{ m}^2$	$A = 12\text{ m}^2$

Example 3 (10 minutes): Decomposing Trapezoids

Drawing one of the diagonals in a trapezoid separates the figure into two non-congruent triangles. Note that the height of these triangles is the same if the two bases of the trapezoid are used as bases of the triangles. If students want to consider the area of the rectangle around the trapezoid, two exterior right triangles should be formed. For isosceles trapezoids, these triangles are congruent. For scalene trapezoids, two non-congruent triangles result. A reproducible copy of trapezoids is included at the end of this lesson for use in further investigation. In all cases, the area can be found by averaging the length of the bases and multiplying by the height.

- What is the area of the garden plot? Use what you know about decomposing and composing to determine the area.

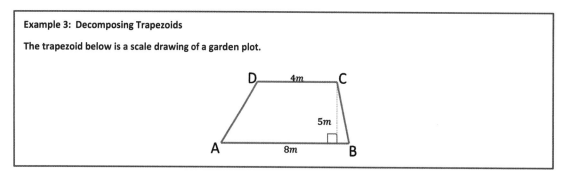

Example 3: Decomposing Trapezoids

The trapezoid below is a scale drawing of a garden plot.

If students need prompting, ask them to draw a diagonal from A to C.

Find the area of both triangles ABC and ACD. Then find the area of the trapezoid.

Student drawing and calculations are shown here.

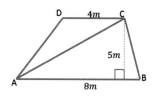

Triangle ABC

$$A = \frac{1}{2}bh$$

$$A = \frac{1}{2}(8 \text{ m})(5 \text{ m})$$

$$A = 20 \text{ m}^2$$

Triangle ACD

$$A = \frac{1}{2}bh$$

$$A = \frac{1}{2}(4 \text{ m})(5 \text{ m})$$

$$A = 10 \text{ m}^2$$

$$A = 20 \text{ m}^2 + 10 \text{ m}^2 = 30 \text{ m}^2$$

If necessary, further prompt students to draw in the other diagonal, from B to D.

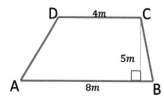

EUREKA
MATH

©2015 Great Minds. eureka-math.org
G6-M5-TE-B5-1.3.1-01.2016

Find the area of both triangles ABD and BCD. Then find the area of the trapezoid.

Student drawing and calculations are shown here.

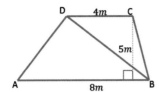

Triangle ABD

$A = \dfrac{1}{2}bh$

$A = \dfrac{1}{2}(8\ \text{m})(5\ \text{m})$

$A = 20\ \text{m}^2$

Triangle BCD

$A = \dfrac{1}{2}bh$

$A = \dfrac{1}{2}(4\ \text{m})(5\ \text{m})$

$A = 10\ \text{m}^2$

$$A = 20\ \text{m}^2 + 10\ \text{m}^2 = 30\ \text{m}^2$$

How else could we find this area?

We could consider the rectangle that surrounds the trapezoid. Find the area of that rectangle, and then subtract the area of both right triangles.

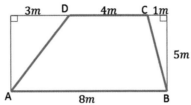

Student drawing and calculations are shown here.

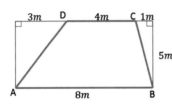

Area of Rectangle

$A = bh$

$A = (8\ \text{m})(5\ \text{m})$

$A = 40\ \text{m}^2$

Triangle 1

$A = \dfrac{1}{2}bh$

$A = \dfrac{1}{2}(3\ \text{m})(5\ \text{m})$

$A = 7.5\ \text{m}^2$

Triangle 2

$A = \dfrac{1}{2}bh$

$A = \dfrac{1}{2}(1\ \text{m})(5\ \text{m})$

$A = 2.5\ \text{m}^2$

$$A = 40\ \text{m}^2 - 7.5\ \text{m}^2 - 2.5\ \text{m}^2 = 30\ \text{m}^2$$

OR

$$A = 40\ \text{m}^2 - (7.5\ \text{m}^2 + 2.5\ \text{m}^2) = 30\ \text{m}^2$$

Closing (2 minutes)

- How can we find the area of irregularly shaped polygons?
  - *They can be broken into rectangles and triangles; we can then calculate the area of the figure using the formulas we already know.*
- Which operations did we use today to find the area of our irregular polygons?
  - *Some methods used addition of the area of the parts. Others used subtraction from a surrounding rectangle.*

Exit Ticket (3 minutes)

Name _____   Date _____

Lesson 5: The Area of Polygons Through Composition and Decomposition

Exit Ticket

1. Find the missing dimensions of the figure below, and then find the area. The figure is not drawn to scale.

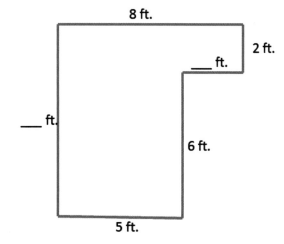

2. Find the area of the parallelogram below by decomposing into two triangles. The figure is not drawn to scale.

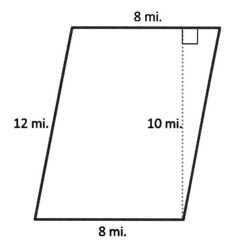

EUREKA MATH™

Exit Ticket Sample Solutions

1. Find the missing dimensions of the figure below, and then find the area. The figure is not drawn to scale.

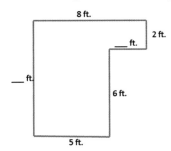

Solutions can be any of those below.

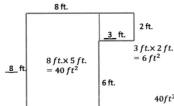

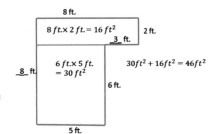

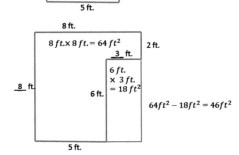

2. Find the area of the parallelogram below by decomposing into two triangles. The figure is not drawn to scale.

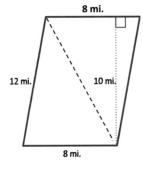

Area of Triangle 1

$A = \frac{1}{2}bh$

$A = \frac{1}{2} \times 8 \text{ mi.} \times 10 \text{ mi.}$

$A = 40 \text{ mi}^2$

Area of Triangle 2

$A = \frac{1}{2}bh$

$A = \frac{1}{2} \times 8 \text{ mi.} \times 10 \text{ mi.}$

$A = 40 \text{ mi}^2$

$$\text{Area of Parallelogram} = \text{Area of Triangle 1} + \text{Area of Triangle 2}$$

$$A = 40 \text{ mi}^2 + 40 \text{ mi}^2 = 80 \text{ mi}^2$$

The area of the parallelogram is 80 mi^2.

©2015 Great Minds. eureka-math.org
G6-M5-TE-B5-1.3.1-01.2016

Problem Set Sample Solutions

1. If $AB = 20$ units, $FE = 12$ units, $AF = 9$ units, and $DE = 12$ units, find the length of the other two sides. Then, find the area of the irregular polygon.

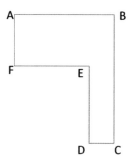

$CD = 8$ *units*, $BC = 21$ *units*, Area $= 276$ *square units*

2. If $DC = 1.9$ cm, $FE = 5.6$ cm, $AF = 4.8$ cm, and $BC = 10.9$ cm, find the length of the other two sides. Then, find the area of the irregular polygon.

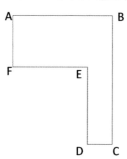

$AB = 7.5$ cm, $DE = 6.1$ cm, Area $= 47.59$ cm^2

3. Determine the area of the trapezoid below. The trapezoid is not drawn to scale.

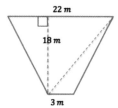

Area of Triangle 1

$A = \dfrac{1}{2}bh$

$A = \dfrac{1}{2} \times 22 \text{ m} \times 18 \text{ m}$

$A = 198 \text{ m}^2$

Area of Triangle 2

$A = \dfrac{1}{2}bh$

$A = \dfrac{1}{2} \times 3 \text{ m} \times 18 \text{ m}$

$A = 27 \text{ m}^2$

Area of Trapezoid = Area of Triangle 1 + Area of Triangle 2
Area $= 198 \text{ m}^2 + 27 \text{ m}^2 = 225 \text{ m}^2$

Lesson 5:   The Area of Polygons Through Composition and Decomposition

EUREKA MATH™

4. Determine the area of the shaded isosceles trapezoid below. The image is not drawn to scale.

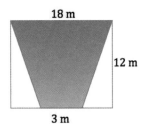

18 m

12 m

3 m

Area of Rectangle

$A = bh$

$A = 18 \text{ m} \times 12 \text{ m}$

$A = 216 \text{ m}^2$

Area of Triangles 1 and 2

$A = \frac{1}{2}bh$

$A = \frac{1}{2} \times 7.5 \text{ m} \times 12 \text{ m}$

$A = 45 \text{ m}^2$

Area of Trapezoid = Area of Rectangle − Area of Triangle 1 − Area of Triangle 2

$A = 216 \text{ m}^2 - 45 \text{ m}^2 - 45 \text{ m}^2 = 126 \text{ m}^2$

5. Here is a sketch of a wall that needs to be painted:

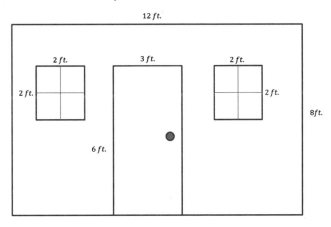

12 ft.

2 ft.

2 ft.

3 ft.

2 ft.

2 ft.

8 ft.

6 ft.

a. The windows and door will not be painted. Calculate the area of the wall that will be painted.

Whole wall: 12 ft. × 8 ft. = 96 ft²

Window: 2 ft. × 2 ft. = 4 ft² *There are two identical windows,* 4 ft² × 2 = 8 ft²

Door: 6 ft. × 3 ft. = 18 ft²

96 ft² − 8 ft² − 18 ft² = 70 ft²

b. If a quart of Extra-Thick Gooey Sparkle paint covers 30 ft², how many quarts must be purchased for the painting job?

$70 \div 30 = 2\frac{1}{3}$

Therefore, 3 quarts must be purchased.

6. The figure below shows a floor plan of a new apartment. New carpeting has been ordered, which will cover the living room and bedroom but not the kitchen or bathroom. Determine the carpeted area by composing or decomposing in two different ways, and then explain why they are equivalent.

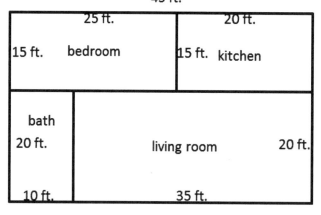

Answers will vary. Sample student responses are shown.

Bedroom: $15 \text{ ft.} \times 25 \text{ ft.} = 375 \text{ ft}^2$

Living room: $35 \text{ ft.} \times 20 \text{ ft.} = 700 \text{ ft}^2$

Sum of bedroom and living room: $375 \text{ ft}^2 + 700 \text{ ft}^2 = 1,075 \text{ ft}^2$

Alternatively, the whole apartment is $45 \text{ ft.} \times 35 \text{ ft.} = 1,575 \text{ ft}^2$.

Subtracting the kitchen and bath (300 ft^2 *and* 200 ft^2) *still gives* $1,075 \text{ ft}^2$.

The two areas are equivalent because they both represent the area of the living room and bedroom.

MP.7

EUREKA
MATH™

©2015 Great Minds. eureka-math.org
G6-M5-TE-B5-1.3.1-01.2016

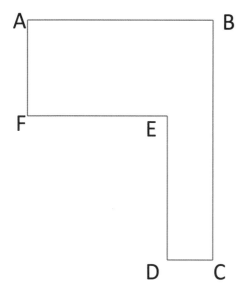

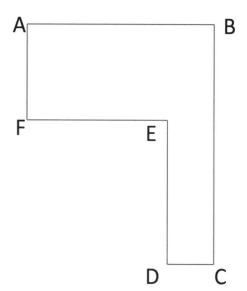

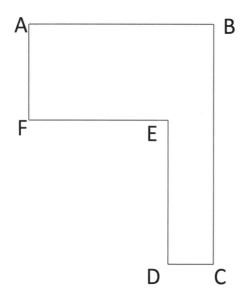

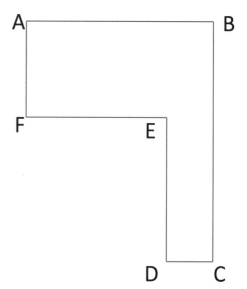

Lesson 5:   The Area of Polygons Through Composition and Decomposition

EUREKA MATH™

©2015 Great Minds. eureka-math.org
G6-M5-TE-B5-1.3.1-01.2016

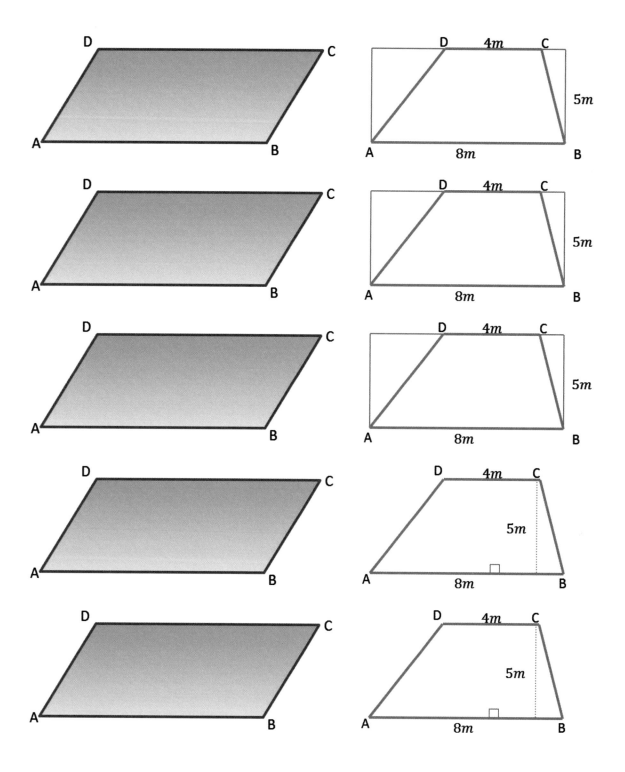

Lesson 5:   The Area of Polygons Through Composition and Decomposition

EUREKA MATH

©2015 Great Minds. eureka-math.org
G6-M5-TE-B5-1.3.1-01.2016

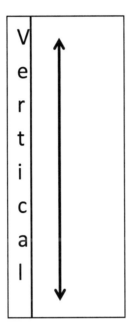

Lesson 6: Area in the Real World

Student Outcomes

- Students determine the area of composite figures in real-life contextual situations using composition and decomposition of polygons.
- Students determine the area of a missing region using composition and decomposition of polygons.

Lesson Notes

Finding area in real-world contexts can be done around the classroom, in a hallway, or in different locations around the school. This lesson requires the teacher to measure and record the dimensions of several objects and calculate the area ahead of time. Choices are dependent on time available and various students' needs. Different levels of student autonomy can be taken into account when grouping and deciding which objects to measure. Further, the measurement units and precision can be adjusted to students' ability level.

Floor tile, carpet area, walls, and furniture in the classroom can be used for this lesson. Smaller objects within the classroom may also be used, such as bulletin boards, notebooks, windows, and file cabinets. Exploring the school building for other real-world area problems might lead to a stage in an auditorium or walkway around a school pool. Of course, adhere to school policy regarding supervision of students, and be vigilant about safety. Students should not have to climb to make measurements.

Throughout the lesson, there are opportunities to compare unsimplified numerical expressions. These are important and should be emphasized because they help prepare students for algebra.

Classwork

MP.5 & MP.6

Gauge students' ability level regarding which units and level of precision will be used in this lesson. Using metric units for length and height of the classroom wall most likely requires measuring to the nearest 0.1 meter or 0.01 meter and multiplying decimals to calculate area. Choosing standard units allows precision to be set to the nearest foot, half foot, etc., but it could require multiplying fractional lengths.

Discussion (5 minutes)

Decide whether the whole group stays in the classroom or if carefully selected groups are sent out on a measurement mission to somewhere outside the classroom. All students should understand which measurement units to use and to what precision they are expected to measure.

- Area problems in the real world are all around us. Can you give an example of when you might need to know the area of something?

    □ *Area needs to be considered when covering an area with paint, carpet, tile, or wallpaper; wrapping a present; etc.*

> **Scaffolding:**
> As noted in the classwork section, there is great flexibility in this lesson, so it can be tailored to the needs of the class and can be easily individualized for both struggling and advanced learners. English language learners might need a mini-lesson on the concept of wallpaper with accompanying visuals and video, if possible.

- The Problem Set from the last lesson had a wall that was to be painted. What measurement units were used in that problem?
  - *All linear measurements were made in feet. Paint was calculated in quarts.*
- How precisely were the measurements made?
  - *Measurements were most likely measured to the nearest foot. Paint was rounded up to the next quart.*
- Could those measurements have been made more precisely?
  - *Yes, measurements could have been made to the nearest inch, half inch, or some other smaller fraction of an inch. Paint can be purchased in pints.*
- We can measure the dimensions of objects and use those measurements to calculate the surface area of the object. Our first object will be a wall in this classroom.

Exploratory Challenge 1 (34 minutes): Classroom Wall Paint

> **Scaffolding:**
> This same context can be worded more simply for English language learners, and students working below grade level would benefit from a quick pantomime of painting a wall. A short video clip might also set the context quickly.

Exploratory Challenge 1: Classroom Wall Paint

The custodians are considering painting our classroom next summer. In order to know how much paint they must buy, the custodians need to know the total surface area of the walls. Why do you think they need to know this, and how can we find the information?

All classroom walls are different. Taking overall measurements and then subtracting windows, doors, or other areas will give a good approximation.

Make a prediction of how many square feet of painted surface there are on one wall in the room. If the floor has square tiles, these can be used as a guide.

Students make a prediction of how many square feet of painted surface there are on one wall in the room. If the floor has square tiles, these can be used as a guide.

Decide beforehand the information in the first three columns. Measure lengths and widths, and calculate areas. Ask students to explain their predictions.

Estimate the dimensions and the area. Predict the area before you measure. My prediction: _____ ft².

a. Measure and sketch one classroom wall. Include measurements of windows, doors, or anything else that would not be painted.

Student responses will depend on the teacher's choice of wall.

Object or Item to Be Measured	Measurement Units	Precision (measure to the nearest)	Length	Width	Expression That Shows the Area	Area
Door	feet	half foot	$6\frac{1}{2}$ ft.	$3\frac{1}{2}$ ft.	$6\frac{1}{2}$ ft. $\times$ $3\frac{1}{2}$ ft.	$22\frac{3}{4}$ ft²

b. Work with your partners and your sketch of the wall to determine the area that needs paint. Show your sketch and calculations below; clearly mark your measurements and area calculations.

c. A gallon of paint covers about 350 ft^2. Write an expression that shows the total area of the wall. Evaluate it to find how much paint is needed to paint the wall.

Answers will vary based on the size of the wall. Fractional answers are to be expected.

d. How many gallons of paint would need to be purchased to paint the wall?

Answers will vary based on the size of the wall. The answer from part (d) should be an exact quantity because gallons of paint are discrete units. Fractional answers from part (c) must be rounded up to the nearest whole gallon.

Exploratory Challenge 2 (Optional—15 minutes)

Assign other walls in the classroom for groups to measure and calculate the area, or send some students to measure and sketch other real-world area problems found around the school. The teacher should measure the objects prior to the lesson using the same units and precision students are using. Objects may have to be measured multiple times if the activity has been differentiated using different units or levels of precision.

Exploratory Challenge 2

Object or Item to Be Measured	Measurement Units	Precision (measure to the nearest)	Length	Width	Area
Door	feet	half foot	$6\frac{1}{2}$ ft.	$3\frac{1}{2}$ ft.	$22\frac{3}{4}$ ft^2

Closing (3 minutes)

- What real-life situations require us to use area?
    - *Floor covering, like carpets and tiles, require area measurements. Wallpaper and paint also call for area measurements. Fabric used for clothing and other items also demand that length and width be considered. Wrapping a present; installing turf on a football field; or laying bricks, pavers, or concrete for a deck or patio are other real-world examples.*
- Sometimes measurements are given in inches and area is calculated in square feet. How many square inches are in a square foot?
    - *There are 144 square inches in a square foot, $12 \text{ in.} \times 12 \text{ in.} = 144 \text{ in}^2$.*

Exit Ticket (3 minutes)

Name _____   Date _____

Lesson 6: Area in the Real World

Exit Ticket

Find the area of the deck around this pool. The deck is the white area in the diagram.

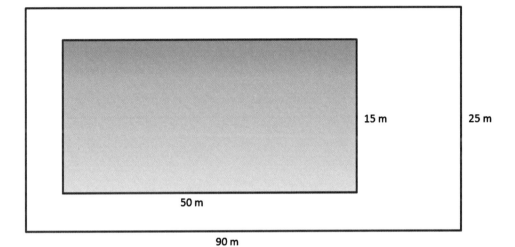

Exit Ticket Sample Solutions

Find the area of the deck around this pool. The deck is the white area in the diagram.

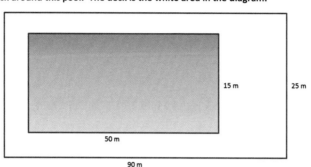

Area of Walkway and Pool	Area of Pool	Area of Walkway
$A = bh$	$A = bh$	$2,250 \text{ m}^2 - 750 \text{ m}^2 = 1,500 \text{ m}^2$
$A = 90 \text{ m} \times 25 \text{ m}$	$A = 50 \text{ m} \times 15 \text{ m}$	
$A = 2,250 \text{ m}^2$	$A = 750 \text{ m}^2$	

Problem Set Sample Solutions

1. Below is a drawing of a wall that is to be covered with either wallpaper or paint. The wall is 8 ft. high and 16 ft. wide. The window, mirror, and fireplace are not to be painted or papered. The window measures 18 in. wide and 14 ft. high. The fireplace is 5 ft. wide and 3 ft. high, while the mirror above the fireplace is 4 ft. wide and 2 ft. high. (Note: this drawing is not to scale.)

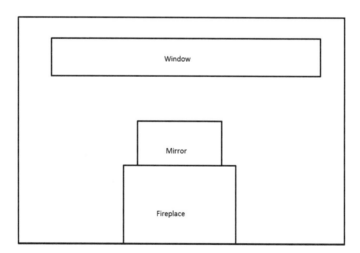

   a. How many square feet of wallpaper are needed to cover the wall?

   Total wall area = $8 \text{ ft.} \times 16 \text{ ft.} = 128 \text{ ft}^2$ *Window area* = $14 \text{ ft.} \times 1.5 \text{ ft.} = 21 \text{ ft}^2$

   Fireplace area = $3 \text{ ft.} \times 5 \text{ ft.} = 15 \text{ ft}^2$ *Mirror area* = $4 \text{ ft.} \times 2 \text{ ft.} = 8 \text{ ft}^2$

   Net wall area to be covered $128 \text{ ft}^2 - (21 \text{ ft}^2 + 15 \text{ ft}^2 + 8 \text{ ft}^2) = 84 \text{ ft}^2$

EUREKA MATH™

b. The wallpaper is sold in rolls that are 18 in. wide and 33 ft. long. Rolls of solid color wallpaper will be used, so patterns do not have to match up.

   i.   What is the area of one roll of wallpaper?

       Area of one roll of wallpaper: $33 \text{ ft.} \times 1.5 \text{ ft.} = 49.5 \text{ ft}^2$

   ii. How many rolls would be needed to cover the wall?

       $84 \text{ ft}^2 \div 49.5 \text{ ft}^2 \approx 1.7$; *therefore, 2 rolls would need to be purchased.*

c. This week, the rolls of wallpaper are on sale for $\$11.99$/roll. Find the cost of covering the wall with wallpaper.

   We need two rolls of wallpaper to cover the wall, which will cost $\$11.99 \times 2 = \$23.98$.

d. A gallon of special textured paint covers 200 ft^2 and is on sale for $\$22.99$/gallon. The wall needs to be painted twice (the wall needs two coats of paint). Find the cost of using paint to cover the wall.

   Total wall area $= 8 \text{ ft.} \times 16 \text{ ft.} = 128 \text{ ft}^2$

   Window area $= 14 \text{ ft.} \times 1.5 \text{ ft.} = 21 \text{ ft}^2$

   Fireplace area $= 3 \text{ ft.} \times 5 \text{ ft.} = 15 \text{ ft}^2$

   Mirror area $= 4 \text{ ft.} \times 2 \text{ ft.} = 8 \text{ ft}^2$

   Net wall area to be covered $128 \text{ ft}^2 - (21 \text{ ft}^2 + 15 \text{ ft}^2 + 8 \text{ ft}^2) = 84 \text{ ft}^2$

   If the wall needs to be painted twice, we need to paint a total area of $84 \text{ ft}^2 \times 2 = 168 \text{ ft}^2$. *One gallon is enough paint for this wall, so the cost will be* $\$22.99$.

2. A classroom has a length of 30 ft. and a width of 20 ft. The flooring is to be replaced by tiles. If each tile has a length of 36 in. and a width of 24 in., how many tiles are needed to cover the classroom floor?

   Area of the classroom: $30 \text{ ft.} \times 20 \text{ ft.} = 600 \text{ ft}^2$

   Area of each tile: $3 \text{ ft.} \times 2 \text{ ft.} = 6 \text{ ft}^2$

$$\frac{\text{Area of the classroom}}{\text{Area of each tile}} = \frac{600 \text{ ft}^2}{6 \text{ ft}^2} = 100$$

   100 *tiles are needed to cover the classroom floor. Allow for students who say that if the tiles are* $3 \text{ ft.} \times 2 \text{ ft.}$, *and they orient them in a way that corresponds to the* $30 \text{ ft.} \times 20 \text{ ft.}$ *room, then they will have ten rows of ten tiles giving them 100 tiles. Using this method, the students do not need to calculate the areas and divide. Orienting the tiles the other way, students could say that they will need 105 tiles as they will need* $6\frac{2}{3}$ *rows of 15 tiles, and since* $\frac{2}{3}$ *of a tile cannot be purchased, they will need 7 rows of 15 tiles.*

3. Challenge: Assume that the tiles from Problem 2 are unavailable. Another design is available, but the tiles are square, 18 in. on a side. If these are to be installed, how many must be ordered?

   Solutions will vary. An even number of tiles fit on the 30 foot length of the room (20 tiles), but the width requires $13\frac{1}{3}$ *tiles. This accounts for a 20 tile by 13 tile array.* $20 \times 13 = 260$. *260 tiles need to be ordered.*

   The remaining area is $30 \text{ ft.} \times 0.5 \text{ ft.}$ ($20 \times \frac{1}{3}$ *tile*)

   Since 20 of the $\frac{1}{3}$ *tiles are needed, 7 additional tiles must be cut to form* $\frac{21}{3}$. *20 of these will be used with* $\frac{1}{3}$ *of 1 tile left over.*

   Using the same logic as above, some students may correctly say they will need 280 tiles.

4. A rectangular flower bed measures 10 m by 6 m. It has a path 2 m wide around it. Find the area of the path.

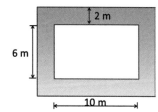

Total area: $14 \text{ m} \times 10 \text{ m} = 140 \text{ m}^2$

Flower bed area: $10 \text{ m} \times 6 \text{ m} = 60 \text{ m}^2$

Area of path: $140 \text{ m}^2 - 60 \text{ m}^2 = 80 \text{ m}^2$

5. A diagram of Tracy's deck is shown below, shaded blue. He wants to cover the missing portion of his deck with soil in order to grow a garden.

  a. Find the area of the missing portion of the deck. Write the expression and evaluate it.

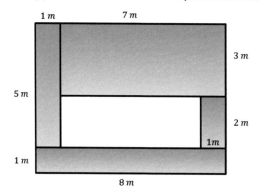

Students should use one of two methods to find the area: finding the dimensions of the garden area (interior rectangle, 6 m × 2 m) or finding the total area minus the sum of the four wooden areas, shown below.

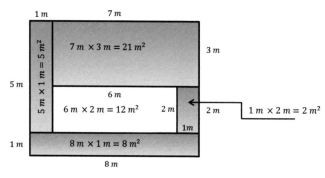

$6 \text{ m} \times 2 \text{ m} = 12 \text{ m}^2$

OR

$8 \times 6 - 7 \times 3 - 5 \times 1 - 8 \times 1 - 2 \times 1 = 12$ *(All linear units are in meters; area is in square meters.)*

  b. Find the area of the missing portion of the deck using a different method. Write the expression and evaluate it.

  Students should choose whichever method was not used in part (a).

Lesson 6:   Area in the Real World

EUREKA
MATH

c. Write two equivalent expressions that could be used to determine the area of the missing portion of the deck.

$8 \times 6 - 7 \times 3 - 5 \times 1 - 8 \times 1 - 2 \times 1$

6×2

d. Explain how each expression demonstrates a different understanding of the diagram.

One expression shows the dimensions of the garden area (interior rectangle, 6 m × 2 m), and one shows finding the total area minus the sum of the four wooden areas.

6. The entire large rectangle below has an area of $3\frac{1}{2}$ ft². If the dimensions of the white rectangle are as shown below, write and solve an equation to find the area, A, of the shaded region.

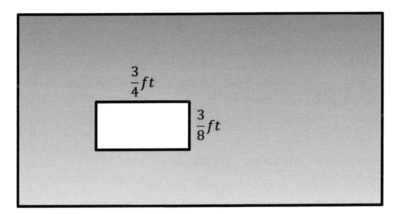

$$\frac{3}{4} \text{ ft.} \times \frac{3}{8} \text{ ft.} = \frac{9}{32} \text{ ft}^2$$

$$\frac{9}{32} \text{ ft}^2 + A = 3\frac{1}{2} \text{ ft}^2$$

$$A = 3\frac{7}{32} \text{ ft}^2$$

©2015 Great Minds. eureka-math.org
G6-M5-TE-B5-1.3.1-01.2016

Mathematics Curriculum

Topic B

Polygons on the Coordinate Plane

6.G.A.3

Focus Standard:	6.G.A.3	Draw polygons in the coordinate plane given coordinates for the vertices; use coordinates to find the length of a side joining points with the same first coordinate or the same second coordinate. Apply these techniques in the context of solving real-world and mathematical problems.
Instructional Days:	4	
Lesson 7:	Distance on the Coordinate Plane (P)[1]	
Lesson 8:	Drawing Polygons in the Coordinate Plane (P)	
Lesson 9:	Determining Perimeter and Area of Polygons on the Coordinate Plane (P)	
Lesson 10:	Distance, Perimeter, and Area in the Real World (E)	

In Lesson 7 of Topic B, students apply prior knowledge from Module 3 by using absolute value to determine the distance between integers on the coordinate plane in order to find side lengths of polygons. Then they move to Lesson 8, where students draw polygons in the coordinate plane when given coordinates for vertices. They find the area enclosed by a polygon by composing and decomposing, using polygons with known area formulas. They name coordinates that define a polygon with specific properties. In Lesson 9, students find the perimeter of rectilinear figures using coordinates to find the length of a side joining points with the same first coordinate or the same second coordinate. They continue to find the area enclosed by a polygon on the coordinate plane by composition and decomposition. The topic concludes with Lesson 10, where students apply their knowledge of distance, perimeter, and area to real-life contextual situations. Students learn more than a key-word reading of contexts. They comprehend different problem contexts and apply concepts accordingly.

---

[1]Lesson Structure Key: **P**-Problem Set Lesson, **M**-Modeling Cycle Lesson, **E**-Exploration Lesson, **S**-Socratic Lesson

Lesson 7: Distance on the Coordinate Plane

Student Outcomes

- Students use absolute value to determine distance between integers on the coordinate plane in order to find side lengths of polygons.

Lesson Notes

Students build on their work in Module 3. More specifically, they build on their work with absolute value from Lessons 11 and 12 as well as on their work with coordinate planes from Lessons 17–19.

Also note that each square unit on the coordinate plane represents 1 unit.

Classwork

Fluency Exercise (5 minutes): Addition of Decimals

Sprint: Refer to the Sprints and the Sprint Delivery Script sections of the Module 4 Module Overview for directions to administer Sprints.

Example (15 minutes)

Example

Determine the lengths of the given line segments by determining the distance between the two endpoints.

Line Segment	Point	Point	Distance	Proof
$\overline{AB}$	$(-2, 8)$	$(9, 8)$	11	
$\overline{BC}$	$(9, 8)$	$(9, 2)$	6	
$\overline{CD}$	$(9, 2)$	$(9, -5)$	7	
$\overline{BD}$	$(9, 8)$	$(9, -5)$	13	
$\overline{DE}$	$(9, -5)$	$(-2, -5)$	11	
$\overline{EF}$	$(-2, -5)$	$(-2, -2)$	3	
$\overline{FG}$	$(-2, -2)$	$(-2, 6)$	8	
$\overline{EG}$	$(-2, -5)$	$(-2, 6)$	11	
$\overline{GA}$	$(-2, 6)$	$(-2, 8)$	2	
$\overline{FA}$	$(-2, -2)$	$(-2, 8)$	10	
$\overline{EA}$	$(-2, -5)$	$(-2, 8)$	13	

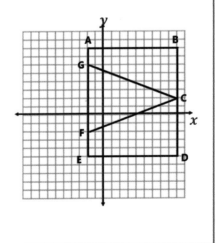

MP.8

- What do you notice about each pair of points?

  □ *In each pair, either the x-coordinates are the same or the y-coordinates are the same.*

- How could you calculate the lengths of the segments using only the coordinates of their endpoints? (Please note, it is possible that English language learners may not understand this question and may need modeling to understand. In addition, students may need to be reminded that distances or lengths are positive.)

  □ *Either the x-values are the same or the y-values are the same. Let's ignore these and focus on the coordinates that are different. We can subtract the absolute values of the endpoints if both points have the same sign. If the signs are different, we can add the absolute values.*

- Why are the steps different? For example, why are the steps for $\overline{EA}$ different than the steps for $\overline{GA}$?

It may be helpful for students to go back to the image and walk through the steps visually when trying to describe the steps and the difference between the two.

MP.8

  □ *When we determine the distance from A to E, we are really adding together the distance from A to the x-axis and the distance from E to the x-axis. We add the distances together because they are on opposite sides of the x-axis. When determining the distance from A to G, we are taking the distance from A to the x-axis and G to the x-axis and finding the difference because they are on the same side of the x-axis.*

- Add a fourth column to the table to show proof of your distances.

Line Segment	Point	Point	Distance	Proof
$\overline{AB}$	$(-2, 8)$	$(9, 8)$	11	$\lvert 9 \rvert + \lvert -2 \rvert = 11$
$\overline{BC}$	$(9, 8)$	$(9, 2)$	6	$\lvert 8 \rvert - \lvert 2 \rvert = 6$
$\overline{CD}$	$(9, 2)$	$(9, -5)$	7	$\lvert 2 \rvert + \lvert -5 \rvert = 7$
$\overline{BD}$	$(9, 8)$	$(9, -5)$	13	$\lvert 8 \rvert + \lvert -5 \rvert = 13$
$\overline{DE}$	$(9, -5)$	$(-2, -5)$	11	$\lvert 9 \rvert + \lvert -2 \rvert = 11$
$\overline{EF}$	$(-2, -5)$	$(-2, -2)$	3	$\lvert -5 \rvert - \lvert -2 \rvert = 3$
$\overline{FG}$	$(-2, -2)$	$(-2, 6)$	8	$\lvert -2 \rvert + \lvert 6 \rvert = 8$
$\overline{EG}$	$(-2, -5)$	$(-2, 6)$	11	$\lvert -5 \rvert + \lvert 6 \rvert = 11$
$\overline{GA}$	$(-2, 6)$	$(-2, 8)$	2	$\lvert 8 \rvert - \lvert 6 \rvert = 2$
$\overline{FA}$	$(-2, -2)$	$(-2, 8)$	10	$\lvert -2 \rvert + \lvert 8 \rvert = 10$
$\overline{EA}$	$(-2, -5)$	$(-2, 8)$	13	$\lvert -5 \rvert + \lvert 8 \rvert = 13$

- How would the distances from one point to another change if each square unit on the plane were 2 units in length? Or 3 units in length?

  □ *The distance would double if each square unit were worth 2 units. The distance would triple if each square unit were actually equal to 3 units in length.*

Exercise (15 minutes)

Exercise

Complete the table using the diagram on the coordinate plane.

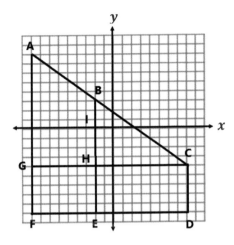

Line Segment	Point	Point	Distance	Proof
$\overline{BI}$	$(-2,3)$	$(-2,0)$	3	$|3|+|0|=3$
$\overline{BH}$	$(-2,3)$	$(-2,-4)$	7	$|3|+|-4|=7$
$\overline{BE}$	$(-2,3)$	$(-2,-9)$	12	$|3|+|-9|=12$
$\overline{GH}$	$(-9,-4)$	$(-2,-4)$	7	$|-9|-|-2|=7$
$\overline{HC}$	$(-2,-4)$	$(8,-4)$	10	$|-2|+|8|=10$
$\overline{GC}$	$(-9,-4)$	$(8,-4)$	17	$|-9|+|8|=17$
$\overline{CD}$	$(8,-4)$	$(8,-9)$	5	$|-9|-|-4|=5$
$\overline{FG}$	$(-9,-9)$	$(-9,-4)$	5	$|-9|-|-4|=5$
$\overline{GA}$	$(-9,-4)$	$(-9,8)$	12	$|-4|+|8|=12$
$\overline{AF}$	$(-9,8)$	$(-9,-9)$	17	$|8|+|-9|=17$

Extension (3 minutes)

Extension

For each problem below, write the coordinates of two points that are 5 units apart with the segment connecting these points having the following characteristics.

a. The segment is vertical.

Answers may vary. One possible solution is $(2,1)$ and $(2,6)$.

b. The segment intersects the x-axis.

Answers may vary. One possible solution is $(3,-4)$ and $(3,1)$.

c.   The segment intersects the y-axis.

Answers may vary. One possible solution is $(-4, 3)$ and $(1, 3)$.

d.   The segment is vertical and lies above the x-axis.

Answers may vary. One possible solution is $(-3, 5)$ and $(-3, 10)$.

Closing (2 minutes)

- What did all of the segments used in the lesson have in common?
  - *They were all either vertical or horizontal.*
- How could you determine whether the segments were vertical or horizontal given the coordinates of their endpoints?
  - *If the x-coordinates were the same for both points, then the segment was vertical. If the y-coordinates were the same, then the segment was horizontal.*
- How did you calculate the length of the segments given the coordinates of the endpoints?
  - *If the coordinates that were not the same had the same sign, we subtracted the absolute values of the coordinates.*
  - *If the coordinates that were not the same had different signs, we added the absolute values of the coordinates.*

Exit Ticket (5 minutes)

©2015 Great Minds. eureka-math.org
G6-M5-TE-B5-1.3.1-01.2016

Name _____   Date _____

Lesson 7: Distance on the Coordinate Plane

Exit Ticket

Use absolute value to show the lengths of $\overline{AB}$, $\overline{BC}$, $\overline{CD}$, $\overline{DE}$, and $\overline{EF}$.

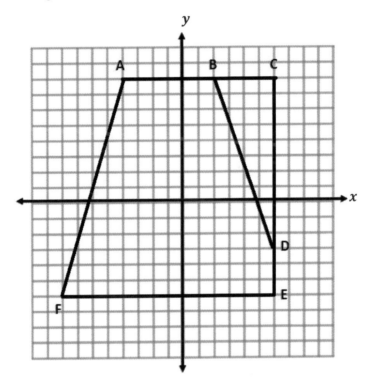

Line Segment	Point	Point	Distance	Proof
$\overline{AB}$				
$\overline{BC}$				
$\overline{CD}$				
$\overline{DE}$				
$\overline{EF}$				

Exit Ticket Sample Solutions

Use absolute value to show the lengths of $\overline{AB}, \overline{BC}, \overline{CD}, \overline{DE},$ and $\overline{EF}$.

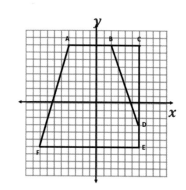

Line Segment	Point	Point	Distance	Proof
$\overline{AB}$	$(-4,8)$	$(2,8)$	6	$\lvert-4\rvert+\lvert2\rvert=6$
$\overline{BC}$	$(2,8)$	$(6,8)$	4	$\lvert6\rvert-\lvert2\rvert=4$
$\overline{CD}$	$(6,8)$	$(6,-3)$	11	$\lvert8\rvert+\lvert-3\rvert=11$
$\overline{DE}$	$(6,-3)$	$(6,-6)$	3	$\lvert-6\rvert-\lvert-3\rvert=3$
$\overline{EF}$	$(6,-6)$	$(-8,-6)$	14	$\lvert6\rvert+\lvert-8\rvert=14$

Problem Set Sample Solutions

1. Given the pairs of points, determine whether the segment that joins them is horizontal, vertical, or neither.

    a. $X(3,5)$ and $Y(-2,5)$ _Horizontal_

    b. $M(-4,9)$ and $N(4,-9)$ _Neither_

    c. $E(-7,1)$ and $F(-7,4)$ _Vertical_

2. Complete the table using absolute value to determine the lengths of the line segments.

Line Segment	Point	Point	Distance	Proof
$\overline{AB}$	$(-3,5)$	$(7,5)$	10	$\lvert-3\rvert+\lvert7\rvert=10$
$\overline{CD}$	$(1,-3)$	$(-6,-3)$	7	$\lvert1\rvert+\lvert-6\rvert=7$
$\overline{EF}$	$(2,-9)$	$(2,-3)$	6	$\lvert-9\rvert-\lvert-3\rvert=6$
$\overline{GH}$	$(6,1)$	$(6,16)$	15	$\lvert16\rvert-\lvert1\rvert=15$
$\overline{JK}$	$(-3,0)$	$(-3,12)$	12	$\lvert12\rvert+\lvert0\rvert=12$

EUREKA MATH

3. Complete the table using the diagram and absolute value to determine the lengths of the line segments.

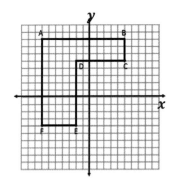

Line Segment	Point	Point	Distance	Proof
$\overline{AB}$	$(-7, 8)$	$(5, 8)$	12	$|-7| + |5| = 12$
$\overline{BC}$	$(5, 8)$	$(5, 5)$	3	$|8| - |5| = 3$
$\overline{CD}$	$(5, 5)$	$(-2, 5)$	7	$|5| + |-2| = 7$
$\overline{DE}$	$(-2, 5)$	$(-2, -4)$	9	$|5| + |-4| = 9$
$\overline{EF}$	$(-2, -4)$	$(-7, -4)$	5	$|-7| - |-2| = 5$
$\overline{FA}$	$(-7, -4)$	$(-7, 8)$	12	$|-4| + |8| = 12$

4. Complete the table using the diagram and absolute value to determine the lengths of the line segments.

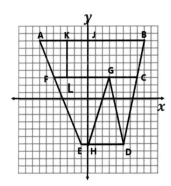

Line Segment	Point	Point	Distance	Proof
$\overline{AB}$	$(-7, 8)$	$(8, 8)$	15	$|-7| + |8| = 15$
$\overline{CG}$	$(7, 3)$	$(3, 3)$	4	$|7| - |3| = 4$
$\overline{CF}$	$(7, 3)$	$(-5, 3)$	12	$|7| + |-5| = 12$
$\overline{GF}$	$(3, 3)$	$(-5, 3)$	8	$|3| + |-5| = 8$
$\overline{DH}$	$(5, -6)$	$(0, -6)$	5	$|5| + |0| = 5$
$\overline{DE}$	$(5, -6)$	$(-1, -6)$	6	$|5| + |-1| = 6$
$\overline{HJ}$	$(0, -6)$	$(0, 8)$	14	$|-6| + |8| = 14$
$\overline{KL}$	$(-3, 8)$	$(-3, 3)$	5	$|8| - |3| = 5$

5. Name two points in different quadrants that form a vertical line segment that is 8 units in length.

   Answers will vary. One possible solution is $(2, 5)$ and $(2, -3)$.

6. Name two points in the same quadrant that form a horizontal line segment that is 5 units in length.

   Answers will vary. One possible solution is $(-4, -11)$ and $(-9, -11)$.

Number Correct: _____

Addition of Decimals II—Round 1

Directions: Evaluate each expression.

1.	2.5 + 4	
2.	2.5 + 0.4	
3.	2.5 + 0.04	
4.	2.5 + 0.004	
5.	2.5 + 0.0004	
6.	6 + 1.3	
7.	0.6 + 1.3	
8.	0.06 + 1.3	
9.	0.006 + 1.3	
10.	0.0006 + 1.3	
11.	0.6 + 13	
12.	7 + 0.2	
13.	0.7 + 0.02	
14.	0.07 + 0.2	
15.	0.7 + 2	
16.	7 + 0.02	
17.	6 + 0.3	
18.	0.6 + 0.03	
19.	0.06 + 0.3	
20.	0.6 + 3	
21.	6 + 0.03	
22.	0.6 + 0.3	

23.	4.5 + 3.1	
24.	4.5 + 0.31	
25.	4.5 + 0.031	
26.	0.45 + 0.031	
27.	0.045 + 0.031	
28.	12 + 0.36	
29.	1.2 + 3.6	
30.	1.2 + 0.36	
31.	1.2 + 0.036	
32.	0.12 + 0.036	
33.	0.012 + 0.036	
34.	0.7 + 3	
35.	0.7 + 0.3	
36.	0.07 + 0.03	
37.	0.007 + 0.003	
38.	5 + 0.5	
39.	0.5 + 0.5	
40.	0.05 + 0.05	
41.	0.005 + 0.005	
42.	0.11 + 19	
43.	1.1 + 1.9	
44.	0.11 + 0.19	

Addition of Decimals II—Round 1 [KEY]

Directions: Evaluate each expression.

1.	2.5 + 4	6.5	23.	4.5 + 3.1	7.6
2.	2.5 + 0.4	2.9	24.	4.5 + 0.31	4.81
3.	2.5 + 0.04	2.54	25.	4.5 + 0.031	4.531
4.	2.5 + 0.004	2.504	26.	0.45 + 0.031	0.481
5.	2.5 + 0.0004	2.5004	27.	0.045 + 0.031	0.076
6.	6 + 1.3	7.3	28.	12 + 0.36	12.36
7.	0.6 + 1.3	1.9	29.	1.2 + 3.6	4.8
8.	0.06 + 1.3	1.36	30.	1.2 + 0.36	1.56
9.	0.006 + 1.3	1.306	31.	1.2 + 0.036	1.236
10.	0.0006 + 1.3	1.3006	32.	0.12 + 0.036	0.156
11.	0.6 + 13	13.6	33.	0.012 + 0.036	0.048
12.	7 + 0.2	7.2	34.	0.7 + 3	3.7
13.	0.7 + 0.02	0.72	35.	0.7 + 0.3	1
14.	0.07 + 0.2	0.27	36.	0.07 + 0.03	0.1
15.	0.7 + 2	2.7	37.	0.007 + 0.003	0.01
16.	7 + 0.02	7.02	38.	5 + 0.5	5.5
17.	6 + 0.3	6.3	39.	0.5 + 0.5	1
18.	0.6 + 0.03	0.63	40.	0.05 + 0.05	0.1
19.	0.06 + 0.3	0.36	41.	0.005 + 0.005	0.01
20.	0.6 + 3	3.6	42.	0.11 + 19	19.11
21.	6 + 0.03	6.03	43.	1.1 + 1.9	3
22.	0.6 + 0.3	0.9	44.	0.11 + 0.19	0.3

Number Correct: _____

Improvement: _____

Addition of Decimals II—Round 2

Directions: Evaluate each expression.

1.	7.4 + 3	
2.	7.4 + 0.3	
3.	7.4 + 0.03	
4.	7.4 + 0.003	
5.	7.4 + 0.0003	
6.	6 + 2.2	
7.	0.6 + 2.2	
8.	0.06 + 2.2	
9.	0.006 + 2.2	
10.	0.0006 + 2.2	
11.	0.6 + 22	
12.	7 + 0.8	
13.	0.7 + 0.08	
14.	0.07 + 0.8	
15.	0.7 + 8	
16.	7 + 0.08	
17.	0.5 + 0.4	
18.	0.5 + 0.04	
19.	0.05 + 0.4	
20.	0.5 + 4	
21.	5 + 0.04	
22.	5 + 0.4	

23.	3.6 + 2.3	
24.	3.6 + 0.23	
25.	3.6 + 0.023	
26.	0.36 + 0.023	
27.	0.036 + 0.023	
28.	0.13 + 56	
29.	1.3 + 5.6	
30.	1.3 + 0.56	
31.	1.3 + 0.056	
32.	0.13 + 0.056	
33.	0.013 + 0.056	
34.	2 + 0.8	
35.	0.2 + 0.8	
36.	0.02 + 0.08	
37.	0.002 + 0.008	
38.	0.16 + 14	
39.	1.6 + 1.4	
40.	0.16 + 0.14	
41.	0.016 + 0.014	
42.	15 + 0.15	
43.	1.5 + 1.5	
44.	0.15 + 0.15	

Lesson 7:   Distance on the Coordinate Plane

EUREKA MATH

©2015 Great Minds. eureka-math.org
G6-M5-TE-B5-1.3.1-01.2016

Addition of Decimals II—Round 2 [KEY]

Directions: Evaluate each expression.

1.	$7.4 + 3$	10.4		23.	$3.6 + 2.3$	5.9
2.	$7.4 + 0.3$	7.7		24.	$3.6 + 0.23$	3.83
3.	$7.4 + 0.03$	7.43		25.	$3.6 + 0.023$	3.623
4.	$7.4 + 0.003$	7.403		26.	$0.36 + 0.023$	0.383
5.	$7.4 + 0.0003$	7.4003		27.	$0.036 + 0.023$	0.059
6.	$6 + 2.2$	8.2		28.	$0.13 + 56$	56.13
7.	$0.6 + 2.2$	2.8		29.	$1.3 + 5.6$	6.9
8.	$0.06 + 2.2$	2.26		30.	$1.3 + 0.56$	1.86
9.	$0.006 + 2.2$	2.206		31.	$1.3 + 0.056$	1.356
10.	$0.0006 + 2.2$	2.2006		32.	$0.13 + 0.056$	0.186
11.	$0.6 + 22$	22.6		33.	$0.013 + 0.056$	0.069
12.	$7 + 0.8$	7.8		34.	$2 + 0.8$	2.8
13.	$0.7 + 0.08$	0.78		35.	$0.2 + 0.8$	1
14.	$0.07 + 0.8$	0.87		36.	$0.02 + 0.08$	0.1
15.	$0.7 + 8$	8.7		37.	$0.002 + 0.008$	0.01
16.	$7 + 0.08$	7.08		38.	$0.16 + 14$	14.16
17.	$0.5 + 0.4$	0.9		39.	$1.6 + 1.4$	3
18.	$0.5 + 0.04$	0.54		40.	$0.16 + 0.14$	0.3
19.	$0.05 + 0.4$	0.45		41.	$0.016 + 0.014$	0.03
20.	$0.5 + 4$	4.5		42.	$15 + 0.15$	15.15
21.	$5 + 0.04$	5.04		43.	$1.5 + 1.5$	3
22.	$5 + 0.4$	5.4		44.	$0.15 + 0.15$	0.3

EUREKA
MATH™

Lesson 7:   Distance on the Coordinate Plane   **103**

©2015 Great Minds. eureka-math.org
G6-M5-TE-B5-1.3.1-01.2016

Lesson 8: Drawing Polygons in the Coordinate Plane

Student Outcomes

- Given coordinates for the vertices, students draw polygons in the coordinate plane. Students find the area enclosed by a polygon by composing or decomposing using polygons with known area formulas.
- Students name coordinates that define a polygon with specific properties.

Lesson Notes

Helping students understand the contextual pronunciation of the word *coordinate* may be useful. Compare it to the verb *coordinate*, which has a slightly different pronunciation and a different stress. In addition, it may be useful to revisit the singular and plural forms of the word *vertex (vertices)*.

Classwork

Examples 1–4 (20 minutes)

Students graph all four examples on the same coordinate plane.

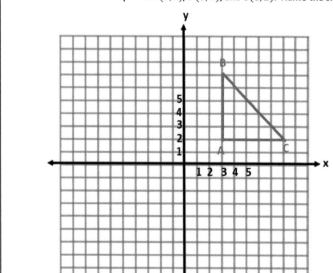

Examples

1. Plot and connect the points $A(3,2)$, $B(3,7)$, and $C(8,2)$. Name the shape, and determine the area of the polygon.

Right Triangle

$$A = \frac{1}{2}bh$$

$$A = \frac{1}{2}(5 \text{ units})(5 \text{ units})$$

$$A = \frac{1}{2}(25 \text{ units}^2)$$

$$A = 12.5 \text{ units}^2$$

EUREKA
MATH™

- How did you determine the length of the base and height?
  - *In this example, I subtracted the values of the coordinates. For AB, I subtracted the absolute value of the y-coordinates. For AC, I subtracted the absolute value of the x-coordinates.*

---

2. Plot and connect the points $E(-8, 8)$, $F(-2, 5)$, and $G(-7, 2)$. Then give the best name for the polygon, and determine the area.

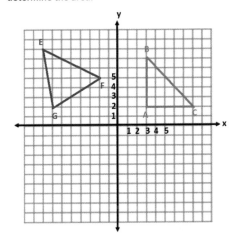

The shape is a triangle.

Area of Square

$A = s^2$

$A = (6 \text{ units})^2$

$A = 36 \text{ units}^2$

Area of Triangle 1

$A = \frac{1}{2}bh$

$A = \frac{1}{2}(1 \text{ unit})(6 \text{ units})$

$A = \frac{1}{2}(6 \text{ units}^2)$

$A = 3 \text{ units}^2$

Area of Triangle 2

$A = \frac{1}{2}bh$

$A = \frac{1}{2}(6 \text{ units})(3 \text{ units})$

$A = \frac{1}{2}(18 \text{ units}^2)$

$A = 9 \text{ units}^2$

Area of Triangle 3

$A = \frac{1}{2}bh$

$A = \frac{1}{2}(5 \text{ units})(3 \text{ units})$

$A = \frac{1}{2}(15 \text{ units}^2)$

$A = 7.5 \text{ units}^2$

Total Area of Triangle

$A = 36 \text{ units}^2 - 3 \text{ units}^2 - 9 \text{ units}^2 - 7.5 \text{ units}^2$

$A = 16.5 \text{ units}^2$

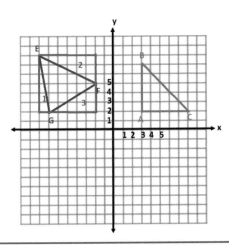

- How is this example different than the first?
  - *The base and height are not on vertical and horizontal lines. This makes it difficult to determine the measurements and calculate the area.*

MP.1

- What other methods might we try?

Students may not come up with the correct method in discussion and may need to be led to the idea. If this is the case, ask students if the shape can be divided into smaller pieces. Try drawing lines on the figure to show this method does not work. Then draw one of the outside triangles to show a triangle whose area could be determined, and help lead students to determine that the areas of the surrounding triangles can be found.

Lesson 8: Drawing Polygons in the Coordinate Plane

105

©2015 Great Minds. eureka-math.org
G6-M5-TE-B5-1.3.1-01.2016

MP.1

□ *Answers will vary. We can draw a square around the outside of the shape. Using these vertical and horizontal lines, we can find the area of the triangles that would be formed around the original triangle. These areas would be subtracted from the area of the square leaving us with the area of the triangle in the center.*

- What expression could we write to represent the area of the triangle?

  □ $6^2 - \frac{1}{2}(1)(6) - \frac{1}{2}(6)(3) - \frac{1}{2}(5)(3)$

- Explain what each part of the expression corresponds to in this situation.

  □ *The 6^2 represents the area of the square surrounding the triangle.*

MP.2

  □ *The $\frac{1}{2}(1)(6)$ represents the area of triangle 1 that needs to be subtracted from the area of the square.*

  □ *The $\frac{1}{2}(6)(3)$ represents the area of triangle 2 that needs to be subtracted from the area of the square.*

  □ *The $\frac{1}{2}(5)(3)$ represents the area of triangle 3 that needs to be subtracted from the area of the square.*

---

3. Plot and connect the following points: $K(-9, -7)$, $L(-4, -2)$, $M(-1, -5)$, and $N(-5, -5)$. Give the best name for the polygon, and determine the area.

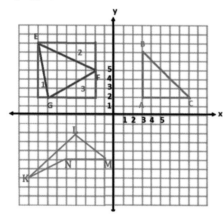

This polygon has 4 sides and has no pairs of parallel sides. Therefore, the best name for this shape is a quadrilateral.

To determine the area, I will separate the shape into two triangles.

Area of Triangle 1

$A = \frac{1}{2}bh$

$A = \frac{1}{2}(6 \text{ units})(3 \text{ units})$

$A = \frac{1}{2}(18 \text{ units}^2)$

$A = 9 \text{ units}^2$

MP.1

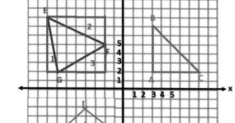

Area of Triangle 2

$A = \frac{1}{2}bh$

$A = \frac{1}{2}(2 \text{ units})(2 \text{ units})$

$A = \frac{1}{2}(4 \text{ units}^2)$

$A = 2 \text{ units}^2$

Total Area $= 9 \text{ units}^2 + 2 \text{ units}^2$

Total Area $= 11 \text{ units}^2$

- ▪ What method(s) could be used to determine the area of this shape?
  - □ *We could decompose the shape, or break the shape, into two triangles using a horizontal line segment to separate the two pieces.*
  - □ *We could also have used a similar method to Example 2, where we draw a rectangle around the outside of the shape, find the area of the pieces surrounding the quadrilateral and then subtract these areas from the area of the rectangle.*

MP.1

- ▪ In this case, which method is more efficient?
  - □ *It would be more efficient to only have to find the area of the two triangles and then add them together.*

- ▪ What expression could we write to represent the area of the triangle?
  - □ $\frac{1}{2}(6)(3) + \frac{1}{2}(2)(2)$

MP.2

- ▪ Explain what each part of the expression corresponds to in this situation.
  - □ *The expression $\frac{1}{2}(6)(3)$ represents the area of triangle 1 that makes up a portion of the quadrilateral.*
  - □ *The expression $\frac{1}{2}(2)(2)$ represents the area of triangle 2 that makes up a portion of the quadrilateral.*

MP.1

4. **Plot and connect the following points:** $P(1, -4)$, $Q(5, -2)$, $R(9, -4)$, $S(7, -8)$, and $T(3, -8)$. **Give the best name for the polygon, and determine the area.**

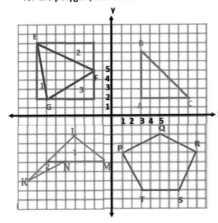

To determine the area, I will decompose this pentagon into four smaller shapes.

Area of Shape 1

$A = \frac{1}{2}bh$

$A = \frac{1}{2}(8 \text{ units})(2 \text{ units})$

$A = \frac{1}{2}(16 \text{ units}^2)$

$A = 8 \text{ units}^2$

Area of Shape 2 and Shape 4

$A = \frac{1}{2}bh$

$A = \frac{1}{2}(4 \text{ units})(2 \text{ units})$

$A = \frac{1}{2}(8 \text{ units}^2)$

$A = 4 \text{ units}^2$

Because there are two of the same triangle, that makes a total of 8 units².

Area of Shape 3

$A = bh$

$A = (4 \text{ units})(4 \text{ units})$

$A = 16 \text{ units}^2$

Total Area = 8 units² + 8 units² + 16 units²

Total Area = 32 units²

- What is the best name for this polygon?

  □ *This shape has 5 sides. Therefore, the best name is pentagon.*

- Do we have a formula that we typically use to calculate the area of a pentagon?

MP.1

  □ *No, we have formulas for different types of triangles and quadrilaterals.*

- How could we use what we know to determine the area of the pentagon?

  □ *Answers will vary. We can break up the shape into triangles and rectangles, find the areas of these pieces, and then add them together to get the total area.*

- What expression could we write to represent the area of the pentagon?

  □ $\frac{1}{2}(8)(2) + 2\left(\frac{1}{2}(4)(2)\right) + (4)(4)$

- Explain what each part of the expression corresponds to in this situation.

MP.2

  □ *The $\frac{1}{2}(8)(2)$ represents the area of triangle 1 that needs to be added to the rest of the areas.*

  □ *The $\frac{1}{2}(4)(2)$ represents the area of triangles 2 and 4 that needs to be added to the rest of the areas. It is multiplied by 2 because there are two triangles with the same area.*

  □ *The $(4)(4)$ represents the area of rectangle 3 that also needs to be added to the rest of the areas.*

Example 5 (5 minutes)

> 5. Two of the coordinates of a rectangle are $A(3, 7)$ and $B(3, 2)$. The rectangle has an area of 30 square units. Give the possible locations of the other two vertices by identifying their coordinates. (Use the coordinate plane to draw and check your answer.)
>
>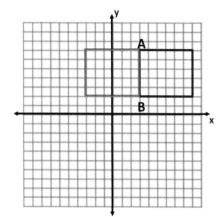
>
> *One possible location of the other two vertices is $(9, 2)$ and $(9, 7)$. Using these coordinates will result in a distance, or side length, of 6 units.*
>
> *Since the height is 5 units, 5 units $\times$ 6 units $= 30$ units^2.*
>
> *Another possible location of the other two vertices is $(-3, 2)$ and $(-3, 7)$. Using these coordinates will result in a distance, or side length, of 6 units.*
>
> *Since the height is 5 units, 5 units $\times$ 6 units $= 30$ units^2.*

Allow students a chance to try this question on their own first and then compare solutions with a partner.

- What is the length of $\overline{AB}$?

  □ *$|7| - |2| = 7 - 2 = 5$; therefore, $AB = 5$ units.*

- If one side of the rectangle is 5 units, what must be the length of the other side?

  □ *Since the area is 30 square units, the other length must be 6 units so that 5×6 makes 30.*

- How many different rectangles can be created with segment AB as one side and the two sides adjacent to segment AB having a length of 6 units?
  - *There are two different solutions. I could make a rectangle with two new points at $(9, 7)$ and $(9, 2)$, or I could make a rectangle with two new points at $(-3, 7)$ and $(-3, 2)$.*
- How are the x-coordinates in the two new points related to the x-coordinates in point A and point B?
  - *They are 6 units apart.*

Exercises (10 minutes)

Students should work independently.

Exercises

For Exercises 1 and 2, plot the points, name the shape, and determine the area of the shape. Then write an expression that could be used to determine the area of the figure. Explain how each part of the expression corresponds to the situation.

1. $A(4, 6)$, $B(8, 6)$, $C(10, 2)$, $D(8, -3)$, $E(5, -3)$, and $F(2, 2)$

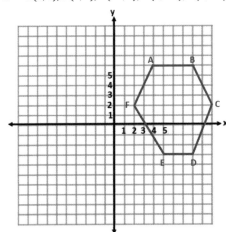

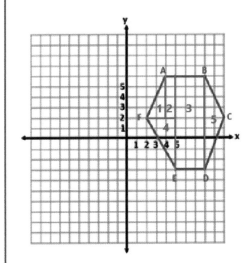

This shape is a hexagon.

Area of Shape 1

$A = \dfrac{1}{2}bh$

$A = \dfrac{1}{2}(2 \text{ units})(4 \text{ units})$

$A = \dfrac{1}{2}(8 \text{ units}^2)$

$A = 4 \text{ units}^2$

Area of Shape 2

$A = bh$

$A = (1 \text{ unit})(4 \text{ units})$

$A = 4 \text{ units}^2$

Area of Shape 3

$A = bh$

$A = (3 \text{ units})(9 \text{ units})$

$A = 27 \text{ units}^2$

Area of Shape 4

$A = \dfrac{1}{2}bh$

$A = \dfrac{1}{2}(3 \text{ units})(5 \text{ units})$

$A = \dfrac{1}{2}(15 \text{ units}^2)$

$A = 7.5 \text{ units}^2$

Area of Shape 5

$A = \dfrac{1}{2}bh$

$A = \dfrac{1}{2}(2 \text{ units})(9 \text{ units})$

$A = \dfrac{1}{2}(18 \text{ units}^2)$

$A = 9 \text{ units}^2$

Total Area $= 4 \text{ units}^2 + 4 \text{ units}^2 + 27 \text{ units}^2 + 7.5 \text{ units}^2 + 9 \text{ units}^2$

Total Area $= 51.5 \text{ units}^2$

Expression:

$\dfrac{1}{2}(2)(4) + (1)(4) + (3)(9) + \dfrac{1}{2}(3)(5) + \dfrac{1}{2}(2)(9)$

Each term represents the area of a section of the hexagon. They must be added together to get the total.
The first term is the area of triangle 1 on the left.
The second term is the area of rectangle 2.
The third term is the area of the large rectangle 3.
The fourth term is the area of triangle 4 on the left.
The fifth term is the area of triangle 5 on the right.

---

2. $X(-9, 6)$, $Y(-2, -1)$, and $Z(-8, -7)$

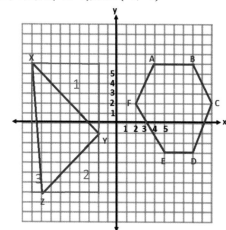

This shape is a triangle.

Area of Outside Rectangle

$A = lw$

$A = (7 \text{ units}) (13 \text{ units})$

$A = 91 \text{ units}^2$

Area of Triangle 1

$A = \dfrac{1}{2} bh$

$A = \dfrac{1}{2}(7 \text{ units})(7 \text{ units})$

$A = \dfrac{1}{2}(49 \text{ units}^2)$

$A = 24.5 \text{ units}^2$

Area of Triangle 2

$A = \dfrac{1}{2} bh$

$A = \dfrac{1}{2}(6 \text{ units})(6 \text{ units})$

$A = \dfrac{1}{2}(36 \text{ units}^2)$

$A = 18 \text{ units}^2$

Area of Triangle 3

$A = \dfrac{1}{2} bh$

$A = \dfrac{1}{2}(13 \text{ units})(1 \text{ unit})$

$A = \dfrac{1}{2}(13 \text{ units}^2)$

$A = 6.5 \text{ units}^2$

Total Area = $91 \text{ units}^2 - 24.5 \text{ units}^2 - 18 \text{ units}^2 - 6.5 \text{ units}^2$

Total Area = 42 units^2

Expression:

$$(7)(13) - \frac{1}{2}(7)(7) - \frac{1}{2}(6)(6) - \frac{1}{2}(13)(1)$$

The first term in the expression represents the area of the rectangle that goes around the outside of the triangle.

The next three terms represent the areas that need to be subtracted from the rectangle so that we are only left with the given triangle.

The second term is the area of the top right triangle.

The third term is the area of the bottom right triangle.

The fourth term is the area of the triangle on the left.

3.   A rectangle with vertices located at $(-3, 4)$ and $(5, 4)$ has an area of 32 square units. Determine the location of the other two vertices.

The other two points could be located at $(-3, 8)$ and $(5, 8)$ or $(-3, 0)$ and $(5, 0)$.

4.   Challenge: A triangle with vertices located at $(-2, -3)$ and $(3, -3)$ has an area of 20 square units. Determine one possible location of the other vertex.

Answers will vary. Possible solutions include points that are 8 units from the base. $(-2, 5)$ or $(3, -11)$.

EUREKA MATH™

Closing (5 minutes)

- What different methods could you use to determine the area of a polygon plotted on the coordinate plane?

  □ *In order to find the area of a polygon on a coordinate plane, it is important to have vertical and horizontal lines. Therefore, the polygon can be decomposed to triangles and rectangles or a large rectangle can be drawn around the polygon.*

- How did the shape of the polygon influence the method you used to determine the area?

  □ *If the shape is easily decomposed with horizontal and vertical lines, then this is the method that I would use to calculate the area. If this is not the case, then it would be easier to draw a rectangle around the outside of the shape.*

Exit Ticket (5 minutes)

©2015 Great Minds. eureka-math.org
G6-M5-TE-B5-1.3.1-01.2016

Name _____   Date _____

Lesson 8: Drawing Polygons in the Coordinate Plane

Exit Ticket

Determine the area of both polygons on the coordinate plane, and explain why you chose the methods you used. Then write an expression that could be used to determine the area of the figure. Explain how each part of the expression corresponds to the situation.

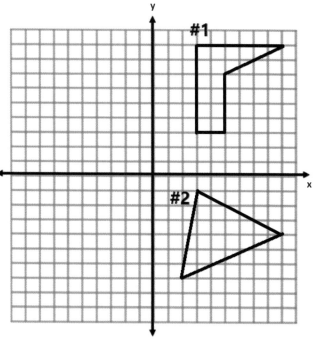

EUREKA MATH

©2015 Great Minds. eureka-math.org
G6-M5-TE-B5-1.3.1-01.2016

Exit Ticket Sample Solutions

Determine the area of both polygons on the coordinate plane, and explain why you chose the methods you used. Then write an expression that could be used to determine the area of the figure. Explain how each part of the expression corresponds to the situation.

Methods to calculate the answer will vary.

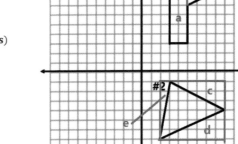

#1 Area of shape a

$A = lw$
$A = (2 \text{ units})(6 \text{ units})$
$A = 12 \text{ units}^2$

Area of shape b

$A = \frac{1}{2}bh$
$A = \frac{1}{2}(4 \text{ units})(2 \text{ units})$
$A = \frac{1}{2}(8 \text{ units}^2)$
$A = 4 \text{ units}^2$

Total Area $= 12 \text{ units}^2 + 4 \text{ units}^2 = 16 \text{ units}^2$

Explanations will vary depending on the method chosen.

Expression: $(2)(6) + \frac{1}{2}(4)(2)$

The first term represents the area of the rectangle on the left, which makes up part of the figure.

The second term represents the area of the triangle on the right that completes the figure.

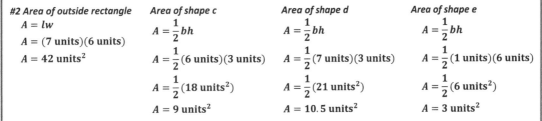

#2 Area of outside rectangle
$A = lw$
$A = (7 \text{ units})(6 \text{ units})$
$A = 42 \text{ units}^2$

Area of shape c
$A = \frac{1}{2}bh$
$A = \frac{1}{2}(6 \text{ units})(3 \text{ units})$
$A = \frac{1}{2}(18 \text{ units}^2)$
$A = 9 \text{ units}^2$

Area of shape d
$A = \frac{1}{2}bh$
$A = \frac{1}{2}(7 \text{ units})(3 \text{ units})$
$A = \frac{1}{2}(21 \text{ units}^2)$
$A = 10.5 \text{ units}^2$

Area of shape e
$A = \frac{1}{2}bh$
$A = \frac{1}{2}(1 \text{ units})(6 \text{ units})$
$A = \frac{1}{2}(6 \text{ units}^2)$
$A = 3 \text{ units}^2$

Total Area $= 42 \text{ units}^2 - 9 \text{ units}^2 - 10.5 \text{ units}^2 - 3 \text{ units}^2$

Total Area $= 19.5 \text{ units}^2$

Explanations will vary depending on method chosen.

Expression: $(7)(6) - \frac{1}{2}(6)(3) - \frac{1}{2}(7)(3) - \frac{1}{2}(1)(6)$

The first term in the expression is the area of a rectangle that goes around the triangle.

Each of the other terms represents the triangles that need to be subtracted from the rectangle so that we are left with just the figure in the center.

Problem Set Sample Solutions

Plot the points for each shape, determine the area of the polygon, and then write an expression that could be used to determine the area of the figure. Explain how each part of the expression corresponds to the situation.

1. $A(1,3)$, $B(2,8)$, $C(8,8)$, $D(10,3)$, and $E(5,-2)$

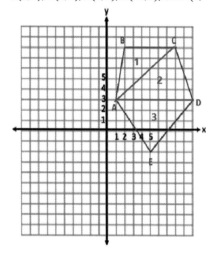

Area of Triangle 1

$A = \dfrac{1}{2}bh$

$A = \dfrac{1}{2}(6 \text{ units})(5 \text{ units})$

$A = \dfrac{1}{2}(30 \text{ units}^2)$

$A = 15 \text{ units}^2$

Area of Triangle 3

$A = \dfrac{1}{2}bh$

$A = \dfrac{1}{2}(9 \text{ units})(5 \text{ units})$

$A = \dfrac{1}{2}(45 \text{ units}^2)$

$A = 22.5 \text{ units}^2$

Area of Triangle 2

$A = \dfrac{1}{2}bh$

$A = \dfrac{1}{2}(9 \text{ units})(5 \text{ units})$

$A = \dfrac{1}{2}(45 \text{ units}^2)$

$A = 22.5 \text{ units}^2$

Pentagon total area $= 15 \text{ units}^2 + 22.5 \text{ units}^2 + 22.5 \text{ units}^2$

Total Area $= 60 \text{ units}^2$

Expression:

$$\dfrac{1}{2}(6)(5) + \dfrac{1}{2}(9)(5) + \dfrac{1}{2}(9)(5)$$

Each term in the expression represents the area of one of the triangular pieces that fits inside the pentagon. They are all added together to form the complete figure.

EUREKA
MATH

2. $X(-10, 2)$, $Y(-3, 6)$, and $Z(-6, -5)$

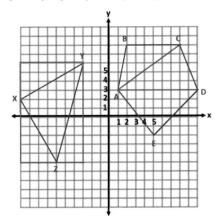

Area of Outside Rectangle

$A = lw$

$A = (11 \text{ units})(7 \text{ units})$

$A = 77 \text{ units}^2$

Area of Top Triangle

$A = \dfrac{1}{2}bh$

$A = \dfrac{1}{2}(7 \text{ units})(4 \text{ units})$

$A = \dfrac{1}{2}(28 \text{ units}^2)$

$A = 14 \text{ units}^2$

Area of Bottom Left Triangle

$A = \dfrac{1}{2}bh$

$A = \dfrac{1}{2}(4 \text{ units})(7 \text{ units})$

$A = \dfrac{1}{2}(28 \text{ units}^2)$

$A = 14 \text{ units}^2$

Area of Bottom Right Triangle

$A = \dfrac{1}{2}bh$

$A = \dfrac{1}{2}(3 \text{ units})(11 \text{ units})$

$A = \dfrac{1}{2}(33 \text{ units}^2)$

$A = 16.5 \text{ units}^2$

Area of center triangle $= 77 \text{ units}^2 - 14 \text{ units}^2 - 14 \text{ units}^2 - 16.5 \text{ units}^2$

Area of center triangle $= 32.5 \text{ units}^2$

Expression:

$(11)(7) - \dfrac{1}{2}(7)(4) - \dfrac{1}{2}(4)(7) - \dfrac{1}{2}(3)(11)$

The first term in the expression represents the area of the rectangle that would enclose the triangle. Then the three terms after represent the areas of the triangles that need to be removed from the area of the rectangle to find the area of the given triangle.

3. $E(5, 7)$, $F(9, -5)$, and $G(1, -3)$

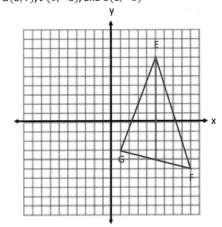

Area of Triangle on the Left

$A = \dfrac{1}{2}bh$

$A = \dfrac{1}{2}(11 \text{ units})(4 \text{ units})$

$A = 22 \text{ units}^2$

Area of Triangle on the Right

$A = \dfrac{1}{2}bh$

$A = \dfrac{1}{2}(11 \text{ units})(4 \text{ units})$

$A = 22 \text{ units}^2$

Total Area $= 22 \text{ units}^2 + 22 \text{ units}^2 = 44 \text{ units}^2$

Expression:

$\dfrac{1}{2}(11)(4) + \dfrac{1}{2}(11)(4)$

Each term in the expression represents the area of a triangle that makes up the total area. The first term is the area of the triangle on the left, and the second term is the area of the triangle on the right.

4. Find the area of the triangle in Problem 3 using a different method. Then, compare the expressions that can be used for both solutions in Problems 3 and 4.

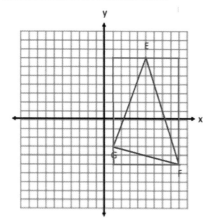

Area of Rectangle

$A = lw$

$A = (12 \text{ units})(8 \text{ units})$

$A = 96 \text{ units}^2$

Area of Triangle on Top Left

$A = \frac{1}{2}bh$

$A = \frac{1}{2}(4 \text{ units})(10 \text{ units})$

$A = 20 \text{ units}^2$

Area of Triangle on Bottom Left

$A = \frac{1}{2}bh$

$A = \frac{1}{2}(8 \text{ units})(2 \text{ units})$

$A = 8 \text{ units}^2$

Area of Triangle on Right

$A = \frac{1}{2}bh$

$A = \frac{1}{2}(4 \text{ units})(12 \text{ units})$

$A = 24 \text{ units}^2$

Total Area = $96 \text{ units}^2 - 20 \text{ units}^2 - 8 \text{ units}^2 - 24 \text{ units}^2$
Total Area = 44 units^2

Expression: $(12)(8) - \frac{1}{2}(4)(10) - \frac{1}{2}(8)(2) - \frac{1}{2}(4)(12)$

The first term in the expression is the area of a rectangle around the outside of the figure. Then we subtracted all of the extra areas with the next three terms.

The two expressions are different because of the way we divided up the figure. In the first expression, we split the shape into two triangles that had to be added together to get the whole. In the second expression, we enclosed the triangle inside a new figure and then had to subtract the extra area.

5. Two vertices of a rectangle are $(8, -5)$ and $(8, 7)$. If the area of the rectangle is 72 square units, name the possible location of the other two vertices.

    $(2, -5)$ and $(2, 7)$ or $(14, -5)$ and $(14, 7)$

6. A triangle with two vertices located at $(5, -8)$ and $(5, 4)$ has an area of 48 square units. Determine one possible location of the other vertex.

    Answers will vary. Possible solutions include points that are 8 units from the base such as $(13, -2)$ or $(-3, -2)$.

EUREKA
MATH™

©2015 Great Minds. eureka-math.org
G6-M5-TE-B5-1.3.1-01.2016

Lesson 9: Determining Perimeter and Area of Polygons on the Coordinate Plane

Student Outcomes

- Students find the perimeter of irregular figures using coordinates to find the length of a side joining points with the same first coordinate or the same second coordinate.
- Students find the area enclosed by a polygon on the coordinate plane by composing or decomposing using polygons with known area formulas.

Lesson Notes

The solutions given throughout the lesson only represent some of the correct answers to the problems. Discussion throughout the lesson about other possible solutions should be welcomed.

Please note that in each coordinate plane, each square unit is one unit in length.

The formulas $A = lw$ and $A = bh$ are used intermittently. Both are correct strategies for determining the area of a rectangle and should be accepted.

Please also note that some of the formulas are solved in a different order depending on the problem. For example, when using the formula for the area of triangles, students could multiply the base and the height and then multiply by $\frac{1}{2}$ or they could take $\frac{1}{2}$ of either the base or the height before multiplying by the other. Because multiplication is commutative, multiplying in different orders is mathematically sound. Students should be comfortable with using either order and may see opportunities when it is more advantageous to use one order over another.

Classwork

Fluency Exercise (5 minutes): Addition and Subtraction Equations

Sprint: Refer to the Sprints and the Sprint Delivery Script sections in the Module 4 Module Overview for directions to administer a Sprint.

©2015 Great Minds. eureka-math.org
G6-M5-TE-B5-1.3.1-01.2016

Example 1 (8 minutes)

Example 1

Jasjeet has made a scale drawing of a vegetable garden she plans to make in her backyard. She needs to determine the perimeter and area to know how much fencing and dirt to purchase. Determine both the perimeter and area.

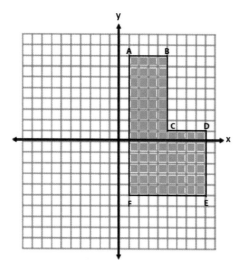 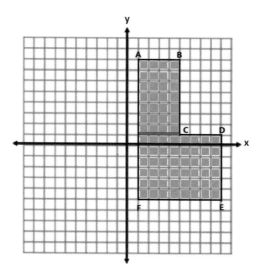

$AB = 4$ units $BC = 7$ units $CD = 4$ units

$DE = 6$ units $EF = 8$ units $AF = 13$ units

Perimeter $= 4$ units $+ 7$ units $+ 4$ units $+ 6$ units $+ 8$ units $+ 13$ units

Perimeter $= 42$ units

The area is determined by making a horizontal cut from $(1, 1)$ *to point C.*

Area of Top   *Area of Bottom*

$A = lw$ $A = lw$

$A = (4$ units$)(7$ units$)$ $A = (8$ units$)(6$ units$)$

$A = 28$ units^2 $A = 48$ units^2

Total Area $= 28$ units$^2 + 48$ units^2

Total Area $= 76$ units^2

- How can we use what we worked on in Lessons 7 and 8 to help us calculate the perimeter and area?
    - *We can determine the lengths of each side first. Then, we add the lengths together to get the perimeter.*
    - *Next, we can break the shape into two rectangles, find the area of each rectangle using the side lengths, and add the areas together to get the total area of the polygon.*

©2015 Great Minds. eureka-math.org
G6-M5-TE-B5-1.3.1-01.2016

Example 2 (8 minutes)

Example 2

Calculate the area of the polygon using two different methods. Write two expressions to represent the two methods, and compare the structure of the expressions.

Answers will vary. The following are two possible methods. However, students could also break the shape into two triangles and a rectangle or use another correct method.

Method One: *Method Two:*

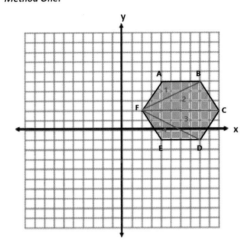   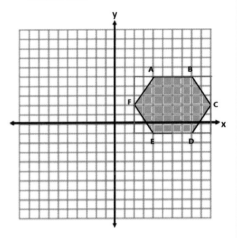

Area of Triangle 1 and 4	*Area of Triangle 2 and 3*	$A = lw$
$A = \dfrac{1}{2}bh$	$A = \dfrac{1}{2}bh$	$A = (8 \text{ units})(6 \text{ units})$
$A = \dfrac{1}{2}(4 \text{ units})(3 \text{ units})$	$A = \dfrac{1}{2}(8 \text{ units})(3 \text{ units})$	$A = 48 \text{ units}^2$
$A = \dfrac{1}{2}(12 \text{ units}^2)$	$A = \dfrac{1}{2}(24 \text{ units}^2)$	$A = \dfrac{1}{2}bh$
$A = 6 \text{ units}^2$	$A = 12 \text{ units}^2$	$A = \dfrac{1}{2}(2 \text{ units})(3 \text{ units})$

Since there are 2, we have a total area of 12 units^2. | *Since there are 2, we have a total area of* 24 units^2. | $A = 3 \text{ units}^2$

There are 4 triangles of equivalent base and height.

$4(3 \text{ units}^2) = 12 \text{ units}^2$

Total Area $= 12 \text{ units}^2 + 24 \text{ units}^2 = 36 \text{ units}^2$

Total Area $= 48 \text{ units}^2 - 12 \text{ units}^2$

Total area $= 36 \text{ units}^2$

Expressions:

$$2\left(\frac{1}{2}(4)(3)\right) + 2\left(\frac{1}{2}(8)(3)\right) \quad or \quad (8)(6) - 4\left(\frac{1}{2}(2)(3)\right)$$

The first expression shows terms being added together because I separated the hexagon into smaller pieces and had to add their areas back together.

The second expression shows terms being subtracted because I made a larger outside shape and then had to take away the extra pieces.

MP.1 & MP.3

Allow time for students to share and explain one of their methods.

- What were the strengths and weaknesses of the methods that you tried?
  - *Responses will vary. Some students may prefer methods that require fewer steps while others may prefer methods that only include rectangles and triangles.*

Scaffolding:

As English language learners discuss their thinking, it may be useful to provide support for their conversations. Sentence starters may include, "My favorite method is ..." or "First, I ...."

Exercises (16 minutes)

Students work on the practice problems in pairs, so they can discuss different methods for calculating the areas. Discussions should include explaining the method they chose and why they chose it. Students should also be looking to see if both partners got the same answer.

Consider asking students to write explanations of their thinking in terms of decomposition and composition as they solve each problem.

Exercises

1. Determine the area of the following shapes.

    a.

    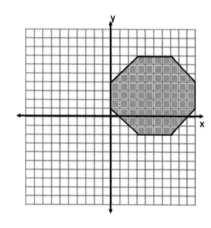

    Area of Rectangle
    $$A = lw$$
    $$A = (10 \text{ units})(9 \text{ units})$$
    $$A = 90 \text{ units}^2$$

    Area of Triangle
    $$A = \frac{1}{2}bh$$
    $$A = \frac{1}{2}(3 \text{ units})(3 \text{ units})$$
    $$A = 4.5 \text{ units}^2$$

    4 triangles with equivalent base and height
    $$4(4.5 \text{ units}^2) = 18 \text{ units}^2$$

    $$\text{Area} = 90 \text{ units}^2 - 18 \text{ units}^2$$
    $$\text{Area} = 72 \text{ units}^2$$

    Please note that students may also choose to solve by decomposing. Here is another option:

    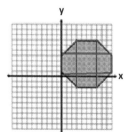

Lesson 9:   Determining Perimeter and Area of Polygons on the Coordinate Plane

EUREKA MATH

b.

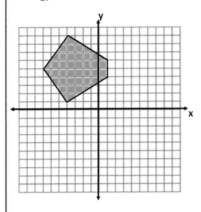

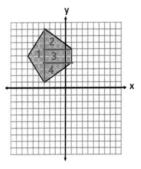

Area of Triangle 1

$A = \frac{1}{2}bh$

$A = \frac{1}{2}(8 \text{ units})(3 \text{ units})$

$A = (4 \text{ units})(3 \text{ units})$

$A = 12 \text{ units}^2$

Area of Triangles 2 and 4

$A = \frac{1}{2}bh$

$A = \frac{1}{2}(5 \text{ units})(3 \text{ units})$

$A = \frac{1}{2}(15 \text{ units}^2)$

$A = 7.5 \text{ units}^2$

Another correct solution might start with the following diagram:

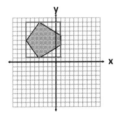

Since triangles 2 and 4 have the same base and height measurements, the combined area is 15 units².

Area of Rectangle 3

$A = bh$

$A = (5 \text{ units})(2 \text{ units})$

$A = 10 \text{ units}^2$

Total Area = 12 units² + 15 units² + 10 units²
Total Area = 37 units²

2. Determine the area and perimeter of the following shapes.

a.

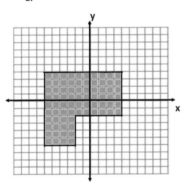

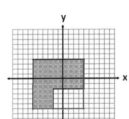

Area

Large Square
$A = s^2$
$A = (10 \text{ units})^2$
$A = 100 \text{ units}^2$

Removed Piece
$A = bh$
$A = (6 \text{ units})(4 \text{ units})$
$A = 24 \text{ units}^2$

Area = 100 units² − 24 units²
Area = 76 units²

Perimeter = 10 units + 6 units + 6 units + 4 units + 4 units + 10 units

Perimeter = 40 units

Other correct solutions might start with the following diagrams:

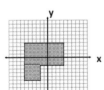

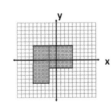

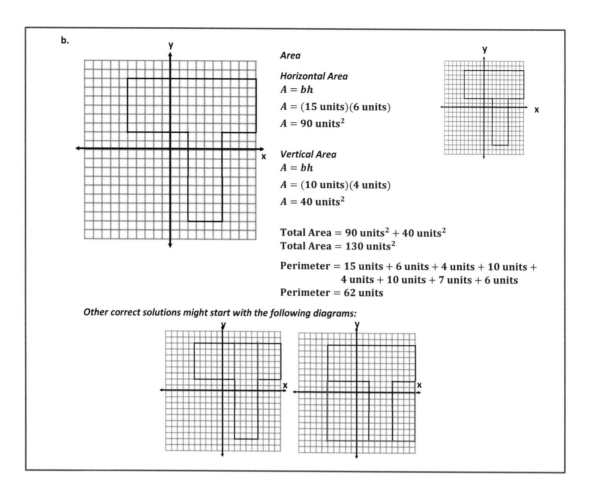

b.

Area

Horizontal Area
$A = bh$
$A = (15 \text{ units})(6 \text{ units})$
$A = 90 \text{ units}^2$

Vertical Area
$A = bh$
$A = (10 \text{ units})(4 \text{ units})$
$A = 40 \text{ units}^2$

Total Area $= 90 \text{ units}^2 + 40 \text{ units}^2$
Total Area $= 130 \text{ units}^2$

Perimeter $= 15 \text{ units} + 6 \text{ units} + 4 \text{ units} + 10 \text{ units} +$
$4 \text{ units} + 10 \text{ units} + 7 \text{ units} + 6 \text{ units}$
Perimeter $= 62 \text{ units}$

Other correct solutions might start with the following diagrams:

Closing (4 minutes)

- Share with the class some of the discussions made between partners about the methods for determining area of irregular polygons.

Ask questions to review the key ideas:

- There appear to be multiple ways to determine the area of a polygon. What do all of these methods have in common?
    - *Answers will vary.*
    - *The areas cannot overlap.*
    - *When you decompose the figure, you cannot leave any parts out.*
    - *When drawing a rectangle around the outside of the shape, the vertices of the original shape should be touching the perimeter of the newly formed rectangle.*
- Why did we determine the area and perimeter of some figures and only the area of others?
    - *In problems similar to Exercise 1 parts (a) and (b), the sides were not horizontal or vertical, so we were not able to use the methods for determining length like we did in other problems.*

Exit Ticket (4 minutes)

Lesson 9:   Determining Perimeter and Area of Polygons on the Coordinate Plane

Name _____   Date _____

Lesson 9: Determining Perimeter and Area of Polygons on the Coordinate Plane

Exit Ticket

Determine the area and perimeter of the figure below. Note that each square unit is 1 unit in length.

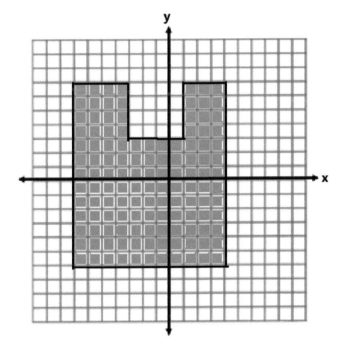

Exit Ticket Sample Solutions

Determine the area and perimeter of the figure below. Note that each square unit is 1 unit in length.

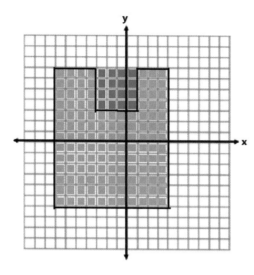

Area

Area of Large Rectangle
$A = bh$
$A = (11 \text{ units})(13 \text{ units})$
$A = 143 \text{ units}^2$

Area of Small Square
$A = s^2$
$A = (4 \text{ units})^2$
$A = 16 \text{ units}^2$

Area of Irregular Shape
$A = 143 \text{ units}^2 - 16 \text{ units}^2$
$A = 127 \text{ units}^2$

Perimeter $= 13 \text{ units} + 4 \text{ units} + 4 \text{ units} + 4 \text{ units} +$
$\qquad\qquad 4 \text{ units} + 3 \text{ units} + 13 \text{ units} + 11 \text{ units}$
Perimeter $= 56 \text{ units}$

Other correct solutions might start with the following diagrams:

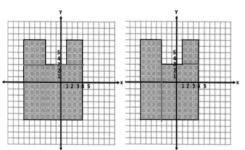 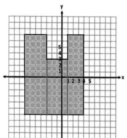 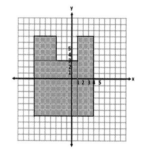

Lesson 9:   Determining Perimeter and Area of Polygons on the Coordinate Plane

Problem Set Sample Solutions

1. Determine the area of the polygon.

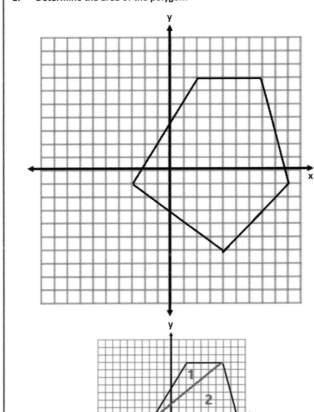

Area of Triangle 1

$A = \dfrac{1}{2}bh$

$A = \dfrac{1}{2}(5 \text{ units})(8 \text{ units})$

$A = \dfrac{1}{2}(40 \text{ units}^2)$

$A = 20 \text{ units}^2$

Area of Triangle 2

$A = \dfrac{1}{2}bh$

$A = \dfrac{1}{2}(12 \text{ units})(8 \text{ units})$

$A = \dfrac{1}{2}(96 \text{ units}^2)$

$A = 48 \text{ units}^2$

Area of Triangle 3

$A = \dfrac{1}{2}bh$

$A = \dfrac{1}{2}(12 \text{ units})(5 \text{ units})$

$A = \dfrac{1}{2}(60 \text{ units}^2)$

$A = 30 \text{ units}^2$

Total Area $= 20 \text{ units}^2 + 48 \text{ units}^2 + 30 \text{ units}^2$

Total Area $= 98 \text{ units}^2$

©2015 Great Minds. eureka-math.org
G6-M5-TE-B5-1.3.1-01.2016

2. Determine the area and perimeter of the polygon.

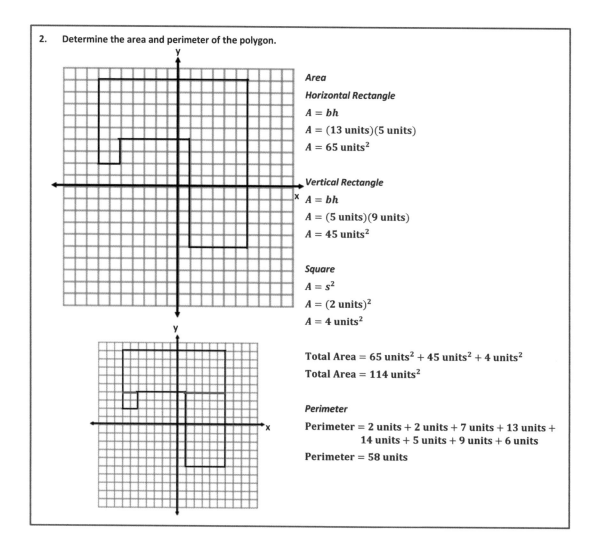

Area

Horizontal Rectangle

$A = bh$

$A = (13 \text{ units})(5 \text{ units})$

$A = 65 \text{ units}^2$

Vertical Rectangle

$A = bh$

$A = (5 \text{ units})(9 \text{ units})$

$A = 45 \text{ units}^2$

Square

$A = s^2$

$A = (2 \text{ units})^2$

$A = 4 \text{ units}^2$

Total Area $= 65 \text{ units}^2 + 45 \text{ units}^2 + 4 \text{ units}^2$

Total Area $= 114 \text{ units}^2$

Perimeter

Perimeter $= 2 \text{ units} + 2 \text{ units} + 7 \text{ units} + 13 \text{ units} +$ $14 \text{ units} + 5 \text{ units} + 9 \text{ units} + 6 \text{ units}$

Perimeter $= 58 \text{ units}$

EUREKA MATH™

3. Determine the area of the polygon. Then, write an expression that could be used to determine the area.

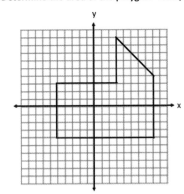 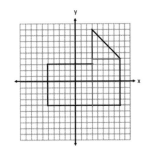

Area of Rectangle on Left

$A = lw$

$A = (8 \text{ units})(7 \text{ units})$

$A = 56 \text{ units}^2$

Area of Rectangle on Right

$A = lw$

$A = (5 \text{ units})(8 \text{ units})$

$A = 40 \text{ units}^2$

Area of Triangle on Top

$A = \frac{1}{2}bh$

$A = \frac{1}{2}(5 \text{ units})(5 \text{ units})$

$A = 12.5 \text{ units}^2$

Total Area $= 56 \text{ units}^2 + 40 \text{ units}^2 + 12.5 \text{ units}^2 = 108.5 \text{ units}^2$

Expression: $(8)(7) + (5)(8) + \frac{1}{2}(5)(5)$

4. If the length of each square was worth 2 instead of 1, how would the area in Problem 3 change? How would your expression change to represent this area?

If each length is twice as long, when they are multiplied, $2l \times 2w = 4lw$. Therefore, the area will be four times larger when the side lengths are doubled.

I could multiply my entire expression by 4 to make it 4 times as big. $4\left[(8)(7) + (5)(8) + \frac{1}{2}(5)(5)\right]$

5. Determine the area of the polygon. Then, write an expression that represents the area.

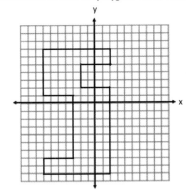 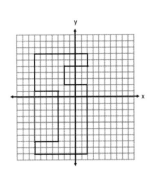

Area of Outside Rectangle

$A = lw$

$A = (9 \text{ units})(16 \text{ units})$

$A = 144 \text{ units}^2$

Area of Rectangle on Left

$A = lw$

$A = (4 \text{ units})(8 \text{ units})$

$A = 32 \text{ units}^2$

Area of Rectangle on Right

$A = lw$

$A = (4 \text{ units})(3 \text{ units})$

$A = 12 \text{ units}^2$

Total Area $= 144 \text{ units}^2 - 32 \text{ units}^2 - 12 \text{ units}^2$

Total Area $= 100 \text{ units}^2$

Expression: $(9)(16) - (4)(8) - (4)(3)$

6. Describe another method you could use to find the area of the polygon in Problem 5. Then, state how the expression for the area would be different than the expression you wrote.

I could have broken up the large shape into many smaller rectangles. Then I would need to add all the areas of these rectangles together to determine the total area.

My expression showed subtraction because I created a rectangle that was larger than the original polygon, and then I had to subtract the extra areas. If I break the shape into pieces, I would need to add the terms together instead of subtracting them to get the total area.

7. Write one of the letters from your name using rectangles on the coordinate plane. Then, determine the area and perimeter. (For help see Exercise 2(b). This irregular polygon looks sort of like a T.)

Answers will vary.

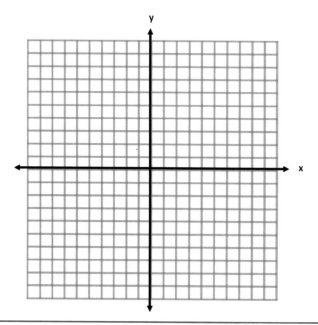

Lesson 9:   Determining Perimeter and Area of Polygons on the Coordinate Plane

Addition and Subtraction Equations—Round 1

Directions: Find the value of m in each equation.

1.	$m + 4 = 11$		18.	$m - 54 = 37$	
2.	$m + 2 = 5$		19.	$4 + m = 9$	
3.	$m + 5 = 8$		20.	$6 + m = 13$	
4.	$m - 7 = 10$		21.	$2 + m = 31$	
5.	$m - 8 = 1$		22.	$15 = m + 11$	
6.	$m - 4 = 2$		23.	$24 = m + 13$	
7.	$m + 12 = 34$		24.	$32 = m + 28$	
8.	$m + 25 = 45$		25.	$4 = m - 7$	
9.	$m + 43 = 89$		26.	$3 = m - 5$	
10.	$m - 20 = 31$		27.	$12 = m - 14$	
11.	$m - 13 = 34$		28.	$23.6 = m - 7.1$	
12.	$m - 45 = 68$		29.	$14.2 = m - 33.8$	
13.	$m + 34 = 41$		30.	$2.5 = m - 41.8$	
14.	$m + 29 = 52$		31.	$64.9 = m + 23.4$	
15.	$m + 37 = 61$		32.	$72.2 = m + 38.7$	
16.	$m - 43 = 63$		33.	$1.81 = m - 15.13$	
17.	$m - 21 = 40$		34.	$24.68 = m - 56.82$	

Addition and Subtraction Equations—Round 1 [KEY]

Directions: Find the value of m in each equation.

1.	$m + 4 = 11$	$m = 7$	18.	$m - 54 = 37$	$m = 91$
2.	$m + 2 = 5$	$m = 3$	19.	$4 + m = 9$	$m = 5$
3.	$m + 5 = 8$	$m = 3$	20.	$6 + m = 13$	$m = 7$
4.	$m - 7 = 10$	$m = 17$	21.	$2 + m = 31$	$m = 29$
5.	$m - 8 = 1$	$m = 9$	22.	$15 = m + 11$	$m = 4$
6.	$m - 4 = 2$	$m = 6$	23.	$24 = m + 13$	$m = 11$
7.	$m + 12 = 34$	$m = 22$	24.	$32 = m + 28$	$m = 4$
8.	$m + 25 = 45$	$m = 20$	25.	$4 = m - 7$	$m = 11$
9.	$m + 43 = 89$	$m = 46$	26.	$3 = m - 5$	$m = 8$
10.	$m - 20 = 31$	$m = 51$	27.	$12 = m - 14$	$m = 26$
11.	$m - 13 = 34$	$m = 47$	28.	$23.6 = m - 7.1$	$m = 30.7$
12.	$m - 45 = 68$	$m = 113$	29.	$14.2 = m - 33.8$	$m = 48$
13.	$m + 34 = 41$	$m = 7$	30.	$2.5 = m - 41.8$	$m = 44.3$
14.	$m + 29 = 52$	$m = 23$	31.	$64.9 = m + 23.4$	$m = 41.5$
15.	$m + 37 = 61$	$m = 24$	32.	$72.2 = m + 38.7$	$m = 33.5$
16.	$m - 43 = 63$	$m = 106$	33.	$1.81 = m - 15.13$	$m = 16.94$
17.	$m - 21 = 40$	$m = 61$	34.	$24.68 = m - 56.82$	$m = 81.5$

EUREKA MATH

©2015 Great Minds. eureka-math.org
G6-M5-TE-B5-1.3.1-01.2016

Addition and Subtraction Equations—Round 2

Number Correct: _____
Improvement: _____

Directions: Find the value of m in each equation.

1.	$m + 2 = 7$	
2.	$m + 4 = 10$	
3.	$m + 8 = 15$	
4.	$m + 7 = 23$	
5.	$m + 12 = 16$	
6.	$m - 5 = 2$	
7.	$m - 3 = 8$	
8.	$m - 4 = 12$	
9.	$m - 14 = 45$	
10.	$m + 23 = 40$	
11.	$m + 13 = 31$	
12.	$m + 23 = 48$	
13.	$m + 38 = 52$	
14.	$m - 14 = 27$	
15.	$m - 23 = 35$	
16.	$m - 17 = 18$	
17.	$m - 64 = 1$	

18.	$6 = m + 3$	
19.	$12 = m + 7$	
20.	$24 = m + 16$	
21.	$13 = m + 9$	
22.	$32 = m - 3$	
23.	$22 = m - 12$	
24.	$34 = m - 10$	
25.	$48 = m + 29$	
26.	$21 = m + 17$	
27.	$52 = m + 37$	
28.	$\frac{6}{7} = m + \frac{4}{7}$	
29.	$\frac{2}{3} = m - \frac{5}{3}$	
30.	$\frac{1}{4} = m - \frac{8}{3}$	
31.	$\frac{5}{6} = m - \frac{7}{12}$	
32.	$\frac{7}{8} = m - \frac{5}{12}$	
33.	$\frac{7}{6} + m = \frac{16}{3}$	
34.	$\frac{1}{3} + m = \frac{13}{15}$	

Addition and Subtraction Equations—Round 2 [KEY]

Directions: Find the value of m in each equation.

1.	$m + 2 = 7$	$m = 5$	18.	$6 = m + 3$	$m = 3$
2.	$m + 4 = 10$	$m = 6$	19.	$12 = m + 7$	$m = 5$
3.	$m + 8 = 15$	$m = 7$	20.	$24 = m + 16$	$m = 8$
4.	$m + 7 = 23$	$m = 16$	21.	$13 = m + 9$	$m = 4$
5.	$m + 12 = 16$	$m = 4$	22.	$32 = m - 3$	$m = 35$
6.	$m - 5 = 2$	$m = 7$	23.	$22 = m - 12$	$m = 34$
7.	$m - 3 = 8$	$m = 11$	24.	$34 = m - 10$	$m = 44$
8.	$m - 4 = 12$	$m = 16$	25.	$48 = m + 29$	$m = 19$
9.	$m - 14 = 45$	$m = 59$	26.	$21 = m + 17$	$m = 4$
10.	$m + 23 = 40$	$m = 17$	27.	$52 = m + 37$	$m = 15$
11.	$m + 13 = 31$	$m = 18$	28.	$\dfrac{6}{7} = m + \dfrac{4}{7}$	$m = \dfrac{2}{7}$
12.	$m + 23 = 48$	$m = 25$	29.	$\dfrac{2}{3} = m - \dfrac{5}{3}$	$m = \dfrac{7}{3}$
13.	$m + 38 = 52$	$m = 14$	30.	$\dfrac{1}{4} = m - \dfrac{8}{3}$	$m = \dfrac{35}{12}$
14.	$m - 14 = 27$	$m = 41$	31.	$\dfrac{5}{6} = m - \dfrac{7}{12}$	$m = \dfrac{17}{12}$
15.	$m - 23 = 35$	$m = 58$	32.	$\dfrac{7}{8} = m - \dfrac{5}{12}$	$m = \dfrac{31}{24}$
16.	$m - 17 = 18$	$m = 35$	33.	$\dfrac{7}{6} + m = \dfrac{16}{3}$	$m = \dfrac{25}{6}$
17.	$m - 64 = 1$	$m = 65$	34.	$\dfrac{1}{3} + m = \dfrac{13}{15}$	$m = \dfrac{8}{15}$

EUREKA MATH™

Lesson 10: Distance, Perimeter, and Area in the Real World

Student Outcomes

- Students determine distance, perimeter, and area in real-world contexts.

Lesson Notes

This lesson is similar to Lesson 6 from this module. The teacher can determine ahead of time whether to do the exploration in the classroom or venture out into hallways or to some other location. The measuring tools, units, and degree of precision to be used in this activity should be chosen in a manner that best meets the needs of students. For large distances, a long measuring tape or trundle wheel can be used. For very small objects, a millimeter ruler would be more appropriate.

The critical understanding for students is that area involves covering, while perimeter involves surrounding. Since plane objects have both area and perimeter, the distinction between the two concepts must be made.

When choosing objects to be measured, look for composite objects that require more than just measuring length and width. Avoid curved edges, as students cannot find area. When possible, choose objects that explicitly lend themselves to both area and perimeter. Such objects could include a frame or mat around a picture, wood trim around the top of a table, piping around a dinner napkin, or baseboard molding along walls. Some of the objects that were chosen for Lesson 6 of this module can also be used.

It is appropriate for students to use a calculator for this lesson.

Classwork

Opening Exercise (6 minutes)

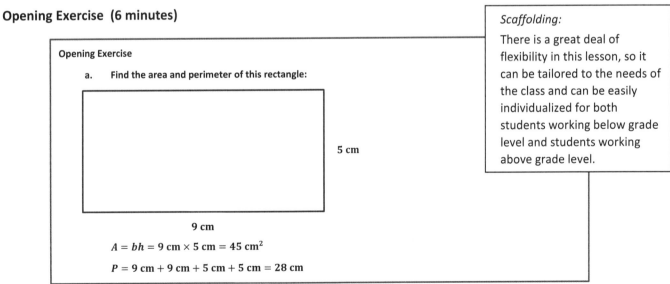

Scaffolding:

There is a great deal of flexibility in this lesson, so it can be tailored to the needs of the class and can be easily individualized for both students working below grade level and students working above grade level.

Opening Exercise

a. Find the area and perimeter of this rectangle:

5 cm

9 cm

$A = bh = 9 \text{ cm} \times 5 \text{ cm} = 45 \text{ cm}^2$

$P = 9 \text{ cm} + 9 \text{ cm} + 5 \text{ cm} + 5 \text{ cm} = 28 \text{ cm}$

b.   **Find the width of this rectangle. The area is $1.2\ m^2$, and the length is 1.5 m.**

$$A = 1.2\ m^2 \qquad w = ?$$

$$l = 1.5\ m$$

$$A = l \times w$$

$$1.2\ \text{m}^2 = 1.5\ \text{m} \times w$$

$$\frac{1.2\ \text{m}^2}{1.5\ \text{m}} = \frac{1.5\ \text{m} \times w}{1.5\ \text{m}}$$

$$0.8\ \text{m} = w$$

Discussion (5 minutes)

- How many dimensions does the rectangle have, and what are they?
  - *Two dimensions: length and width*
- What units are used to express area?
  - *Square units, such as square centimeters as we had in the Opening Exercise 1.*
- What superscript is used to denote square units?
  - *The number 2, for two dimensions*
- What does the prefix *peri-* mean?
  - *Around*
- Are there any other words that use this prefix?
  - *Periscope (seeing around), periodontal (surrounding a tooth), pericardium (the sac around the heart), period (a portion of time that is limited and determined by some recurring phenomenon, as by the completion of a revolution of Earth or the moon), etc.*
- How can focusing on the meaning of the word help you remember the difference between area and perimeter?
  - *Peri- means around; -meter means measure. Perimeter is the measure of the distance around an object. Area is the measure of the surface of an object and has two dimensions.*
- How many dimensions do the line segments around the rectangle have?
  - *The line segments around the rectangle have one dimension; line segments only have length.*
- What units are used to express perimeter?
  - *Linear units*
- We do not typically write linear units with an exponent because the exponent is 1.

> **Scaffolding:**
> The term *dimensions* may be new to English language learners and, as such, may need to be taught and rehearsed. Similarly, the word *superscript* may be new for English language learners and should be taught or reviewed.

Example (6 minutes): Student Desks or Tables

Distribute measuring tools. Explain the units to be used and level of precision expected.

Example 1: Student Desks or Tables

1. Measure the dimensions of the top of your desk.
2. How do you find the area of the top of your desk?
3. How do you find the perimeter?
4. Record these on your paper in the appropriate column.

Scaffolding:

Consider asking some students to measure to the nearest inch, others to the nearest half inch, and others to the nearest quarter inch, depending on ability. Compare these.

- Let's do an example before starting out on this investigation. Measure the dimensions of the top of your desk (or tabletop, etc.).
  - *Dimensions will vary.*
- How do you find the area of the surface?
  - *Multiply the length by the width.*
- How do you find the perimeter?
  - *Any of three ways: Add the length and width (to find the semi-perimeter), and then double the sum; double the length, double the width, and add those two products; or add the length, length, width, and width.*
- Record these on your paper in the appropriate column.

Exploratory Challenge (17 minutes)

Exploratory Challenge

Estimate and predict the area and perimeter of each object. Then measure each object, and calculate both the area and perimeter of each.

Answers are determined by the teacher when objects are chosen. Consider using examples like decorating a bulletin board: bulletin board trim (perimeter), paper for bulletin board (area).

Object or Item to be Measured	Measurement Units	Precision (measure to the nearest)	Area Prediction (square units)	Area (square units) Write the expression and evaluate it.	Perimeter Prediction (linear units)	Perimeter (linear units)
Ex: door	feet	half foot		$6\frac{1}{2}$ ft. $\times$ $3\frac{1}{2}$ ft. $= 22\frac{3}{4}$ ft^2		$2\left(3\frac{1}{2} \text{ ft.} + 6\frac{1}{2} \text{ ft.}\right)$ $= 20$ ft.
desktop						

Optional Challenge (10 minutes)

If desired, send some students to measure other real-world objects found around the school. Set measurement units and precision parameters in advance. The teacher should measure these objects in advance of the activity and calculate the corresponding perimeters and areas. Measuring the school building from the outside could be a whole group activity or could be assigned as an extra credit opportunity.

Optional Challenge

Object or Item to be Measured	Measurement Units	Precision (measure to the nearest)	Area (square units)	Perimeter (linear units)
Ex: door	feet	half foot	$6\frac{1}{2}$ ft. $\times$ $3\frac{1}{2}$ ft. $= 22\frac{3}{4}$ ft^2	$2\left(3\frac{1}{2}\text{ ft.} + 6\frac{1}{2}\text{ ft.}\right) = 20$ ft.

Closing (4 minutes)

- What are some professions that use area and perimeter regularly?
  - *Surveyors, garment manufacturers, packaging engineers, cabinetmakers, carpenters*
- Can you think of any circumstances where you or someone you know has or might have to calculate perimeter and area?
  - *Answers will vary. Encourage a large quantity of responses.*
- Would you like to work in an occupation that requires measuring and calculating as part of the duties?
  - *Answers will vary.*

Exit Ticket (7 minutes)

Name _____   Date _____

Lesson 10: Distance, Perimeter, and Area in the Real World

Exit Ticket

1. The local school is building a new playground. This plan shows the part of the playground that needs to be framed with wood for the swing set. The unit of measure is feet. Determine the number of feet of wood needed to frame the area.

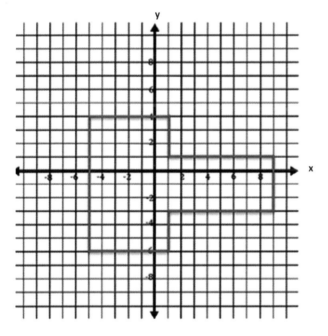

2. The school wants to fill the area enclosed with wood with mulch for safety. Determine the area in square feet that needs to be covered by the mulch.

Exit Ticket Sample Solutions

1. The local school is building a new playground. This plan shows the part of the playground that needs to be framed with wood for the swing set. The unit of measure is feet. Determine the number of feet of wood needed to frame the area.

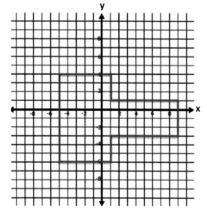

Perimeter: 10 ft. + 6 ft. + 6 ft. + 3 ft. + 3 ft. + 8 ft. + 8 ft. + 4 ft. = 48 ft.

2. The school wants to fill the area enclosed with wood with mulch for safety. Determine the number of square feet that needs to be covered by the mulch.

Area of Left Rectangle $= bh = (6 \text{ ft.} \times 10 \text{ ft.}) = 60 \text{ ft}^2$
Area of Right Rectangle $= bh = (8 \text{ ft.} \times 4 \text{ ft.}) = 32 \text{ ft}^2$
Total Area $= 60 \text{ ft}^2 + 32 \text{ ft}^2 = 92 \text{ ft}^2$

Problem Set Sample Solutions

Note: When columns in a table are labeled with units, students need only enter numerical data in the cells of the table and not include the units each time.

1. How is the length of the side of a square related to its area and perimeter? The diagram below shows the first four squares stacked on top of each other with their upper left-hand corners lined up. The length of one side of the smallest square is 1 foot.

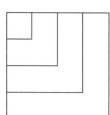

EUREKA MATH

a.   Complete this chart calculating area and perimeter for each square.

Side Length (in feet)	Expression Showing the Area	Area (in square feet)	Expression Showing the Perimeter	Perimeter (in feet)
1	1×1	1	1×4	4
2	2×2	4	2×4	8
3	3×3	9	3×4	12
4	4×4	16	4×4	16
5	5×5	25	5×4	20
6	6×6	36	6×4	24
7	7×7	49	7×4	28
8	8×8	64	8×4	32
9	9×9	81	9×4	36
10	10×10	100	10×4	40
n	$n \times n$	n^2	$4 \times n$	$4n$

b.   In a square, which numerical value is greater, the area or the perimeter?

It depends. For side length less than 4 feet, perimeter is greater; however, for side length greater than 4 feet, area is greater.

c.   When is the numerical value of a square's area (in square units) equal to its perimeter (in units)?

When the side length is exactly 4 feet.

d.   Why is this true?

$n^2 = 4n$ *is only true when* $n = 4$.

2.   This drawing shows a school pool. The walkway around the pool needs special nonskid strips installed but only at the edge of the pool and the outer edges of the walkway.

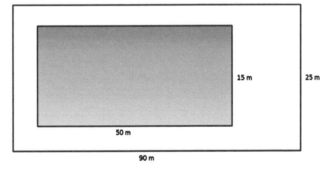

a.   Find the length of nonskid strips that is needed for the job.

$50\,\text{m} + 50\,\text{m} + 15\,\text{m} + 15\,\text{m} + 90\,\text{m} + 90\,\text{m} + 25\,\text{m} + 25\,\text{m} = 360\,\text{m}$

b.   The nonskid strips are sold only in rolls of 50 m. How many rolls need to be purchased for the job?

$360\,\text{m} \div 50\,\dfrac{\text{m}}{\text{roll}} = 7.2\,\text{rolls}$

Therefore, 8 rolls need to be purchased.

3. A homeowner called in a painter to paint the walls and ceiling of one bedroom. His bedroom is 18 ft. long, 12 ft. wide, and 8 ft. high. The room has <u>two</u> doors, each 3 ft. by 7 ft., and <u>three</u> windows each 3 ft. by 5 ft. The doors and windows will not be painted. A gallon of paint can cover 300 ft^2. A hired painter claims he needs a minimum of 4 gallons. Show that his estimate is too high.

Area of 2 long walls: $2(18 \text{ ft.} \times 8 \text{ ft.}) = 288 \text{ ft}^2$

Area of 2 short walls: $2(12 \text{ ft.} \times 8 \text{ ft.}) = 192 \text{ ft}^2$

Area of ceiling: $18 \text{ ft.} \times 12 \text{ ft.} = 216 \text{ ft}^2$

Area of 2 doors: $2(3 \text{ ft.} \times 7 \text{ ft.}) = 42 \text{ ft}^2$

Area of 3 windows: $3(3 \text{ ft.} \times 5 \text{ ft.}) = 45 \text{ ft}^2$

Area to be painted: $(288 \text{ ft}^2 + 192 \text{ ft}^2 + 216 \text{ ft}^2) - (42 \text{ ft}^2 + 45 \text{ ft}^2) = 609 \text{ ft}^2$

Gallons of paint needed: $609 \div 300 = 2.03$

The painter will need a little more than 2 gallons. The painter's estimate for how much paint is necessary was too high.

4. Theresa won a gardening contest and was awarded a roll of deer-proof fencing. The fencing is 36 feet long. She and her husband, John, discuss how to best use the fencing to make a rectangular garden. They agree that they should only use whole numbers of feet for the length and width of the garden.

    a. What are all of the possible dimensions of the garden?

Length of Garden in Feet	Width of Garden in Feet
17	1
16	2
15	3
14	4
13	5
12	6
11	7
10	8
9	9

    b. Which plan yields the maximum area for the garden? Which plan yields the minimum area?

Length of Garden in Feet	Width of Garden in Feet	Area of Garden in Square Feet
17	1	17
16	2	32
15	3	45
14	4	56
13	5	65
12	6	72
11	7	77
10	8	80
9	9	81

The 9 ft. by 9 ft. garden would have the maximum area (81 ft^2), while the 17 ft. by 1 ft. garden would have only 17 ft^2 of garden space.

©2015 Great Minds. eureka-math.org
G6-M5-TE-B5-1.3.1-01.2016

5. Write and then solve the equation to find the missing value below.

$$A = 1.82 \ m^2$$ $w = ?$

$$l = 1.4 \ m$$

$$A = l \times w$$
$$1.82 \ \text{m}^2 = 1.4 \ \text{m} \times w$$
$$\frac{1.82 \ \text{m}^2}{1.4 \ \text{m}} = w$$
$$1.3 \ \text{m} = w$$

6. Challenge: This is a drawing of the flag of the Republic of the Congo. The area of this flag is $3\frac{3}{4} \text{ft}^2$.

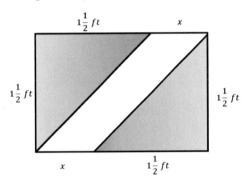

$1\frac{1}{2} ft$ x

$1\frac{1}{2} ft$ $1\frac{1}{2} ft$

x $1\frac{1}{2} ft$

a. Using the area formula, tell how you would determine the value of the base. This figure is not drawn to scale.

$$A = bh$$
$$A \div h = b$$
$$3\frac{3}{4}\text{ft}^2 \div 1\frac{1}{2}\text{ft.} = b$$
$$2\frac{1}{2}\text{ft.} = b$$

b. Using what you found in part (a), determine the missing value of the base.

$$2\frac{1}{2}\text{ft.} = 1\frac{1}{2}\text{ft.} + x$$
$$1 \text{ ft.} = x$$

Name _____   Date _____

1. David is the groundskeeper at Triangle Park, scale shown below.

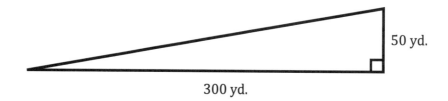

a. David needs to cut the grass four times a month. How many square yards of grass will he cut altogether each month?

b. During the winter, the triangular park and adjacent square parking lot are flooded with water and allowed to freeze so that people can go ice skating. What is the area of the ice?

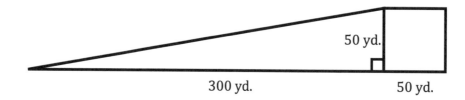

EUREKA MATH™

2. Mariska is looking for a new computer table. Below is a sketch of two computer tables she likes when looking at them from above. All measurements are in feet.

   a. If Mariska needs to choose the one with the greater area, which one should she choose? Justify your answer with evidence, using coordinates to determine side lengths.

   b. If Mariska needs to choose the one with the greater perimeter, which one should she choose? Justify your answer with evidence, using coordinates to determine side lengths.

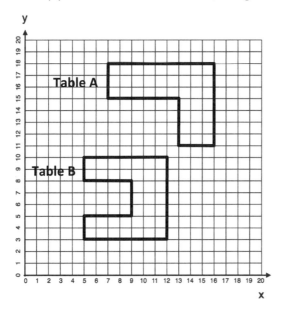

3. Find the area of the triangular region.

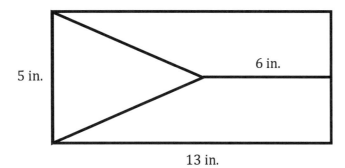

5 in.

6 in.

13 in.

4. The grid below shows a bird's-eye view of a middle school.

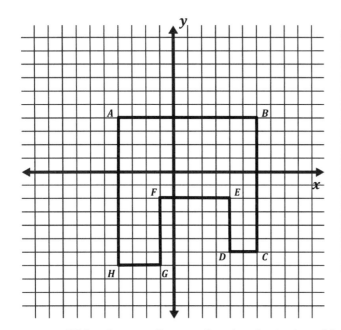

Point	Coordinates		Segment	Length (m)
A			$\overline{AB}$	
B			$\overline{BC}$	
C			$\overline{CD}$	
D			$\overline{DE}$	
E			$\overline{EF}$	
F			$\overline{FG}$	
G			$\overline{GH}$	
H			$\overline{HA}$	

a. Write the coordinates of each point in the table.

b. Each space on the grid stands for 10 meters. Find the length of each wall of the school.

c. Find the area of the entire building. Show your work.

Module 5: Area, Surface Area, and Volume Problems

EUREKA
MATH™

A Progression Toward Mastery

Assessment Task Item		STEP 1 Missing or incorrect answer and little evidence of reasoning or application of mathematics to solve the problem	STEP 2 Missing or incorrect answer but evidence of some reasoning or application of mathematics to solve the problem	STEP 3 A correct answer with some evidence of reasoning or application of mathematics to solve the problem, OR an incorrect answer with substantial evidence of solid reasoning or application of mathematics to solve the problem	STEP 4 A correct answer supported by substantial evidence of solid reasoning or application of mathematics to solve the problem
1	a 6.G.A.1	Student response is incorrect and shows no application of the triangle area formula.	Student uses the triangle area formula but answers incorrectly, perhaps by only calculating the area of the triangle (7,500 yd^2).	Student uses the triangle area formula, correctly finds the area of the park, 7,500 yd^2, and multiplies that area by 4. In the final answer, an arithmetic mistake might be made, or the units are either missing or are in yards instead of square yards.	Student uses the triangle area formula, correctly finds the area of the park, 7,500 yd^2, and multiplies that area by 4. Student response is correct, both in number and in units (30,000 yd^2).
	b 6.G.A.1	Student response is incorrect and shows no application of area formulas.	Student uses the triangle area formula and/or rectangle area formula but response is incorrect because of arithmetic errors. Units are not correct.	Student uses the triangle area formula, and correctly finds the area of the grass, 7,500 yd^2, or correctly finds the area of the parking lot, 2,500 yd^2.	Student uses area formulas and correctly finds the area of the grass, 7,500 yd^2, and parking lot, 2,500 yd^2, and adds them correctly, totaling 10,000 yd^2. Units are correct in the final answer.
2	a 6.G.A.3	Student response is incorrect and shows no application of area formulas. Perimeter calculations may have been made.	Student incorrectly calculates the area of both tables. Student chooses the greater of the two areas calculated, regardless of the mistake. Units are incorrectly identified.	Student correctly calculates the area of one table, either Table A is 39 ft^2 or Table B is 37 ft^2. The student chooses the greater of the two areas calculated, regardless of the mistake. Units are correctly identified.	Student correctly calculates the area of both tables, Table A is 39 ft^2 and Table B is 37 ft^2, and concludes Table A has a larger area. Units are correctly identified, and coordinates are appropriately used in order to determine side lengths.

	b **6.G.A.3**	Student incorrectly calculates the perimeter of both tables. Units are incorrectly identified. Area calculations may have been made.	Student incorrectly calculates the perimeter of both tables. Student chooses the greater of the two calculated perimeters, regardless of the mistake. Units are incorrectly identified.	Student correctly calculates the perimeter of one table, either Table A is 32 ft. or Table B is 36 ft., and concludes Table B has a longer perimeter. Units are correctly identified.	Student correctly calculates the perimeter of both tables, Table A is 32 ft. and Table B is 36 ft., and concludes Table B has a longer perimeter. Units are correctly identified, and coordinates are appropriately used in order to determine side lengths.
3	**6.G.A.1**	Student does not calculate the altitude of the triangle to be 7 in., and the final response is incorrect.	Student correctly calculates the altitude of the triangle to be 7 in., but the final area of the triangle is incorrect.	Student correctly calculates the altitude and area of the triangle, but the units are incorrectly identified.	Student correctly calculates the area of the triangle as 17.5 in^2.
4	**a** **6.G.A.3**	Student correctly identifies fewer than 4 of the 8 points.	Student correctly identifies at least 4 of the 8 points.	Student correctly identifies at least 6 of the 8 points.	Student correctly identifies all 8 points.

For the rightmost cell in row 4a:

Point	Coordinates
A	$(-4, 4)$
B	$(6, 4)$
C	$(6, -6)$
D	$(4, -6)$
E	$(4, -2)$
F	$(-1, -2)$
G	$(-1, -7)$
H	$(-4, -7)$

	b **6.G.A.3**	Student correctly identifies fewer than 4 of the 8 lengths.	Student correctly identifies at least 4 of the 8 lengths; alternatively, the response ignores the scale factor and finds 6 of the 8 lengths to be one-tenth of the correct answers.	Student correctly identifies at least 6 of the 8 lengths; alternatively, the response ignores the scale factor and finds all 8 lengths to be one-tenth of the correct answers.	Student correctly identifies all 8 lengths.

For the rightmost cell in row 4b:

Segment	Length (m)
$\overline{AB}$	100
$\overline{BC}$	100
$\overline{CD}$	20
$\overline{DE}$	40
$\overline{EF}$	50
$\overline{FG}$	50
$\overline{GH}$	30
$\overline{HA}$	110

	c **6.G.A.3**	Student response is incorrect in both number and units.	Student ignores the scale and incorrectly calculates the area of the building as 83 m^2. Units can be correct, incorrect, or missing.	Student incorrectly calculates the area of the building to be something other than $8,300 \text{ m}^2$ due to an arithmetic error. Units are correct.	Student correctly calculates the area of the building: $8,300 \text{ m}^2$. Both the number and units are correct.

©2015 Great Minds. eureka-math.org
G6-M5-TE-B5-1.3.1-01.2016

Name _____   Date _____

1.   David is the groundskeeper at Triangle Park, scale shown below.

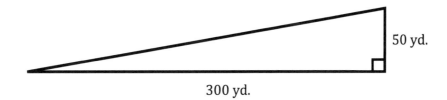

a.   David needs to cut the grass four times a month. How many square yards of grass will he cut altogether each month?

$A = \frac{1}{2}bh$

$A = \frac{1}{2} \cdot 300\,yd. \cdot 50\,yd.$

$A = \frac{1}{2} \cdot 15,000\,yd.^2$

$A = 7,500\,yd.^2$

$4 \cdot 7,500\,yd.^2 = 30,000\,yd.^2$

b.   During the winter, the triangular park and adjacent square parking lot are flooded with water and allowed to freeze so that people can go ice skating. What is the area of the ice?

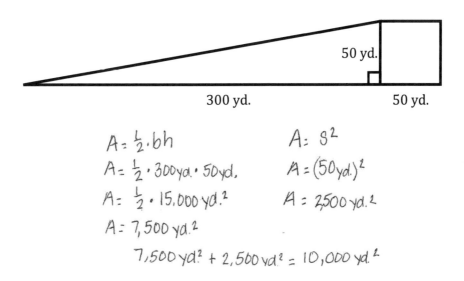

$A = \frac{1}{2} \cdot bh$ $A = s^2$

$A = \frac{1}{2} \cdot 300\,yd. \cdot 50\,yd.$ $A = (50\,yd.)^2$

$A = \frac{1}{2} \cdot 15,000\,yd.^2$ $A = 2,500\,yd.^2$

$A = 7,500\,yd.^2$

$7,500\,yd.^2 + 2,500\,yd.^2 = 10,000\,yd.^2$

2. Mariska is looking for a new computer table. Below is a sketch of two computer tables she likes when looking at them from above. All measurements are in feet.

    a. If Mariska needs to choose the one with the greater area, which one should she choose? Justify your answer with evidence, using coordinates to determine side lengths.

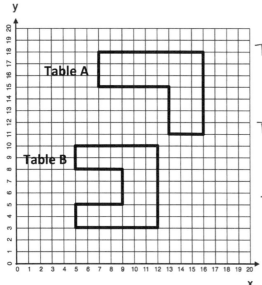

Table A
$(7,15) \rightarrow (7,18) = 3$ ft.
$(7,18) \rightarrow (16,18) = 9$ ft.
$(16,18) \rightarrow (16,11) = 7$ ft.
$(16,11) \rightarrow (13,11) = 3$ ft.
$(13,11) \rightarrow (13,15) = 4$ ft.
$(13,15) \rightarrow (7,15) = 6$ ft.

Table B
$(5,8) \rightarrow (5,10) = 2$ ft.
$(5,10) \rightarrow (12,10) = 7$ ft.
$(12,10) \rightarrow (12,3) = 7$ ft.
$(12,3) \rightarrow (5,3) = 7$ ft.
$(5,3) \rightarrow (5,5) = 2$ ft.
$(5,5) \rightarrow (9,5) = 4$ ft.
$(9,5) \rightarrow (9,8) = 3$ ft.
$(9,8) \rightarrow (5,8) = 4$ ft.

Table A

$A = bh$ $A = bh$
$A = 9$ ft. $\cdot$ 3ft. $A = 3$ ft. $\cdot$ 4ft.
$A = 27$ ft.^{2} $A = 12$ ft.^{2}

27 ft.^{2} + 12 ft.^{2} = 39 ft.^{2}

Table B

$A = bh$ $A = b \cdot h$ $A = bh$
$A = 7$ ft. $\cdot$ 2 ft. $A = 3$ ft. $\cdot$ 3 ft. $A = 7$ ft. $\cdot$ 2 ft.
$A = 14$ ft.^{2} $A = 9$ ft.^{2} $A = 14$ ft.^{2}

14 ft.^{2} + 9 ft.^{2} + 14 ft.^{2} = 37 ft.^{2}

Mariska will need to choose Table A because it is the table with the greatest area.

    b. If Mariska needs to choose the one with the greater perimeter, which one should she choose? Justify your answer with evidence, using coordinates to determine side lengths.

Table A:
$P = 3$ ft. + 9 ft. + 7 ft. + 3 ft. + 4 ft. + 6 ft.
$P = 32$ ft.

Table B:
$P = 2$ ft. + 7 ft. + 7 ft. + 7 ft. + 2 ft. + 3 ft. + 4 ft. + 4 ft.
$P = 36$ ft.

Table B has a larger perimeter.

EUREKA
MATH

3. Find the area of the triangular region.

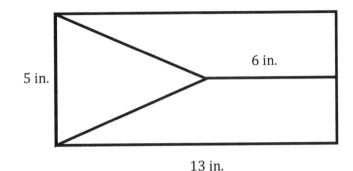

5 in.

6 in.

13 in.

$A = \frac{1}{2}bh$

$A = \frac{1}{2} \cdot 5\,\text{in.} \cdot 7\,\text{in.}$

$A = \frac{1}{2} \cdot 35\,\text{in.}^2$

$A = 17.5\,\text{in.}^2$

4. The grid below shows a bird's-eye view of a middle school.

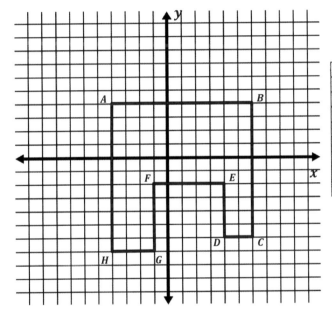

Point	Coordinates		Segment	Length (m)
A	(-4, 4)		$\overline{AB}$	100 m
B	(6, 4)		$\overline{BC}$	100 m
C	(6, -6)		$\overline{CD}$	20 m
D	(4, -6)		$\overline{DE}$	40 m
E	(4, -2)		$\overline{EF}$	50 m
F	(-1, -2)		$\overline{FG}$	50 m
G	(-1, -7)		$\overline{GH}$	30 m
H	(-4, -7)		$\overline{HA}$	110 m

a. Write the coordinates of each point in the table.

b. Each space on the grid stands for 10 meters. Find the length of each wall of the school.

c. Find the area of the entire building. Show your work.

$A = bh$
$A = 100\,\text{m} \cdot 60\,\text{m}$
$A = 6{,}000\,\text{m}^2$

$A = bh$
$A = 30\,\text{m} \cdot 50\,\text{m}$
$A = 1{,}500\,\text{m}^2$

$A = bh$
$A = 20\,\text{m} \cdot 40\,\text{m}$
$A = 800\,\text{m}^2$

$6{,}000\,\text{m}^2 + 1{,}500\,\text{m}^2 + 800\,\text{m}^2 = 8{,}300\,\text{m}^2$

6 GRADE

Mathematics Curriculum

Topic C

Volume of Right Rectangular Prisms

6.G.A.2

Focus Standard:	6.G.A.2	Find the volume of a right rectangular prism with fractional edge lengths by packing it with unit cubes of the appropriate unit fraction edge lengths, and show that the volume is the same as would be found by multiplying the edge lengths of the prism. Apply the formulas $V = lwh$ and $V = bh$ to find volumes of right rectangular prisms with fractional edge lengths in the context of solving real-world and mathematical problems.
Instructional Days:	4	
	Lesson 11:	Volume with Fractional Edge Lengths and Unit Cubes (P)[1]
	Lesson 12:	From Unit Cubes to the Formulas for Volume (P)
	Lesson 13:	The Formulas for Volume (P)
	Lesson 14:	Volume in the Real World (P)

In Topic C, students extend their understanding of the volume of a right rectangular prism with integer side lengths to right rectangular prisms with fractional side lengths. They apply the known volume formula, $V = lwh$, to find the volume of these prisms and use correct volume units when writing the answer. In Lesson 11, students determine the volume of a rectangular prism with edges $\frac{1}{8}, \frac{3}{8}$, and $\frac{5}{8}$ by packing it with 15 cubes with edge length $\frac{1}{8}$; they then compare that volume to the volume computed by multiplying the side lengths. In Lesson 12, students extend the volume formula for a right rectangular prism to the formula $V = $ area of base $\cdot$ height. Students explore the bases of right rectangular prisms and understand that any face can be the base. They find the area of the base first and then multiply by the height. They determine that two formulas can be used to find the volume of a right rectangular prism. In Lesson 13, students apply both formulas from Lesson 12 to application problems dealing with volume formulas of right rectangular prisms and cubes with fractional edge lengths. The topic concludes with Lesson 14, in which students determine the volume of composite solid figures and apply volume formulas to find missing volumes and missing dimensions in real-world contexts.

---

[1]Lesson Structure Key: **P**-Problem Set Lesson, **M**-Modeling Cycle Lesson, **E**-Exploration Lesson, **S**-Socratic Lesson

Lesson 11: Volume with Fractional Edge Lengths and Unit Cubes

Student Outcomes

- Students extend their understanding of the volume of a right rectangular prism with integer side lengths to right rectangular prisms with fractional side lengths. They apply the formula $V = l \cdot w \cdot h$ to find the volume of a right rectangular prism and use the correct volume units when writing the answer.

Lesson Notes

This lesson builds on the work done in Grade 5 Module 5 Topics A and B. Within these topics, students determine the volume of rectangular prisms with side lengths that are whole numbers. Students fill prisms with unit cubes in addition to using the formulas $V = bh$ and $V = l \cdot w \cdot h$ to determine the volume.

Students start their work on volume of prisms with fractional lengths so that they can continue to build an understanding of the units of volume. In addition, they must continue to build the connection between packing and filling. In the following lessons, students move from packing the prisms to using the formula.

The sample activity provided at the end of the lesson fosters an understanding of volume, especially in students not previously exposed to the Common Core standards.

> *Scaffolding:*
> Use unit cubes to help students visualize the problems in this lesson.
>
> One way to do this would be to have students make a conjecture about how many cubes it takes to fill the prism, and then use the cubes to test their ideas.
>
> Provide different examples of *volume* (electronic devices, loudness of voice), and explain that although this is the same word, the context of *volume* in this lesson refers to three-dimensional figures.

Classwork

Fluency Exercise (5 minutes): Multiplication of Fractions II

Sprint: Refer to the Sprints and the Sprint Delivery Script sections in the Module 4 Module Overview for directions to administer a Sprint.

Opening Exercise (3 minutes)

Please note that although scaffolding questions are provided, this Opening Exercise is an excellent chance to let students work on their own, persevering and making sense of the problem.

MP.1

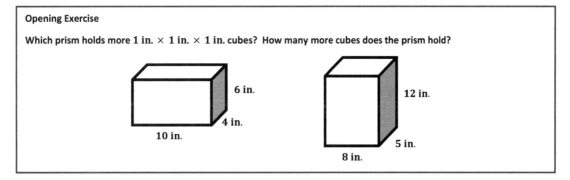

Opening Exercise

Which prism holds more 1 in. × 1 in. × 1 in. cubes? How many more cubes does the prism hold?

Students discuss their solutions with a partner.

- How many 1 in. × 1 in. × 1 in. cubes can fit across the bottom of the first rectangular prism?
    - *40 cubes can fit across the bottom.*
- How did you determine this number?
    - *Answers will vary. I determined how many cubes could fill the bottom layer of the prism and then decided how many layers were needed.*

Students who are English language learners may need a model of what "layers" means in this context.

MP.1

- How many layers of 1 in. × 1 in. × 1 in. cubes can fit inside the rectangular prism?
    - *There are 6 inches in the height; therefore, 6 layers of cubes can fit inside.*
- How many 1 in. × 1 in. × 1 in. cubes can fit across the bottom of the second rectangular prism?
    - *40 cubes can fit across the bottom.*
- How many layers do you need?
    - *I need 12 layers because the prism is 12 in. tall.*
- Which rectangular prism can hold more cubes?
    - *The second rectangular prism can hold more cubes.*
- How did you determine this?
    - *Both rectangular prisms hold the same number of cubes in one layer, but the second rectangular prism has more layers.*
- How many more layers does the second rectangular prism hold?
    - *It holds 6 more layers.*
- How many more cubes does the second rectangular prism hold?
    - *The second rectangular prism has 6 more layers than the first, with 40 cubes in each layer.*
    - *6 × 40 = 240, so the second rectangular prism holds 240 more cubes than the first.*
- What other ways can you determine the volume of a rectangular prism?
    - *We can also use the formula $V = l \cdot w \cdot h$.*

Example 1 (5 minutes)

Example 1

A box with the same dimensions as the prism in the Opening Exercise is used to ship miniature dice whose side lengths have been cut in half. The dice are $\frac{1}{2}$ in. × $\frac{1}{2}$ in. × $\frac{1}{2}$ in. cubes. How many dice of this size can fit in the box?

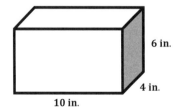

6 in.

4 in.

10 in.

Scaffolding:

Students may need a considerable amount of time to make sense of cubes with fractional side lengths.

An additional exercise has been included at the end of this lesson to use if needed.

EUREKA
MATH

- How many cubes could we fit across the length? The width? The height?
  - □ *Two cubes would fit across a 1-inch length. So, I would need to double the lengths to get the number of cubes. Twenty cubes will fit across the 10-inch length, 8 cubes will fit across the 4-inch width, and 12 cubes will fit across the 6-inch height.*

- How can you use this information to determine the number of $\frac{1}{2}$ in. $\times \frac{1}{2}$ in. $\times \frac{1}{2}$ in. cubes it takes to fill the box?
  - □ *I can multiply the number of cubes in the length, width, and height.*
  - □ $20 \times 8 \times 12 = 1{,}920$, *so 1,920 of the smaller cubes will fill the box.*

- How many of these smaller cubes can fit into the 1 in. $\times$ 1 in. $\times$ 1 in. cube?
  - □ *Two can fit across the length, two across the width, and two for the height.* $2 \times 2 \times 2 = 8.$ *Eight smaller cubes can fit in the larger cube.*

- How does the number of cubes in this example compare to the number of cubes that would be needed in the Opening Exercise?
  - □ $\dfrac{\text{new}}{\text{old}} = \dfrac{1{,}920}{240} = \dfrac{8}{1}$
  - □ *If I fill the same box with cubes that are half the length, I need 8 times as many.*

- How is the volume of the box related to the number of cubes that will fit in it?
  - □ *The volume of the box is* $\frac{1}{8}$ *of the number of cubes that will fit in it.*

- What is the volume of 1 cube?
  - □ $V = \frac{1}{2}$ in. $\times \frac{1}{2}$ in. $\times \frac{1}{2}$ in.
    $V = \frac{1}{8}$ in^3

- What is the product of the number of cubes and the volume of the cubes? What does this product represent?
  - □ $1{,}920 \times \frac{1}{8} = 240$
  - □ *The product represents the volume of the original box.*

Example 2 (5 minutes)

Example 2

A $\frac{1}{4}$ in. cube is used to fill the prism.

How many $\frac{1}{4}$ in. cubes does it take to fill the prism?

What is the volume of the prism?

How is the number of cubes related to the volume?

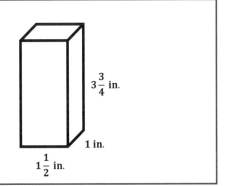

- How would you determine, or find, the number of cubes that fill the prism?

  - *One method would be to determine the number of cubes that will fit across the length, width, and height. Then, I would multiply.*

    6 will fit across the length, 4 across the width, and 15 across the height.

    6 × 4 × 15 = 360, so 360 cubes will fill the prism.

- How are the number of cubes and the volume related?

  - *The volume is equal to the number of cubes times the volume of one cube.*

    The volume of one cube is $\frac{1}{4}$ in. × $\frac{1}{4}$ in. × $\frac{1}{4}$ in. = $\frac{1}{64}$ in³.

    360 cubes × $\frac{1}{64}$ in³ = $\frac{360}{64}$ in³ = $\frac{540}{64}$ in³ = $5\frac{5}{8}$ in³

- What other method can be used to determine the volume?

  - *$V = l\,w\,h$*

    $V = \left(1\frac{1}{2}\text{ in.}\right)(1\text{ in.})\left(3\frac{3}{4}\text{ in.}\right)$

    $V = \frac{3}{2}\text{in.} \times \frac{1}{1}\text{in.} \times \frac{15}{4}\text{in.}$

    $V = \frac{45}{8}\text{in}^3 = 5\frac{5}{8}\text{in}^3$

- Would any other size cubes fit perfectly inside the prism with no space left over?

  - *We would not be able to use cubes with side lengths of $\frac{1}{2}$ in., $\frac{1}{3}$ in., or $\frac{2}{3}$ in. because there would be spaces left over. However, we could use a cube with a side length of $\frac{1}{8}$ in. without having spaces left over.*

Exercises (20 minutes)

Have students work in pairs.

Exercises

1. Use the prism to answer the following questions.

   a. Calculate the volume.

      $V = l\,w\,h$

      $V = \left(5\frac{1}{3}\text{ cm}\right)\left(\frac{2}{3}\text{ cm}\right)\left(1\frac{1}{3}\text{ cm}\right)$

      $V = \frac{16}{3}\text{ cm} \times \frac{2}{3}\text{ cm} \times \frac{4}{3}\text{ cm}$

      $V = \frac{128}{27}\text{ cm}^3 \text{ or } 4\frac{20}{27}\text{ cm}^3$

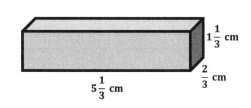

$1\frac{1}{3}$ cm

$\frac{2}{3}$ cm

$5\frac{1}{3}$ cm

   b. If you have to fill the prism with cubes whose side lengths are less than 1 cm, what size would be best?

      The best choice would be a cube with side lengths of $\frac{1}{3}$ cm.

EUREKA MATH

    c.   **How many of the cubes would fit in the prism?**

        $16 \times 2 \times 4 = 128$, so 128 cubes will fit in the prism.

    d.   **Use the relationship between the number of cubes and the volume to prove that your volume calculation is correct.**

        The volume of one cube would be $\frac{1}{3}$ cm $\times \frac{1}{3}$ cm $\times \frac{1}{3}$ cm $= \frac{1}{27}$ cm^3.

        Since there are 128 cubes, the volume would be $128 \times \frac{1}{27}$ cm$^3 = \frac{128}{27}$ cm^3 or $4\frac{20}{27}$ cm^3.

2.   **Calculate the volume of the following rectangular prisms.**

    a.

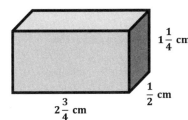

$$V = l\,w\,h$$
$$V = \left(2\frac{3}{4}\text{ cm}\right)\left(\frac{1}{2}\text{ cm}\right)\left(1\frac{1}{4}\text{ cm}\right)$$
$$V = \frac{11}{4}\text{ cm} \times \frac{1}{2}\text{ cm} \times \frac{5}{4}\text{ cm}$$
$$V = \frac{55}{32}\text{ cm}^3 \text{ or } 1\frac{23}{32}\text{ cm}^3$$

    b.

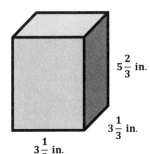

$$V = l\,w\,h$$
$$V = \left(3\frac{1}{3}\text{in.}\right)\left(3\frac{1}{3}\text{in.}\right)\left(5\frac{2}{3}\text{in.}\right)$$
$$V = \frac{10}{3}\text{in.} \times \frac{10}{3}\text{in.} \times \frac{17}{3}\text{in.}$$
$$V = \frac{1,700}{27}\text{ in}^3 \text{ or } 62\frac{26}{27}\text{ in}^3$$

3.   **A toy company is packaging its toys to be shipped. Each small toy is placed inside a cube-shaped box with side lengths of $\frac{1}{2}$ in. These smaller boxes are then placed into a larger box with dimensions of 12 in. $\times\, 4\frac{1}{2}$ in. $\times\, 3\frac{1}{2}$ in.**

    a.   **What is the greatest number of small toy boxes that can be packed into the larger box for shipping?**

        $24 \times 9 \times 7 = 1,512$, so 1,512 toys can be packed into the larger box.

    b.   **Use the number of small toy boxes that can be shipped in the larger box to help determine the volume of the shipping box.**

        One small box would have a volume of $\frac{1}{2}$ in. $\times \frac{1}{2}$ in. $\times \frac{1}{2}$ in. $= \frac{1}{8}$ in^3.

        Now, I multiply the number of cubes by the volume of the cube.

        $1,512 \times \frac{1}{8}$ in$^3 = \frac{1,512}{8}$ in$^3 = 189$ in^3

©2015 Great Minds. eureka-math.org
G6-M5-TE-B5-1.3.1-01.2016

4.   A rectangular prism with a volume of 8 cubic units is filled with cubes twice: once with cubes with side lengths of $\frac{1}{2}$ unit and once with cubes with side lengths of $\frac{1}{3}$ unit.

   a.   How many more of the cubes with $\frac{1}{3}$-unit side lengths than cubes with $\frac{1}{2}$-unit side lengths are needed to fill the prism?

There are 8 cubes with $\frac{1}{2}$-unit side lengths in 1 cubic unit because the volume of one cube is $\frac{1}{8}$ cubic unit.

Since we have 8 cubic units, we would have 64 total cubes with $\frac{1}{2}$-unit side lengths because $8 \times 8 = 64$.

There are 27 cubes with $\frac{1}{3}$-unit side lengths in 1 cubic unit because the volume of one cube is $\frac{1}{27}$ cubic units.

Since we have 8 cubic units, we would have 216 total cubes with $\frac{1}{3}$-unit side lengths because $8 \times 27 = 216$.

$216 - 64 = 152$, so 152 more cubes with $\frac{1}{3}$-unit side lengths are needed to fill the prism.

   b.   Why does it take more cubes with $\frac{1}{3}$-unit side lengths to fill the prism than it does with cubes with $\frac{1}{2}$-unit side lengths?

$\frac{1}{3} < \frac{1}{2}$. The side length is shorter for the cube with a $\frac{1}{3}$-unit side length, so it takes more to fill the rectangular prism.

5.   Calculate the volume of the rectangular prism. Show two different methods for determining the volume.

Method 1:

$V = l\,w\,h$

$V = \left(1\frac{1}{2}\ \text{m}\right)\left(\frac{3}{4}\ \text{m}\right)\left(4\frac{1}{2}\ \text{m}\right)$

$V = \left(\frac{3}{2}\ \text{m}\right)\left(\frac{3}{4}\ \text{m}\right)\left(\frac{9}{2}\ \text{m}\right)$

$V = \frac{81}{16}\ \text{m}^3$

$V = 5\frac{1}{16}\ \text{m}^3$

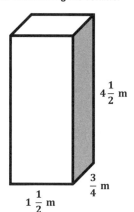

$4\frac{1}{2}$ m

$\frac{3}{4}$ m

$1\frac{1}{2}$ m

Method 2:

Fill the rectangular prism with cubes that are $\frac{1}{4}$ m $\times$ $\frac{1}{4}$ m $\times$ $\frac{1}{4}$ m.

The volume of each cube is $\frac{1}{64}$ m^3.

We would have 6 cubes across the length, 3 cubes across the width, and 18 cubes across the height.

$6 \times 3 \times 18 = 324$, so the rectangular prism could be filled with 324 cubes with $\frac{1}{4}$ m side lengths.

$324 \times \frac{1}{64}\ \text{m}^3 = 5\frac{1}{16}\ \text{m}^3$

EUREKA MATH

Closing (2 minutes)

- When you want to find the volume of a rectangular prism that has sides with fractional lengths, what are some methods you can use?

    □   *One method to find the volume of a right rectangular prism that has fractional side lengths is to use the volume formula $V = lwh$.*

    □   *Another method to find the volume is to determine how many cubes of fractional side lengths are inside the right rectangular prism, and then find the volume of the cube. To determine the volume of the right rectangular prism, find the product of these two numbers.*

Exit Ticket (5 minutes)

Name _____   Date _____

Lesson 11: Volume with Fractional Edge Lengths and Unit Cubes

Exit Ticket

Calculate the volume of the rectangular prism using two different methods. Label your solutions Method 1 and Method 2.

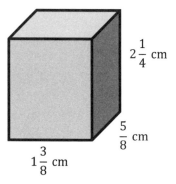

$2\frac{1}{4}$ cm

$\frac{5}{8}$ cm

$1\frac{3}{8}$ cm

EUREKA
MATH™

©2015 Great Minds. eureka-math.org
G6-M5-TE-B5-1.3.1-01.2016

Exit Ticket Sample Solutions

Calculate the volume of the rectangular prism using two different methods. Label your solutions Method 1 and Method 2.

Method 1:

$V = l\,w\,h$

$V = \left(1\frac{3}{8} \text{ cm}\right)\left(\frac{5}{8} \text{ cm}\right)\left(2\frac{1}{4} \text{ cm}\right)$

$V = \frac{11}{8} \text{ cm} \times \frac{5}{8} \text{ cm} \times \frac{9}{4} \text{ cm}$

$V = \frac{495}{256} \text{ cm}^3$

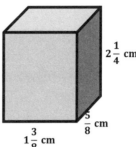

$2\frac{1}{4}$ cm

$\frac{5}{8}$ cm

$1\frac{3}{8}$ cm

Method 2:

Fill shape with $\frac{1}{8}$ cm cubes.

$11 \times 5 \times 18 = 990$, *so 990 cubes could be used to fill the prism.*

Each cube has a volume of $\frac{1}{8}$ cm $\times \frac{1}{8}$ cm $\times \frac{1}{8}$ cm $= \frac{1}{512}$ cm^3.

$V = 990 \times \frac{1}{512} \text{ cm}^3 = \frac{990}{512} \text{ cm}^3 = \frac{495}{256} \text{ cm}^3$

Problem Set Sample Solutions

1. Answer the following questions using this rectangular prism:

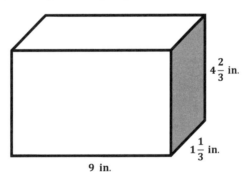

$4\frac{2}{3}$ in.

$1\frac{1}{3}$ in.

9 in.

a. What is the volume of the prism?

$V = l\,w\,h$

$V = (9 \text{ in.})\left(1\frac{1}{3} \text{ in.}\right)\left(4\frac{2}{3} \text{ in.}\right)$

$V = \left(\frac{9}{1} \text{ in.}\right)\left(\frac{4}{3} \text{ in.}\right)\left(\frac{14}{3} \text{ in.}\right)$

$V = \frac{504}{9} \text{ in}^3$

$V = 56 \text{ in}^3$

b. Linda fills the rectangular prism with cubes that have side lengths of $\frac{1}{3}$ in. How many cubes does she need to fill the rectangular prism?

She needs 27 across by 4 wide and 14 high.

Number of cubes = 27 × 4 × 14 = 1,512.

Linda needs 1,512 cubes with $\frac{1}{3}$ in. side lengths to fill the rectangular prism.

c. How is the number of cubes related to the volume?

$56 \times 27 = 1,512$

The number of cubes needed is 27 times larger than the volume.

d. Why is the number of cubes needed different from the volume?

Because the cubes are not each 1 in., the volume is different from the number of cubes. However, I could multiply the number of cubes by the volume of one cube and still get the original volume.

e. Should Linda try to fill this rectangular prism with cubes that are $\frac{1}{2}$ in. long on each side? Why or why not?

Because some of the lengths are $\frac{1}{3}$ in. and some are $\frac{2}{3}$ in., it would not be possible to use side lengths of $\frac{1}{2}$ in. to fill the prism.

2. Calculate the volume of the following prisms.

a.

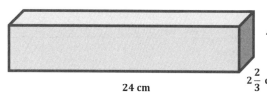

$V = l\,w\,h$

$V = (24 \text{ cm})\left(2\frac{2}{3}\text{ cm}\right)\left(4\frac{1}{2}\text{cm}\right)$

$V = (24 \text{ cm})\left(\frac{8}{3}\text{ cm}\right)\left(\frac{9}{2}\text{ cm}\right)$

$V = \frac{1,728}{6}\text{ cm}^3$

$V = 288 \text{ cm}^3$

b.

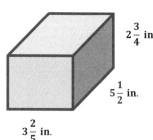

$V = l\,w\,h$

$V = \left(3\frac{2}{5}\text{in.}\right)\left(5\frac{1}{2}\text{in.}\right)\left(2\frac{3}{4}\text{in.}\right)$

$V = \left(\frac{17}{5}\text{in.}\right)\left(\frac{11}{2}\text{in.}\right)\left(\frac{11}{4}\text{in.}\right)$

$V = \frac{2057}{40}\text{ in}^3$

$V = 51\frac{17}{40}\text{ in}^3$

EUREKA
MATH™

3. A rectangular prism with a volume of 12 cubic units is filled with cubes twice: once with cubes with $\frac{1}{2}$-unit side lengths and once with cubes with $\frac{1}{3}$-unit side lengths.

    a. How many more of the cubes with $\frac{1}{3}$-unit side lengths than cubes with $\frac{1}{2}$-unit side lengths are needed to fill the prism?

    There are 8 cubes with $\frac{1}{2}$-unit side lengths in 1 cubic unit because the volume of one cube is $\frac{1}{8}$ cubic unit.

    Since we have 12 cubic units, we would have 96 total cubes with $\frac{1}{2}$-unit side lengths because $12 \times 8 = 96$.

    There are 27 cubes with $\frac{1}{3}$-unit side lengths in 1 cubic unit because the volume of one cube is $\frac{1}{27}$ cubic unit.

    Since we have 12 cubic units, we would have 324 total cubes with $\frac{1}{3}$-unit side lengths because $12 \times 27 = 324$.

    $324 - 96 = 228$, so there are 228 more cubes with $\frac{1}{3}$-unit side lengths needed than there are cubes with $\frac{1}{2}$-unit side lengths needed.

    b. Finally, the prism is filled with cubes whose side lengths are $\frac{1}{4}$ unit. How many $\frac{1}{4}$ unit cubes would it take to fill the prism?

    There are 64 cubes with $\frac{1}{4}$-unit side lengths in 1 cubic unit because the volume of one cube is $\frac{1}{64}$ cubic unit.

    Since there are 12 cubic units, we would have 768 total cubes with side lengths of $\frac{1}{4}$ unit because $12 \times 64 = 768$.

4. A toy company is packaging its toys to be shipped. Each toy is placed inside a cube-shaped box with side lengths of $3\frac{1}{2}$ in. These smaller boxes are then packed into a larger box with dimensions of 14 in. $\times$ 7 in. $\times$ $3\frac{1}{2}$ in.

    a. What is the greatest number of toy boxes that can be packed into the larger box for shipping?

    $4 \times 2 \times 1 = 8$, so 8 toy boxes can be packed into the larger box for shipping.

    b. Use the number of toy boxes that can be shipped in the large box to determine the volume of the shipping box.

    One small box would have a volume of $3\frac{1}{2}$ in. $\times$ $3\frac{1}{2}$ in. $\times$ $3\frac{1}{2}$ in. $= 42\frac{7}{8}$ in³.

    Now, I will multiply the number of cubes by the volume of the cube. $8 \times 42\frac{7}{8}$ in³ $= 343$ in³

5. A rectangular prism has a volume of 34.224 cubic meters. The height of the box is 3.1 meters, and the length is 2.4 meters.

    a. Write an equation that relates the volume to the length, width, and height. Let w represent the width, in meters.

    $34.224 = (3.1)(2.4)w$

    b. Solve the equation.

    $34.224 = 7.44w$

    $w = 4.6$

    The width is 4.6 m.

Additional Exercise from Scaffolding Box

This is a sample activity that fosters understanding of a cube with fractional edge lengths. It begins with three (two-dimensional) squares with side lengths of 1 unit, $\frac{1}{2}$ unit, and $\frac{1}{3}$ unit, which leads to an understanding of three-dimensional cubes that have edge lengths of 1 unit, $\frac{1}{2}$ unit, and $\frac{1}{3}$ unit.

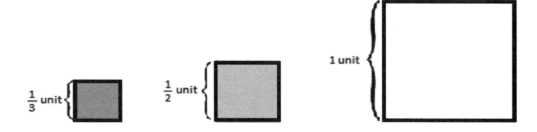

- How many squares with $\frac{1}{2}$-unit side lengths can fit in a square with 1-unit side lengths?

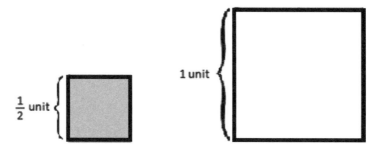

   □ *Four squares with $\frac{1}{2}$-unit side lengths can fit in the square with 1-unit side lengths.*

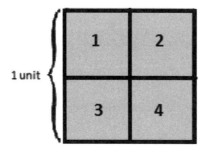

- What does this mean about the area of a square with $\frac{1}{2}$-unit side lengths?

   □ *The area of a square with $\frac{1}{2}$-unit side lengths is $\frac{1}{4}$ of the area of a square with 1-unit side lengths, so it has an area of $\frac{1}{4}$ square unit.*

EUREKA
MATH™

- How many squares with side lengths of $\frac{1}{3}$ unit can fit in a square with side lengths of 1 unit?

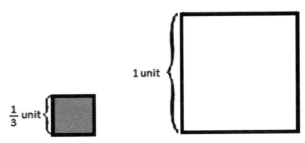

   □ *Nine squares with side lengths of $\frac{1}{3}$ unit will fit in a square with side lengths of 1 unit.*

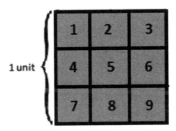

- What does this mean about the area of a square with $\frac{1}{3}$-unit side lengths?

   □ *The area of a square with $\frac{1}{3}$-unit side lengths is $\frac{1}{9}$ of the area of a square with 1-unit side lengths, so it has an area of $\frac{1}{9}$ square unit.*

- Let's look at what we have seen so far:

Side Length of Square (units)	How Many Small Squares Fit into One Unit Square?
1	1
$\frac{1}{2}$	4
$\frac{1}{3}$	9

Sample questions to pose:

- Make a prediction about how many squares with $\frac{1}{4}$-unit side lengths can fit into a unit square; then, draw a picture to justify your prediction.

   □ 16 *squares*

- How could you determine the number of $\frac{1}{2}$-unit side length squares that would cover a figure with an area of 15 square units? How many $\frac{1}{3}$-unit side length squares would cover the same figure?

  - *4 squares of $\frac{1}{2}$-unit side lengths fit in each 1 square unit. So, if there are 15 square units, there are 15 × 4 = 60, so 60 squares of $\frac{1}{2}$-unit side lengths will cover a figure with an area of 15 square units.*

  - *9 squares of $\frac{1}{3}$-unit side lengths fit in each 1 square unit. So, if there are 15 square units, there are 15 × 9 = 135, so 135 squares of $\frac{1}{3}$-unit side lengths will cover a figure with an area of 15 square units.*

- Now let's see what happens when we consider cubes of 1-, $\frac{1}{2}$-, and $\frac{1}{3}$-unit side lengths.

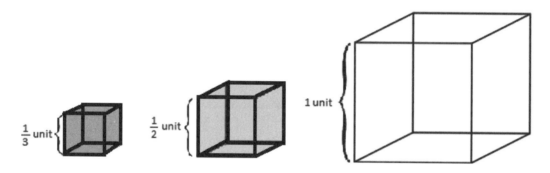

- How many cubes with $\frac{1}{2}$-unit side lengths can fit in a cube with 1-unit side lengths?

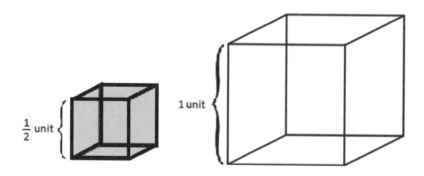

  - *Eight of the cubes with $\frac{1}{2}$-unit side lengths can fit into the cube with a 1-unit side lengths.*

Lesson 11:   Volume with Fractional Edge Lengths and Unit Cubes

EUREKA MATH™

■   What does this mean about the volume of a cube with $\frac{1}{2}$-unit side lengths?

      □   *The volume of a cube with $\frac{1}{2}$-unit side lengths is $\frac{1}{8}$ of the volume of a cube with 1-unit side lengths, so it has a volume of $\frac{1}{8}$ cubic unit.*

■   How many cubes with $\frac{1}{3}$-unit side lengths can fit in a cube with 1-unit side lengths?

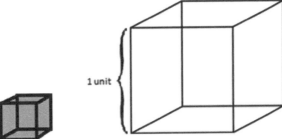

      □   *27 of the cubes with $\frac{1}{3}$-unit side lengths can fit into the cube with 1-unit side lengths.*

■   What does this mean about the volume of a cube with $\frac{1}{3}$-unit side lengths?

      □   *The volume of a cube with $\frac{1}{3}$-unit side lengths is $\frac{1}{27}$ of the volume of a cube with 1-unit side lengths, so it has a volume of $\frac{1}{27}$ cubic unit.*

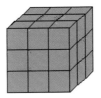

■   Let's look at what we have seen so far:

Side Length of Square (units)	How Many Small Squares Fit into One Unit Square?
1	1
$\frac{1}{2}$	8
$\frac{1}{3}$	27

Sample questions to pose:

- Make a prediction about how many cubes with $\frac{1}{4}$-unit side lengths can fit into a unit cube, and then draw a picture to justify your prediction.
    - *64 cubes*

- How could you determine the number of $\frac{1}{2}$-unit side length cubes that would fill a figure with a volume of 15 cubic units? How many $\frac{1}{3}$-unit side length cubes would fill the same figure?
    - *8 cubes of $\frac{1}{2}$-unit side lengths fit in each 1 cubic unit. So, if there are 15 cubic units, there are 120 cubes because $15 \times 8 = 120$.*
    - *27 cubes of $\frac{1}{3}$-unit side lengths fit in each 1 cubic unit. So, if there are 15 cubic units, there are 405 cubes because $15 \times 27 = 405$.*

Understanding Volume

Volume

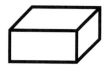

- Volume is the amount of space inside a three-dimensional figure.
- It is measured in cubic units.
- It is the number of cubic units needed to fill the inside of the figure.

Cubic Units

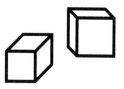

- Cubic units measure the same on all sides. A cubic centimeter is one centimeter on all sides; a cubic inch is one inch on all sides, etc.
- Cubic units can be shortened using the exponent 3.
  6 cubic centimeters $= 6 \text{ cm}^3$
- Different cubic units can be used to measure the volume of space figures—cubic inches, cubic yards, cubic centimeters, etc.

©2015 Great Minds. eureka-math.org
G6-M5-TE-B5-1.3.1-01.2016

Number Correct: _____

Multiplication of Fractions II—Round 1

Directions: Determine the product of the fractions and simplify.

1.	$\frac{1}{2} \times \frac{5}{8}$		16.	$\frac{2}{9} \times \frac{3}{8}$	
2.	$\frac{3}{4} \times \frac{3}{5}$		17.	$\frac{3}{8} \times \frac{8}{9}$	
3.	$\frac{1}{4} \times \frac{7}{8}$		18.	$\frac{3}{4} \times \frac{7}{9}$	
4.	$\frac{3}{9} \times \frac{2}{5}$		19.	$\frac{3}{5} \times \frac{10}{13}$	
5.	$\frac{5}{8} \times \frac{3}{7}$		20.	$1\frac{2}{7} \times \frac{7}{8}$	
6.	$\frac{3}{7} \times \frac{4}{9}$		21.	$3\frac{1}{2} \times 3\frac{5}{6}$	
7.	$\frac{2}{5} \times \frac{3}{8}$		22.	$1\frac{7}{8} \times 5\frac{1}{5}$	
8.	$\frac{4}{9} \times \frac{5}{9}$		23.	$5\frac{4}{5} \times 3\frac{2}{9}$	
9.	$\frac{2}{3} \times \frac{5}{7}$		24.	$7\frac{2}{5} \times 2\frac{3}{8}$	
10.	$\frac{2}{7} \times \frac{3}{10}$		25.	$4\frac{2}{3} \times 2\frac{3}{10}$	
11.	$\frac{3}{4} \times \frac{9}{10}$		26.	$3\frac{3}{5} \times 6\frac{1}{4}$	
12.	$\frac{3}{5} \times \frac{2}{9}$		27.	$2\frac{7}{9} \times 5\frac{1}{3}$	
13.	$\frac{2}{10} \times \frac{5}{6}$		28.	$4\frac{3}{8} \times 3\frac{1}{5}$	
14.	$\frac{5}{8} \times \frac{7}{10}$		29.	$3\frac{1}{3} \times 5\frac{2}{5}$	
15.	$\frac{3}{5} \times \frac{7}{9}$		30.	$2\frac{2}{3} \times 7$	

Multiplication of Fractions II—Round 1 [KEY]

Directions: Determine the product of the fractions and simplify.

1.	$\dfrac{1}{2} \times \dfrac{5}{8}$	$\dfrac{5}{16}$	16.	$\dfrac{2}{9} \times \dfrac{3}{8}$	$\dfrac{6}{72} = \dfrac{1}{12}$
2.	$\dfrac{3}{4} \times \dfrac{3}{5}$	$\dfrac{9}{20}$	17.	$\dfrac{3}{8} \times \dfrac{8}{9}$	$\dfrac{24}{72} = \dfrac{1}{3}$
3.	$\dfrac{1}{4} \times \dfrac{7}{8}$	$\dfrac{7}{32}$	18.	$\dfrac{3}{4} \times \dfrac{7}{9}$	$\dfrac{21}{36} = \dfrac{7}{12}$
4.	$\dfrac{3}{9} \times \dfrac{2}{5}$	$\dfrac{6}{45} = \dfrac{2}{15}$	19.	$\dfrac{3}{5} \times \dfrac{10}{13}$	$\dfrac{30}{65} = \dfrac{6}{13}$
5.	$\dfrac{5}{8} \times \dfrac{3}{7}$	$\dfrac{15}{56}$	20.	$1\dfrac{2}{7} \times \dfrac{7}{8}$	$\dfrac{63}{56} = 1\dfrac{1}{8}$
6.	$\dfrac{3}{7} \times \dfrac{4}{9}$	$\dfrac{12}{63} = \dfrac{4}{21}$	21.	$3\dfrac{1}{2} \times 3\dfrac{5}{6}$	$\dfrac{161}{12} = 13\dfrac{5}{12}$
7.	$\dfrac{2}{5} \times \dfrac{3}{8}$	$\dfrac{6}{40} = \dfrac{3}{20}$	22.	$1\dfrac{7}{8} \times 5\dfrac{1}{5}$	$\dfrac{390}{40} = 9\dfrac{3}{4}$
8.	$\dfrac{4}{9} \times \dfrac{5}{9}$	$\dfrac{20}{81}$	23.	$5\dfrac{4}{5} \times 3\dfrac{2}{9}$	$\dfrac{841}{45} = 18\dfrac{31}{45}$
9.	$\dfrac{2}{3} \times \dfrac{5}{7}$	$\dfrac{10}{21}$	24.	$7\dfrac{2}{5} \times 2\dfrac{3}{8}$	$\dfrac{703}{40} = 17\dfrac{23}{40}$
10.	$\dfrac{2}{7} \times \dfrac{3}{10}$	$\dfrac{6}{70} = \dfrac{3}{35}$	25.	$4\dfrac{2}{3} \times 2\dfrac{3}{10}$	$\dfrac{322}{30} = 10\dfrac{11}{15}$
11.	$\dfrac{3}{4} \times \dfrac{9}{10}$	$\dfrac{27}{40}$	26.	$3\dfrac{3}{5} \times 6\dfrac{1}{4}$	$\dfrac{450}{20} = 22\dfrac{1}{2}$
12.	$\dfrac{3}{5} \times \dfrac{2}{9}$	$\dfrac{6}{45} = \dfrac{2}{15}$	27.	$2\dfrac{7}{9} \times 5\dfrac{1}{3}$	$\dfrac{400}{27} = 14\dfrac{22}{27}$
13.	$\dfrac{2}{10} \times \dfrac{5}{6}$	$\dfrac{10}{60} = \dfrac{1}{6}$	28.	$4\dfrac{3}{8} \times 3\dfrac{1}{5}$	$\dfrac{560}{40} = 14$
14.	$\dfrac{5}{8} \times \dfrac{7}{10}$	$\dfrac{35}{80} = \dfrac{7}{16}$	29.	$3\dfrac{1}{3} \times 5\dfrac{2}{5}$	$\dfrac{270}{15} = 18$
15.	$\dfrac{3}{5} \times \dfrac{7}{9}$	$\dfrac{21}{45} = \dfrac{7}{15}$	30.	$2\dfrac{2}{3} \times 7$	$\dfrac{56}{3} = 18\dfrac{2}{3}$

Lesson 11: Volume with Fractional Edge Lengths and Unit Cubes

EUREKA
MATH

Number Correct: _____

Improvement: _____

Multiplication of Fractions II—Round 2

Directions: Determine the product of the fractions and simplify.

1.	$\frac{2}{3} \times \frac{5}{7}$	
2.	$\frac{1}{4} \times \frac{3}{5}$	
3.	$\frac{2}{3} \times \frac{2}{5}$	
4.	$\frac{5}{9} \times \frac{5}{8}$	
5.	$\frac{5}{8} \times \frac{3}{7}$	
6.	$\frac{3}{4} \times \frac{7}{8}$	
7.	$\frac{2}{5} \times \frac{3}{8}$	
8.	$\frac{3}{4} \times \frac{3}{4}$	
9.	$\frac{7}{8} \times \frac{3}{10}$	
10.	$\frac{4}{9} \times \frac{1}{2}$	
11.	$\frac{6}{11} \times \frac{3}{8}$	
12.	$\frac{5}{6} \times \frac{9}{10}$	
13.	$\frac{3}{4} \times \frac{2}{9}$	
14.	$\frac{4}{11} \times \frac{5}{8}$	
15.	$\frac{2}{3} \times \frac{9}{10}$	

16.	$\frac{3}{11} \times \frac{2}{9}$	
17.	$\frac{3}{5} \times \frac{10}{21}$	
18.	$\frac{4}{9} \times \frac{3}{10}$	
19.	$\frac{3}{8} \times \frac{4}{5}$	
20.	$\frac{6}{11} \times \frac{2}{15}$	
21.	$1\frac{2}{3} \times \frac{3}{5}$	
22.	$2\frac{1}{6} \times \frac{3}{4}$	
23.	$1\frac{2}{5} \times 3\frac{2}{3}$	
24.	$4\frac{2}{3} \times 1\frac{1}{4}$	
25.	$3\frac{1}{2} \times 2\frac{4}{5}$	
26.	$3 \times 5\frac{3}{4}$	
27.	$1\frac{2}{3} \times 3\frac{1}{4}$	
28.	$2\frac{3}{5} \times 3$	
29.	$1\frac{5}{7} \times 3\frac{1}{2}$	
30.	$3\frac{1}{3} \times 1\frac{9}{10}$	

Multiplication of Fractions II—Round 2 [KEY]

Directions: Determine the product of the fractions and simplify.

1.	$\frac{2}{3} \times \frac{5}{7}$	$\frac{10}{21}$	16.	$\frac{3}{11} \times \frac{2}{9}$	$\frac{6}{99} = \frac{2}{33}$
2.	$\frac{1}{4} \times \frac{3}{5}$	$\frac{3}{20}$	17.	$\frac{3}{5} \times \frac{10}{21}$	$\frac{30}{105} = \frac{2}{7}$
3.	$\frac{2}{3} \times \frac{2}{5}$	$\frac{4}{15}$	18.	$\frac{4}{9} \times \frac{3}{10}$	$\frac{12}{90} = \frac{2}{15}$
4.	$\frac{5}{9} \times \frac{5}{8}$	$\frac{25}{72}$	19.	$\frac{3}{8} \times \frac{4}{5}$	$\frac{12}{40} = \frac{3}{10}$
5.	$\frac{5}{8} \times \frac{3}{7}$	$\frac{15}{56}$	20.	$\frac{6}{11} \times \frac{2}{15}$	$\frac{12}{165} = \frac{4}{55}$
6.	$\frac{3}{4} \times \frac{7}{8}$	$\frac{21}{32}$	21.	$1\frac{2}{3} \times \frac{3}{5}$	$\frac{15}{15} = 1$
7.	$\frac{2}{5} \times \frac{3}{8}$	$\frac{6}{40} = \frac{3}{20}$	22.	$2\frac{1}{6} \times \frac{3}{4}$	$\frac{39}{24} = \frac{13}{8} = 1\frac{5}{8}$
8.	$\frac{3}{4} \times \frac{3}{4}$	$\frac{9}{16}$	23.	$1\frac{2}{5} \times 3\frac{2}{3}$	$\frac{77}{15} = 5\frac{2}{15}$
9.	$\frac{7}{8} \times \frac{3}{10}$	$\frac{21}{80}$	24.	$4\frac{2}{3} \times 1\frac{1}{4}$	$\frac{70}{12} = 5\frac{10}{12} = 5\frac{5}{6}$
10.	$\frac{4}{9} \times \frac{1}{2}$	$\frac{4}{18} = \frac{2}{9}$	25.	$3\frac{1}{2} \times 2\frac{4}{5}$	$\frac{98}{10} = 9\frac{8}{10} = 9\frac{4}{5}$
11.	$\frac{6}{11} \times \frac{3}{8}$	$\frac{18}{88} = \frac{9}{44}$	26.	$3 \times 5\frac{3}{4}$	$\frac{69}{4} = 17\frac{1}{4}$
12.	$\frac{5}{6} \times \frac{9}{10}$	$\frac{45}{60} = \frac{3}{4}$	27.	$1\frac{2}{3} \times 3\frac{1}{4}$	$\frac{65}{12} = 5\frac{5}{12}$
13.	$\frac{3}{4} \times \frac{2}{9}$	$\frac{6}{36} = \frac{1}{6}$	28.	$2\frac{3}{5} \times 3$	$\frac{39}{5} = 7\frac{4}{5}$
14.	$\frac{4}{11} \times \frac{5}{8}$	$\frac{20}{88} = \frac{5}{22}$	29.	$1\frac{5}{7} \times 3\frac{1}{2}$	$\frac{84}{14} = 6$
15.	$\frac{2}{3} \times \frac{9}{10}$	$\frac{18}{30} = \frac{3}{5}$	30.	$3\frac{1}{3} \times 1\frac{9}{10}$	$\frac{190}{30} = 6\frac{10}{30} = 6\frac{1}{3}$

EUREKA MATH

Lesson 12: From Unit Cubes to the Formulas for Volume

Student Outcomes

- Students extend the volume formula for a right rectangular prism to the formula
  $V = \text{Area of base} \cdot \text{height}$. They understand that any face can be the base.

Lesson Notes

This lesson is a continuation of the ideas in Lesson 11 and the lessons in Grade 5 Module 5 Topics A and B.

The word *face*, though referenced in the last lesson, should be taught to students who may not know this meaning of it. A student-friendly definition and illustration can be posted on the wall (along with definitions of *edge(s)* and *vertex/vertices*). Here is a link to a useful illustration: http://www.11plusforparents.co.uk/Maths/shape8.html.

Classwork

Example 1 (10 minutes)

- Look at the rectangular prisms in the first example. Write a numerical expression for the volume of each rectangular prism.
  - *Answers provided below.*
- What do these expressions have in common?
  - *They have the same dimensions for the lengths and widths.*
- What do these dimensions represent?
  - *They represent the area of the bases of the rectangular prisms.*

> **Scaffolding:**
> You may want to use unit cubes to help students visualize the layers in this problem.

 MP.7

- Rewrite each of the numerical expressions to show what they have in common.
  - *Answers provided below.*

 MP.8

- If we know volume for a rectangular prism as length times width times height, what is another formula for volume that we could use based on these examples?
  - *We could use area of the base times the height.*
- What is the area of the base of each of the rectangular prisms?
  - $A = l\,w;\ A = (15\text{ in.})\left(1\frac{1}{2}\text{ in.}\right);\ \text{and } A = 22\frac{1}{2}\text{ in}^2$
- How would we use the area of the base to determine the volume? (Think about the unit cubes we have been using. The area of the base would be the first layer of unit cubes. What would the height represent?)
  - *We would multiply the area of the base times the height. The height would represent how many layers of cubes it would take to fill up the rectangular prism. Sample answers are on the next page.*
- How do the volumes of the first and second rectangular prisms compare? The first and third?
  - *The volume of the second prism is twice that of the first because the height is doubled. The volume of the third prism is three times that of the first because the height is tripled.*

©2015 Great Minds. eureka-math.org
G6-M5-TE-B5-1.3.1-01.2016

Example 1

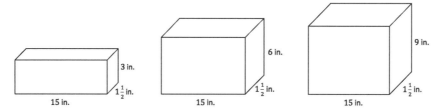

3 in.

$1\frac{1}{2}$ in.

15 in.

6 in.

$1\frac{1}{2}$ in.

15 in.

9 in.

$1\frac{1}{2}$ in.

15 in.

a.   Write a numerical expression for the volume of each of the rectangular prisms above.

$(15 \text{ in.})\left(1\frac{1}{2}\text{ in.}\right)(3\text{ in.})$ $(15 \text{ in.})\left(1\frac{1}{2}\text{ in.}\right)(6\text{ in.})$ $(15 \text{ in.})\left(1\frac{1}{2}\text{ in.}\right)(9\text{ in.})$

b.   What do all of these expressions have in common? What do they represent?

All of the expressions have $(15 \text{ in.})\left(1\frac{1}{2}\text{in.}\right)$. *This is the area of the base.*

c.   Rewrite the numerical expressions to show what they have in common.

$\left(22\frac{1}{2}\text{ in}^2\right)(3\text{ in.})$ $\left(22\frac{1}{2}\text{ in}^2\right)(6\text{ in.})$ $\left(22\frac{1}{2}\text{ in}^2\right)(9\text{ in.})$

d.   If we know volume for a rectangular prism as length times width times height, what is another formula for volume that we could use based on these examples?

We could use $(\text{area of the base})(\text{height})$*, or area of the base times height.*

e.   What is the area of the base for all of the rectangular prisms?

$(15 \text{ in.})\left(1\frac{1}{2}\text{ in.}\right) = 22\frac{1}{2}\text{ in}^2$

f.   Determine the volume of each rectangular prism using either method.

$(15 \text{ in.})\left(1\frac{1}{2}\text{ in.}\right)(3\text{ in.}) = 67\frac{1}{2}\text{ in}^3$ *or* $\left(22\frac{1}{2}\text{ in}^2\right)(3\text{ in.}) = 67\frac{1}{2}\text{ in}^3$

$(15 \text{ in.})\left(1\frac{1}{2}\text{ in.}\right)(6\text{ in.}) = 135\text{ in}^3$ *or* $\left(22\frac{1}{2}\text{ in}^2\right)(6\text{ in.}) = 135\text{ in}^3$

$(15 \text{ in.})\left(1\frac{1}{2}\text{ in.}\right)(9\text{ in.}) = 202\frac{1}{2}\text{ in}^3$ *or* $\left(22\frac{1}{2}\text{ in}^2\right)(9\text{ in.}) = 202\frac{1}{2}\text{ in}^3$

g.   How do the volumes of the first and second rectangular prisms compare? The volumes of the first and third?

$135 \text{ in}^3 = 67\frac{1}{2}\text{ in}^3 \times 2$

$202\frac{1}{2}\text{ in}^3 = 67\frac{1}{2}\text{ in}^3 \times 3$

The volume of the second prism is twice that of the first because the height is doubled. The volume of the third prism is three times as much as the first because the height is triple the first prism's height.

EUREKA
MATH™

- What do you think would happen to the volume if we turn this prism on its side so that a different face is the base? (Have students calculate the area of the base times the height for this new prism. To help students visualize what is happening with this rotation, you could use a textbook or a stack of index cards and discuss how this prism is similar to and different from the rectangular prisms in part (a).)

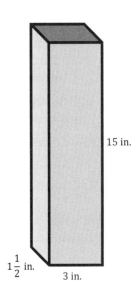

15 in.

$1\frac{1}{2}$ in.

3 in.

  - *Answers will vary. The volume is the same no matter which face is the base.*

    Area of the base $= (3 \text{ in.})\left(1\frac{1}{2}\text{ in.}\right)$

    Area of the base $= 4.5 \text{ in}^2$

    Volume $=$ Area of the base $\times$ height

    Volume $= \left(4\frac{1}{2}\text{ in}^2\right)(15 \text{ in.})$

    Volume $= 67\frac{1}{2}\text{ in}^3$

- How does this volume compare with the volume you calculated using the other face as the base?

  - *The volumes in both solutions are the same.*

- What other expressions could we use to determine the volume of the prism?

  - *Answers will vary. Some possible variations are included below.*

$$15 \text{ in.} \times 1\frac{1}{2}\text{ in.} \times 3 \text{ in.}$$

$$15 \text{ in.} \times 3 \text{ in.} \times 1\frac{1}{2}\text{ in.}$$

$$3 \text{ in.} \times 15 \text{ in.} \times 1\frac{1}{2}\text{ in.}$$

$$45 \text{ in}^2 \times 1\frac{1}{2}\text{ in.}$$

MP.7

- We notice that $3 \text{ in.} \times 15 \text{ in.} \times 1\frac{1}{2}\text{ in.}$ and $45 \text{ in}^2 \times 1\frac{1}{2}\text{ in.}$ are equivalent, and both represent the volume. How do they communicate different information?

  - *The first expression ($3 \text{ in.} \times 15 \text{ in.} \times 1\frac{1}{2}\text{ in.}$) shows that the volume is the product of three edge lengths. The second ($45 \text{ in}^2 \times 1\frac{1}{2}\text{ in.}$) shows that the volume is the product of the area of the base and the height.*

Example 2 (5 minutes)

> **Example 2**
>
> The base of a rectangular prism has an area of $3\frac{1}{4}$ in². The height of the prism is $2\frac{1}{2}$ in. Determine the volume of the rectangular prism.
>
> $V = $ **Area of base** $\times$ **height**
>
> $V = \left(3\frac{1}{4}\ \text{in}^2\right)\left(2\frac{1}{2}\ \text{in.}\right)$
>
> $V = \left(\frac{13}{4}\ \text{in}^2\right)\left(\frac{5}{2}\ \text{in.}\right)$
>
> $V = \frac{65}{8}\ \text{in}^3$

- Do we need to know the length and the width to find the volume of the rectangular prism?
    - *The length and width are needed to calculate the area of the base, and we already know the area of the base. Therefore, we do not need the length and width.*

Exercises (20 minutes)

The cards are printed out and used as stations or hung on the classroom walls so that students can move from question to question. Copies of the questions can be found at the end of the lesson. Multiple copies of each question can be printed so that students visit each question in small groups. Students should spend about three minutes at each station where they should show their work by first writing an equation and then using the equation to calculate the volume of the rectangular prism described. They should use the rest of the time to discuss the answers, and the teacher can answer any questions students have about the lesson.

Card	Sample Response
a. Draw a sketch of the figure. Then, calculate the volume. Rectangular Prism Area of the base $= 4\frac{3}{8}\text{ft}^2$ Height $= 2\frac{1}{2}\text{ft.}$	$V = $ Area of base $\times$ height $V = \left(4\frac{3}{8}\ \text{ft}^2\right)\left(2\frac{1}{2}\ \text{ft.}\right)$ $V = \left(\frac{35}{8}\ \text{ft}^2\right)\left(\frac{5}{2}\ \text{ft.}\right)$ $V = \frac{175}{16}\ \text{ft}^3$
b. Draw a sketch of the figure. Write the length, width, and height in feet. Then, calculate the volume. Rectangular Prism Length is $2\frac{1}{2}$ times as long as the height. Width is $\frac{3}{4}$ as long as the height. Height $= 3$ ft.	Length $= 3$ ft. $\times\ 2\frac{1}{2} = \frac{15}{2}$ ft. Width $= 3$ ft. $\times\ \frac{3}{4} = \frac{9}{4}$ ft. $V = l\,w\,h$ $V = \left(\frac{15}{2}\ \text{ft.}\right)\left(\frac{9}{4}\ \text{ft.}\right)(3\ \text{ft.})$ $V = \frac{405}{8}\ \text{ft}^3$

©2015 Great Minds. eureka-math.org
G6-M5-TE-B5-1.3.1-01.2016

<table>
<tr><td>

MP.7

c. Write two different expressions to represent the volume, and explain what each one represents.

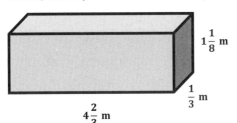

$1\frac{1}{8}$ m

$\frac{1}{3}$ m

$4\frac{2}{3}$ m

</td><td>

Answers will vary. Some possible solutions include $\left(4\frac{2}{3}\text{ m}\right)\left(\frac{1}{3}\text{ m}\right)\left(1\frac{1}{8}\text{ m}\right)$ and $\left(\frac{14}{9}\text{ m}^2\right)\left(1\frac{1}{8}\text{ m}\right)$.

The first expression shows the volume as a product of the three edge lengths. The second expression, $\left(4\frac{2}{3}\text{ m}\right)\left(\frac{1}{3}\text{ m}\right)$, shows the volume as a product of the base area times the height.

</td></tr>
<tr><td>

d. Calculate the volume.

$\frac{3}{10}$ ft.

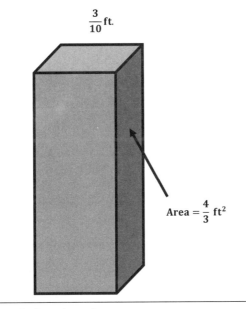

Area $= \frac{4}{3}$ ft^2

</td><td>

$V = $ Area of base $\times$ height

$V = \left(\frac{4}{3}\text{ ft}^2\right)\left(\frac{3}{10}\text{ ft.}\right)$

$V = \frac{12}{30}\text{ ft}^3$

$V = \frac{2}{5}\text{ ft}^3$

</td></tr>
<tr><td>

e. Calculate the volume.

$1\frac{1}{3}$ in.

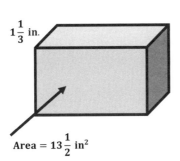

Area $= 13\frac{1}{2}$ in^2

</td><td>

$V = $ Area of base $\times$ height

$V = \left(13\frac{1}{2}\text{ in}^2\right)\left(1\frac{1}{3}\text{ in.}\right)$

$V = \frac{108}{6}\text{ in}^3$

$V = 18\text{ in}^3$

</td></tr>
</table>

f.	Challenge:	Length = 5 ft.
	Determine the volume of a rectangular prism whose length and width are in a ratio of $3:1$. The width and height are in a ratio of $2:3$. The length of the rectangular prism is 5 ft.	Width = 5 ft. $\div 3 = \dfrac{5}{3}$ ft. Height = $\dfrac{5}{3}$ ft. $\times \dfrac{3}{2} = \dfrac{5}{2}$ ft. $V = l\, w\, h$ $V = (5\ \text{ft.})\left(\dfrac{5}{3}\ \text{ft.}\right)\left(\dfrac{5}{2}\ \text{ft.}\right)$ $V = \dfrac{125}{6}\ \text{ft}^3$

Extension (3 minutes)

> **Extension**
>
> A company is creating a rectangular prism that must have a volume of $6\ \text{ft}^3$. The company also knows that the area of the base must be $2\dfrac{1}{2}\ \text{ft}^2$. How can you use what you learned today about volume to determine the height of the rectangular prism?
>
> *I know that the volume can be calculated by multiplying the area of the base times the height. So, if I needed the height instead, I would do the opposite. I would divide the volume by the area of the base to determine the height.*
>
> $$V = \text{Area of base} \times \text{height}$$
> $$6\ \text{ft}^3 = \left(2\frac{1}{2}\ \text{ft}^2\right)h$$
> $$6\ \text{ft}^3 \div 2\frac{1}{2}\ \text{ft}^2 = h$$
> $$2\frac{2}{5}\ \text{ft.} = h$$

Closing (2 minutes)

- How is the formula $V = l \cdot w \cdot h$ related to the formula $V = \text{Area of the base} \cdot \text{height}$?
    □ *When we multiply the length and width of the rectangular prism, we are actually finding the area of the base. Therefore, the two formulas both determine the volume of the rectangular prism.*

Exit Ticket (5 minutes)

Name _____   Date _____

Lesson 12: From Unit Cubes to the Formulas for Volume

Exit Ticket

1. Determine the volume of the rectangular prism in two different ways.

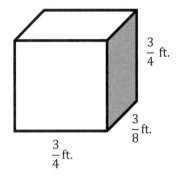

2. The area of the base of a rectangular prism is 12 cm^2, and the height is $3\frac{1}{3}$ cm. Determine the volume of the rectangular prism.

Exit Ticket Sample Solutions

1. Determine the volume of the rectangular prism in two different ways.

   $V = l \cdot w \cdot h$

   $V = \left(\frac{3}{4} \text{ ft.}\right)\left(\frac{3}{8} \text{ ft.}\right)\left(\frac{3}{4} \text{ ft.}\right)$

   $V = \frac{27}{128} \text{ ft}^3$

   $V = \text{Area of base} \cdot \text{height}$

   $V = \left(\frac{9}{32} \text{ ft}^2\right)\left(\frac{3}{4} \text{ ft.}\right)$

   $V = \frac{27}{128} \text{ ft}^3$

   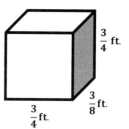

2. The area of the base of a rectangular prism is 12 cm², and the height is $3\frac{1}{3}$ cm. Determine the volume of the rectangular prism.

   $V = \text{Area of base} \cdot \text{height}$

   $V = (12 \text{ cm}^2)\left(3\frac{1}{3} \text{ cm}\right)$

   $V = \frac{120}{3} \text{ cm}^3$

   $V = 40 \text{ cm}^3$

Problem Set Sample Solutions

1. Determine the volume of the rectangular prism.

   $V = l\,w\,h$

   $V = \left(1\frac{1}{2} \text{ m}\right)\left(\frac{1}{2} \text{ m}\right)\left(\frac{7}{8} \text{ m}\right)$

   $V = \frac{21}{32} \text{ m}^3$

   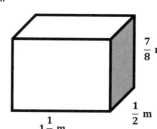

2. The area of the base of a rectangular prism is $4\frac{3}{4}$ ft², and the height is $2\frac{1}{3}$ ft. Determine the volume of the rectangular prism.

   $V = \text{Area of base} \times \text{height}$

   $V = \left(4\frac{3}{4} \text{ ft}^2\right)\left(2\frac{1}{3} \text{ ft.}\right)$

   $V = \left(\frac{19}{4} \text{ ft}^2\right)\left(\frac{7}{3} \text{ ft.}\right)$

   $V = \frac{133}{12} \text{ ft}^3$

EUREKA
MATH™

3. The length of a rectangular prism is $3\frac{1}{2}$ times as long as the width. The height is $\frac{1}{4}$ of the width. The width is 3 cm. Determine the volume.

Width = 3 cm

Length = 3 cm $\times$ $3\frac{1}{2}$ = $\frac{21}{2}$ cm

Height = 3 cm $\times \frac{1}{4} = \frac{3}{4}$ cm

$V = l\,w\,h$

$V = \left(\frac{21}{2}\ \text{cm}\right)(3\ \text{cm})\left(\frac{3}{4}\ \text{cm}\right)$

$V = \frac{189}{8}\ \text{cm}^3$

4.

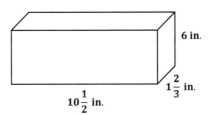

6 in.

$1\frac{2}{3}$ in.

$10\frac{1}{2}$ in.

a. Write numerical expressions to represent the volume in two different ways, and explain what each reveals.

$\left(10\frac{1}{2}\ \text{in.}\right)\left(1\frac{2}{3}\text{in.}\right)(6\ \text{in.})$ *represents the product of three edge lengths.* $\left(\frac{35}{2}\ \text{in}^2\right)(6\ \text{in.})$ *represents the product of the base area times the height. Answers will vary.*

b. Determine the volume of the rectangular prism.

$\left(10\frac{1}{2}\ \text{in.}\right)\left(1\frac{2}{3}\ \text{in.}\right)(6\ \text{in.}) = 105\ \text{in}^3$ or $\left(\frac{35}{2}\ \text{in}^2\right)(6\ \text{in.}) = 105\ \text{in}^3$

5. An aquarium in the shape of a rectangular prism has the following dimensions: length = 50 cm, width = $25\frac{1}{2}$ cm, and height = $30\frac{1}{2}$ cm.

a. Write numerical expressions to represent the volume in two different ways, and explain what each reveals.

$(50\ \text{cm})\left(25\frac{1}{2}\ \text{cm}\right)\left(30\frac{1}{2}\ \text{cm}\right)$ *represents the product of the three edge lengths.*

$(1,275\ \text{cm}^2)\left(30\frac{1}{2}\ \text{cm}\right)$ *represents the base area times the height.*

b. Determine the volume of the rectangular prism.

$(1,275\ \text{cm}^2)\left(30\frac{1}{2}\ \text{cm}\right) = 38,887\frac{1}{2}\ \text{cm}^3$

6. The area of the base in this rectangular prism is fixed at 36 cm^2. As the height of the rectangular prism changes, the volume will also change as a result.

    a.   Complete the table of values to determine the various heights and volumes.

3 cm

12 cm

Height of Prism (in centimeters)	Volume of Prism (in cubic centimeters)
1	36
2	72
3	108
4	144
5	180
6	216
7	252
8	288

    b.   Write an equation to represent the relationship in the table. Be sure to define the variables used in the equation.

Let x be the height of the rectangular prism in centimeters.

Let y be the volume of the rectangular prism in cubic centimeters.

$36x = y$

    c.   What is the unit rate for this proportional relationship? What does it mean in this situation?

The unit rate is 36.

For every centimeter of height, the volume increases by 36 cm^3 because the area of the base is 36 cm^2. In order to determine the volume, multiply the height by 36.

7. The volume of a rectangular prism is 16.328 cm^3. The height is 3.14 cm.

    a.   Let B represent the area of the base of the rectangular prism. Write an equation that relates the volume, the area of the base, and the height.

$16.328 = 3.14B$

    b.   Solve the equation for B.

$$\frac{16.328}{3.14} = \frac{3.14B}{3.14}$$
$$B = 5.2$$

The area of the base is 5.2 cm^2.

EUREKA MATH™

Station A

Draw a sketch of the figure. Then, calculate the volume.

Rectangular Prism

$$\text{Area of the base} = 4\frac{3}{8}\ \text{ft}^2$$

$$\text{Height} = 2\frac{1}{2}\ \text{ft.}$$

Station B

Draw a sketch of the figure. Write the length, width, and height in feet. Then, calculate the volume.

Rectangular Prism

Length is $2\frac{1}{2}$ times as long as the height.

Width is $\frac{3}{4}$ as long as the height.

Height = 3 ft.

EUREKA
MATH

Station C

Write two different expressions to represent the volume, and explain what each one represents.

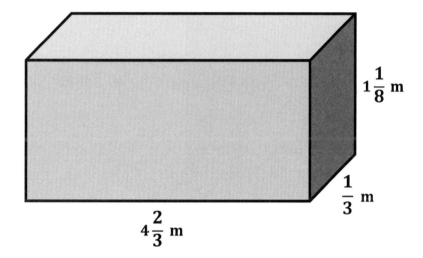

Station D

Calculate the volume.

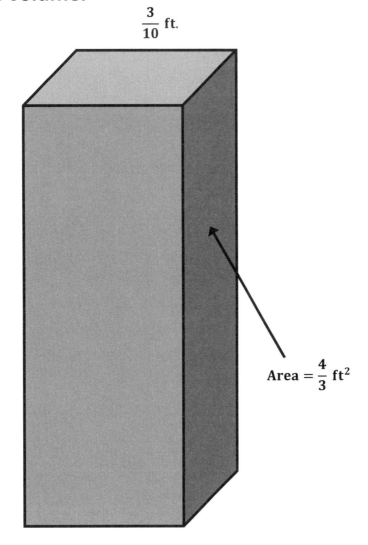

$\frac{3}{10}$ ft.

Area $= \frac{4}{3}$ ft^2

From Unit Cubes to the Formulas for Volume

EUREKA MATH

Station E

Calculate the volume.

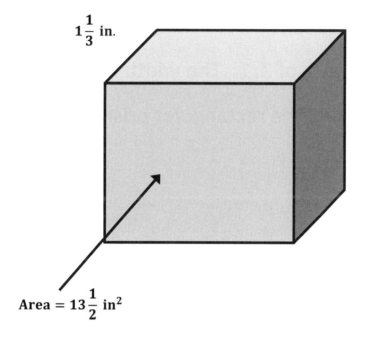

$1\dfrac{1}{3}$ in.

$\text{Area} = 13\dfrac{1}{2}$ in^2

©2015 Great Minds. eureka-math.org
G6-M5-TE-B5-1.3.1-01.2016

Station F

Challenge:

Determine the volume of a rectangular prism whose length and width are in a ratio of $3:1$. The width and height are in a ratio of $2:3$. The length of the rectangular prism is 5 ft.

![icon] **Lesson 13: The Formulas for Volume**

Student Outcomes

- Students develop, understand, and apply formulas for finding the volume of right rectangular prisms and cubes.

Lesson Notes

This lesson is a continuation of the two previous lessons, Lessons 11 and 12, in this module and Grade 5 Module 5 Topics A and B.

Classwork

Fluency Exercise (5 minutes): Multiplication and Division Equations with Fractions

RWBE: Refer to the Rapid White Board Exchanges section in the Module 4 Module Overview for directions to administer an RWBE.

Example 1 (3 minutes)

Example 1

Determine the volume of a cube with side lengths of $2\frac{1}{4}$ cm.

$$V = l\,w\,h$$

$$V = \left(2\frac{1}{4}\ \text{cm}\right)\left(2\frac{1}{4}\ \text{cm}\right)\left(2\frac{1}{4}\ \text{cm}\right)$$

$$V = \frac{9}{4}\ \text{cm} \times \frac{9}{4}\ \text{cm} \times \frac{9}{4}\ \text{cm}$$

$$V = \frac{729}{64}\ \text{cm}^3$$

MP.1

Scaffolding:

Provide a visual of a cube for students to label. If needed, begin with less complex numbers for the edge lengths.

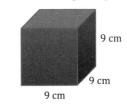

$$V = (9\ \text{cm})(9\ \text{cm})(9\ \text{cm})$$
$$V = 729\ \text{cm}^3$$

Students work through the first problem on their own and then discuss.

- Which method for determining the volume did you choose?
  - *Answers will vary. Sample response: I chose to use the $V = l\,w\,h$ formula to solve.*
- Why did you choose this method?
  - *Explanations will vary according to the method chosen. Sample response: Because I know the length, width, and height of the prism, I used $V = l\,w\,h$ instead of the other formulas.*

Example 2 (3 minutes)

Example 2

Determine the volume of a rectangular prism with a base area of $\frac{7}{12}$ ft^2 and a height of $\frac{1}{3}$ ft.

$$V = \text{Area of base} \times \text{height}$$

$$V = \left(\frac{7}{12} \text{ ft}^2\right)\left(\frac{1}{3} \text{ ft.}\right)$$

$$V = \frac{7}{36} \text{ ft}^3$$

- What makes this problem different from the first example?

  □ *This example gives the area of the base instead of just giving the length and width.*

- Would it be possible to use another method or formula to determine the volume of the prism in this example?

  □ *I could try fitting cubes with fractional lengths. However, I could not use the $V = l\,w\,h$ formula because I do not know the length and width of the base.*

Exercises (27 minutes)

In the exercises, students explore how changes in the lengths of the sides affect the volume. Students can use any method to determine the volume as long as they can explain their solution. Students work in pairs or small groups.

Please note that the relationships between the volumes are more easily determined if the fractions are left in their original form when solving. If time allows, this could be an interesting discussion point, either between partners, groups, or as a whole class when discussing the results of their work.

Exercises

1. Use the rectangular prism to answer the next set of questions.

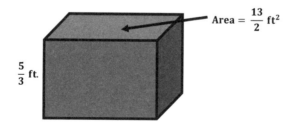

Area = $\frac{13}{2}$ ft^2

$\frac{5}{3}$ ft.

Scaffolding:

- The wording *half as long* may confuse some students. Explain that *half as long* means that the original length was multiplied by one-half or divided by 2. A similar explanation can be used for *one-third as long* and *one-fourth as long*.

- Explain to students that the word *doubled* refers to *twice as many* or *multiplied by two.*

a. Determine the volume of the prism.

$$V = \text{Area of the base} \times \text{height}$$

$$V = \left(\frac{13}{2} \text{ ft}^2\right)\left(\frac{5}{3} \text{ ft.}\right)$$

$$V = \frac{65}{6} \text{ ft}^3$$

©2015 Great Minds. eureka-math.org
G6-M5-TE-B5-1.3.1-01.2016

b.   Determine the volume of the prism if the height of the prism is doubled.

$$\text{Height} \times 2 = \left(\frac{5}{3} \text{ ft.} \times 2\right) = \frac{10}{3} \text{ ft.}$$

$$V = \text{Area of base} \times \text{height}$$

$$V = \left(\frac{13}{2} \text{ ft}^2\right)\left(\frac{10}{3} \text{ ft.}\right)$$

$$V = \frac{130}{6} \text{ ft}^3 \text{ or } 21\frac{2}{3} \text{ ft}^3$$

c.   Compare the volume of the rectangular prism in part (a) with the volume of the prism in part (b). What do you notice?

When the height of the rectangular prism is doubled, the volume is also doubled.

d.   Complete and use the table below to determine the relationship between the height and volume.

Height of Prism (in feet)	Volume of Prism (in cubic feet)
$\frac{5}{3}$	$\frac{65}{6}$
$\frac{10}{3}$	$\frac{130}{6}$
$\frac{15}{3}$	$\frac{195}{6}$
$\frac{20}{3}$	$\frac{260}{6}$

What happened to the volume when the height was tripled?

The volume tripled.

What happened to the volume when the height was quadrupled?

The volume quadrupled.

What conclusions can you make when the base area stays constant and only the height changes?

Answers will vary but should include the idea of a proportional relationship. Each time the height is multiplied by a number, the original volume is multiplied by the same amount.

2.

a.   If B represents the area of the base and h represents the height, write an expression that represents the volume.

Bh

b.   If we double the height, write an expression for the new height.

$2h$

c.   Write an expression that represents the volume with the doubled height.

$B2h$

MP.2

MP.7

MP.7

    d.   Write an equivalent expression using the commutative and associative properties to show the volume is twice the original volume.

$$2(Bh)$$

3.   Use the cube to answer the following questions.

    a.   Determine the volume of the cube.

$$V = l\,w\,h$$
$$V = (3\text{m})(3\text{m})(3\text{m})$$
$$V = 27 \text{ m}^3$$

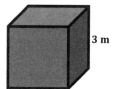

3 m

    b.   Determine the volume of a cube whose side lengths are half as long as the side lengths of the original cube.

$$V = l\,w\,h$$
$$V = \left(\frac{3}{2}\text{m}\right)\left(\frac{3}{2}\text{m}\right)\left(\frac{3}{2}\text{m}\right)$$
$$V = \frac{27}{8} \text{ m}^3$$

    c.   Determine the volume if the side lengths are one-fourth as long as the original cube's side lengths.

$$V = l\,w\,h$$
$$V = \left(\frac{3}{4}\text{ m}\right)\left(\frac{3}{4}\text{ m}\right)\left(\frac{3}{4}\text{ m}\right)$$
$$V = \frac{27}{64} \text{ m}^3$$

    d.   Determine the volume if the side lengths are one-sixth as long as the original cube's side lengths.

$$V = l\,w\,h$$
$$V = \left(\frac{3}{6}\text{ }m\right)\left(\frac{3}{6}m\right)\left(\frac{3}{6}\text{ }m\right)$$
$$V = \frac{27}{216} \ m^3$$

OR

$$V = \frac{1}{8} \ m^3$$

    e.   Explain the relationship between the side lengths and the volumes of the cubes.

If each of the sides are changed by the same fractional amount, $\frac{1}{a}$, of the original, then the volume of the new figure will be $\left(\frac{1}{a}\right)^3$ of the original volume. For example, if the sides are $\frac{1}{2}$ as long, then the volume will be $\left(\frac{1}{2}\right)^3 = \frac{1}{8}$ as much.

EUREKA
MATH

©2015 Great Minds. eureka-math.org
G6-M5-TE-B5-1.3.1-01.2016

4.   Check to see if the relationship you found in Exercise 3 is the same for rectangular prisms.

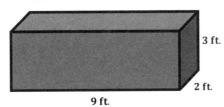

3 ft.

2 ft.

9 ft.

a.   Determine the volume of the rectangular prism.

$$V = l \, w \, h$$
$$V = (9 \, ft.)(2 \, ft.)(3 \, ft.)$$
$$V = 54 \, ft^3$$

b.   Determine the volume if all of the sides are half as long as the original lengths.

$$V = l \, w \, h$$
$$V = \left(\frac{9}{2} \, ft.\right)\left(\frac{2}{2} \, ft.\right)\left(\frac{3}{2} \, ft.\right)$$
$$V = \frac{54}{8} \, ft^3$$

OR

$$V = \frac{27}{4} \, ft^3$$

c.   Determine the volume if all of the sides are one-third as long as the original lengths.

$$V = l \, w \, h$$
$$V = \left(\frac{9}{3} ft.\right)\left(\frac{2}{3} \, ft.\right)\left(\frac{3}{3} \, ft.\right)$$
$$V = \frac{54}{27} \, ft^3$$

OR

$$V = 2 \, ft^3$$

d.   Is the relationship between the side lengths and the volume the same as the one that occurred in Exercise 3? Explain your answer.

Yes, the relationship that was found in the problem with the cubes still holds true with this rectangular prism. When I found the volume of a prism with side lengths that were one-third the original, the volume was $\left(\frac{1}{3}\right)^3 = \frac{1}{27}$ *the original.*

5.   a.   If e represents a side length of the cube, create an expression that shows the volume of the cube.

e^3

MP.2
&
MP.7

b.   If we divide the side lengths by three, create an expression for the new side length.

$\frac{1}{3} e \ or \ \frac{e}{3}$

MP.2
&
MP.7

c. Write an expression that represents the volume of the cube with one-third the side length.

$$\left(\frac{1}{3}e\right)^3 \text{ or } \left(\frac{e}{3}\right)^3$$

d. Write an equivalent expression to show that the volume is $\frac{1}{27}$ of the original volume.

$$\left(\frac{1}{3}e\right)^3$$

$$\left(\frac{1}{3}e\right)\left(\frac{1}{3}e\right)\left(\frac{1}{3}e\right)$$

$$\left(\frac{1}{9}e^2\right)\left(\frac{1}{3}e\right)$$

$$\frac{1}{27}e^3$$

Closing (2 minutes)

- How did you determine which method to use when solving the exercises?
  - *If I were given the length, width, and height, I have many options for determining the volume. I could use $V = l\,w\,h$. I could also determine the area of the base first and then use $V = \text{Area of the base} \times \text{height}$. I could also use a unit cube and determine how many cubes would fit inside.*
  - *If I was given the area of the base and the height, I could use the formula $V = \text{Area of the base} \times \text{height}$, or I could also use a unit cube and determine how many cubes would fit inside.*
- What relationships did you notice between the volume and changes in the length, width, or height?
  - *Answers will vary. Students may mention that if the length, width, or height is changed by a certain factor, the volume is affected by that same factor.*
  - *They may also mention that if all three dimensions are changed by the same factor, the volume will change by that factor cubed. For example, if all the sides are $\frac{1}{2}$ as long as the original, the volume will be $\left(\frac{1}{2}\right)^3$ as large as the original.*

Exit Ticket (5 minutes)

Lesson 13:   The Formulas for Volume

©2015 Great Minds. eureka-math.org
G6-M5-TE-B5-1.3.1-01.2016

Name _____   Date _____

Lesson 13: The Formulas for Volume

Exit Ticket

1. A new company wants to mail out samples of its hair products. The company has a sample box that is a rectangular prism with a rectangular base with an area of $23\frac{1}{3}$ in². The height of the prism is $1\frac{1}{4}$ in.
    Determine the volume of the sample box.

2. A different sample box has a height that is twice as long as the original box described in Problem 1. What is the volume of this sample box? How does the volume of this sample box compare to the volume of the sample box in Problem 1?

Exit Ticket Sample Solutions

1. A new company wants to mail out samples of its hair products. The company has a sample box that is a rectangular prism with a rectangular base with an area of $23\frac{1}{3}$ in^2. The height of the prism is $1\frac{1}{4}$ in. Determine the volume of the sample box.

$$V = \text{Area of base} \times \text{height}$$
$$V = \left(23\frac{1}{3}\text{ in}^2\right)\left(1\frac{1}{4}\text{ in.}\right)$$
$$V = \frac{70}{3}\text{ in}^2 \times \frac{5}{4}\text{ in.}$$
$$V = \frac{350}{12}\text{ in}^3$$

OR

$$V = \frac{175}{6}\text{ in}^3$$

2. A different sample box has a height that is twice as long as the original box described in Problem 1. What is the volume of this sample box? How does the volume of this sample box compare to the volume of the sample box in Problem 1?

$$V = \text{Area of base} \times \text{height}$$
$$V = \left(23\frac{1}{3}\text{ in}^2\right)\left(2\frac{1}{2}\text{ in.}\right)$$
$$V = \left(\frac{70}{3}\text{ in}^2\right)\left(\frac{5}{2}\text{ in.}\right)$$
$$V = \frac{350}{6}\text{ in}^3$$

OR

$$V = \frac{175}{3}\text{ in}^3$$

By doubling the height, we have also doubled the volume.

Problem Set Sample Solutions

1. Determine the volume of the rectangular prism.

$$V = \text{Area of base} \times \text{height}$$
$$V = \left(\frac{30}{7}\text{ cm}^2\right)\left(\frac{1}{3}\text{ cm}\right)$$
$$V = \frac{30}{21}\text{ cm}^3$$

OR

$$V = \frac{10}{7}\text{ cm}^3$$

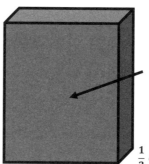

Area $= \frac{30}{7}$ cm^2

$\frac{1}{3}$ cm

©2015 Great Minds. eureka-math.org
G6-M5-TE-B5-1.3.1-01.2016

2. Determine the volume of the rectangular prism in Problem 1 if the height is quadrupled (multiplied by four). Then, determine the relationship between the volumes in Problem 1 and this prism.

$$V = \text{Area of base} \times \text{height}$$

$$V = \left(\frac{30}{7} \text{ cm}^2\right)\left(\frac{4}{3} \text{ cm}\right)$$

$$V = \frac{120}{21} \text{ cm}^3$$

OR

$$V = \frac{40}{7} \text{ cm}^3$$

When the height was quadrupled, the volume was also quadrupled.

3. The area of the base of a rectangular prism can be represented by B, and the height is represented by h.

a. Write an equation that represents the volume of the prism.

$$V = Bh$$

b. If the area of the base is doubled, write an equation that represents the volume of the prism.

$$V = 2Bh$$

c. If the height of the prism is doubled, write an equation that represents the volume of the prism.

$$V = B2h = 2Bh$$

d. Compare the volume in parts (b) and (c). What do you notice about the volumes?

The expressions in part (b) and part (c) are equal to each other.

e. Write an expression for the volume of the prism if both the height and the area of the base are doubled.

$$V = 2B2h = 4Bh$$

4. Determine the volume of a cube with a side length of $5\frac{1}{3}$ in.

$$V = l\,w\,h$$

$$V = \left(5\frac{1}{3} \text{ in.}\right)\left(5\frac{1}{3} \text{ in.}\right)\left(5\frac{1}{3} \text{ in.}\right)$$

$$V = \frac{16}{3} \text{ in.} \times \frac{16}{3} \text{ in.} \times \frac{16}{3} \text{ in.}$$

$$V = \frac{4,096}{27} \text{ in}^3$$

5. Use the information in Problem 4 to answer the following:

a. Determine the volume of the cube in Problem 4 if all of the side lengths are cut in half.

$$V = l\,w\,h$$

$$V = \left(2\frac{2}{3} \text{ in.}\right)\left(2\frac{2}{3} \text{ in.}\right)\left(2\frac{2}{3} \text{ in.}\right)$$

$$V = \frac{8}{3} \text{ in.} \times \frac{8}{3} \text{ in.} \times \frac{8}{3} \text{ in.}$$

$$V = \frac{512}{27} \text{ in}^3$$

©2015 Great Minds. eureka-math.org
G6-M5-TE-B5-1.3.1-01.2016

b. How could you determine the volume of the cube with the side lengths cut in half using the volume in Problem 4?

Because each side is half as long, I know that the volume is $\frac{1}{8}$ the volume of the cube in Problem 4. This is because the length, the width, and the height were all cut in half.

$$\frac{1}{2}l \times \frac{1}{2}w \times \frac{1}{2}h = \frac{1}{8}lwh$$

$$\frac{1}{8} \times \frac{4,096}{27} \text{ in}^3 = \frac{512}{27} \text{ in}^3$$

6. Use the rectangular prism to answer the following questions.

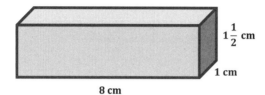

1 cm

$1\frac{1}{2}$ cm

8 cm

a. Complete the table.

Length of Prism	Volume of Prism
$l = 8$ cm	12 cm^3
$\frac{1}{2}l = 4$ cm	6 cm^3
$\frac{1}{3}l = \frac{8}{3}$ cm	4 cm^3
$\frac{1}{4}l = 2$ cm	3 cm^3
$2l = 16$ cm	24 cm^3
$3l = 24$ cm	36 cm^3
$4l = 32$ cm	48 cm^3

b. How did the volume change when the length was one-third as long?

4 is one-third of 12. Therefore, when the length is one-third as long, the volume is also one-third as much.

c. How did the volume change when the length was tripled?

36 is three times as much as 12. Therefore, when the length is three times as long, the volume is also three times as much.

d. What conclusion can you make about the relationship between the volume and the length?

When the length changes but the width and height stay the same, the change in the volume is proportional to the change in the length.

EUREKA
MATH™

7. The sum of the volumes of two rectangular prisms, Box A and Box B, are 14.325 cm^3. Box A has a volume of 5.61 cm^3.

   a. Let B represent the volume of Box B in cubic centimeters. Write an equation that could be used to determine the volume of Box B.

   $$14.325 \text{ cm}^3 = 5.61 \text{ cm}^3 + B$$

   b. Solve the equation to determine the volume of Box B.

   $$B = 8.715 \text{ cm}^3$$

   c. If the area of the base of Box B is 1.5 cm^2, write an equation that could be used to determine the height of Box B. Let h represent the height of Box B in centimeters.

   $$8.715 \text{ cm}^3 = (1.5 \text{ cm}^2)h$$

   d. Solve the equation to determine the height of Box B.

   $$h = 5.81 \text{ cm}$$

©2015 Great Minds. eureka-math.org
G6-M5-TE-B5-1.3.1-01.2016

Multiplication and Division Equations with Fractions

Progression of Exercises

1. $5y = 35$

    $y = 7$

2. $3m = 135$

    $m = 45$

3. $12k = 156$

    $k = 13$

4. $\dfrac{f}{3} = 24$

    $f = 72$

5. $\dfrac{x}{7} = 42$

    $x = 294$

6. $\dfrac{c}{13} = 18$

    $c = 234$

7. $\dfrac{2}{3}g = 6$

    $g = 9$

8. $\dfrac{3}{5}k = 9$

    $k = 15$

9. $\dfrac{3}{4}y = 10$

    $y = \dfrac{40}{3} = 13\dfrac{1}{3}$

EUREKA
MATH™

©2015 Great Minds. eureka-math.org
G6-M5-TE-B5-1.3.1-01.2016

10. $\frac{5}{8}j = 9$

$$j = \frac{72}{5} = 14\frac{2}{5}$$

11. $\frac{3}{7}h = 13$

$$h = \frac{91}{3} = 30\frac{1}{3}$$

12. $\frac{m}{4} = \frac{3}{5}$

$$m = \frac{12}{5} = 2\frac{2}{5}$$

13. $\frac{f}{3} = \frac{2}{7}$

$$f = \frac{6}{7}$$

14. $\frac{2}{5}p = \frac{3}{7}$

$$p = \frac{15}{14} = 1\frac{1}{14}$$

15. $\frac{3}{4}k = \frac{5}{8}$

$$k = \frac{20}{24} = \frac{5}{6}$$

Lesson 14: Volume in the Real World

Student Outcomes

- Students understand that volume is additive, and they apply volume formulas to determine the volume of composite solid figures in real-world contexts.
- Students apply volume formulas to find missing volumes and missing dimensions.

Lesson Notes

This lesson is a continuation of the three previous lessons, Lessons 11–13, in this module and Grade 5 Module 5 Topics A and B.

Classwork

Example 1 (6 minutes)

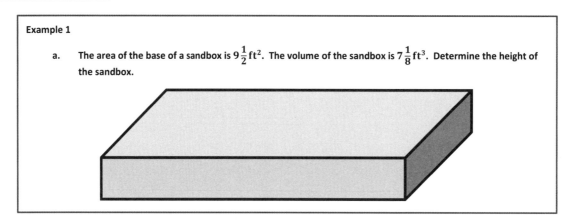

Example 1

a.   The area of the base of a sandbox is $9\frac{1}{2}$ ft^2. The volume of the sandbox is $7\frac{1}{8}$ ft^3. Determine the height of the sandbox.

MP.1

Students make sense of this problem on their own before discussing.

- What information are we given in this problem?
    - *We have been given the area of the base and the volume.*
- How can we use the information to determine the height?
    - *We know that the area of the base times the height gives the volume. Since we already have the volume, we can do the opposite and divide to get the height.*
- Notice that the number for the volume is less than the number for the area. What does that tell us about the height?
    - *If the product of the area of the base and the height is less than the area, we know that the height must be less than 1.*

Note to Teacher:

In these examples, it might be easier for students to use common denominators when dividing and working with dimensions. Students can use the invert and multiply rule, but it may cause more work and make it harder to see the relationships.

EUREKA MATH

- Calculate the height by solving a one step equation.
  - Volume = Area of the base × height

$$V = bh$$

$$7\frac{1}{8} = \left(9\frac{1}{2}\right)h$$

$$\frac{57}{8} = \left(\frac{19}{2}\right)h$$

$$\frac{57}{8} \div \frac{76}{8} = \left(\frac{76}{8}\right)h \div \frac{76}{8}$$

$$\frac{57}{76} = h$$

$$\frac{3}{4} = h$$

MP.1

The height of the sandbox is $\frac{3}{4}$ ft.

- We could also calculate the height using the equation Height = Volume ÷ Area of the base. Solve using this equation to determine if the height will be the same.
  - Height = Volume ÷ Area of the base

$$h = V \div b$$

$$h = 7\frac{1}{8} \div 9\frac{1}{2}$$

$$h = \frac{57}{8} \div \frac{19}{2}$$

$$h = \frac{57}{8} \div \frac{76}{8}$$

$$h = \frac{57}{76}$$

$$h = \frac{3}{4}$$

The height of the sandbox is $\frac{3}{4}$ ft.

> b. The sandbox was filled with sand, but after the kids played, some of the sand spilled out. Now, the sand is at a height of $\frac{1}{2}$ ft. Determine the volume of the sand in the sandbox after the children played in it.

- What new information have we been given in this problem?
  - *This means that the sandbox is not totally filled. Therefore, the volume of sand used is not the same as the volume of the sandbox.*

- How will we determine the volume of the sand?

  □ *To determine the volume of the sand, I use the area of the base of the sandbox, but I use the height of $\frac{1}{2}$ ft. instead of the height of the sandbox.*

$$\text{Volume} = \text{Area of the base} \times \text{height}$$

$$\text{Volume} = 9\frac{1}{2} \text{ ft}^2 \times \frac{1}{2} \text{ ft.}$$

$$\text{Volume} = \frac{19}{2} \text{ ft}^2 \times \frac{1}{2} \text{ ft.}$$

$$\text{Volume} = \frac{19}{4} \text{ ft}^3$$

$$\text{Volume} = 4\frac{3}{4} \text{ ft}^3$$

The volume of the sand is $4\frac{3}{4}$ ft^3.

Example 2 (6 minutes)

Example 2

A special-order sandbox has been created for children to use as an archeological digging area at the zoo. Determine the volume of the sandbox.

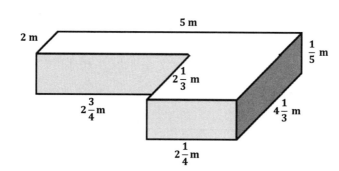

- Describe this three-dimensional figure.

  □ *This figure looks like two rectangular prisms that have been placed together to form one large prism.*

  □ *I could think of it as a piece on the left and a piece on the right.*

MP.7

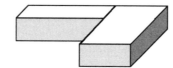

EUREKA MATH

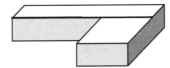

MP.7

- ■ How can we determine the volume of this figure?
  - ▫ *We can find the volume of each piece and then add the volumes together to get the volume of the entire figure.*
- ■ Does it matter which way we divide the shape when we calculate the volume?
  - ▫ *Answers will vary.*
- ■ At this point, you can divide the class in half and have each half determine the volume using one of the described methods.
  - ▫ *If the shape is divided into a figure on the left and a figure on the right, we would have the following:*

  Volume of prism on the left = $l\,w\,h$.

  $$V = 2\frac{3}{4}\text{ m} \times 2\text{ m} \times \frac{1}{5}\text{ m}$$

  $$V = \frac{11}{4}\text{ m} \times 2\text{ m} \times \frac{1}{5}\text{ m}$$

  $$V = \frac{22}{20}\text{ m}^3$$

  - ■ Volume of the prism on the right = $l\,w\,h$.

  $$V = 2\frac{1}{4}\text{ m} \times 4\frac{1}{3}\text{ m} \times \frac{1}{5}\text{ m}$$

  $$V = \frac{9}{4}\text{ m} \times \frac{13}{3}\text{ m} \times \frac{1}{5}\text{ m}$$

  $$V = \frac{117}{60}\text{ m}^3$$

  $$V = \frac{39}{20}\text{ m}^3$$

  Total volume = volume of left + volume of right

  Total volume = $\frac{22}{20}$ m³ + $\frac{39}{20}$ m³

  Total volume = $\frac{61}{20}$ m³ = $3\frac{1}{20}$ m³

□   *If the shape is divided into a figure with a piece in front and piece behind, we have the following:*
Volume of the back piece $= l\,w\,h$

$$V = 5\text{ m} \times 2\text{ m} \times \frac{1}{5}\text{ m}$$

$$V = 2\text{ m}^3$$

Volume of the front piece $= l\,w\,h$

$$V = 2\frac{1}{4}\text{ m} \times 2\frac{1}{3}\text{ m} \times \frac{1}{5}\text{ m}$$

$$V = \frac{9}{4}\text{ m} \times \frac{7}{3}\text{ m} \times \frac{1}{5}\text{ m}$$

$$V = \frac{63}{60}\text{ m}^3 = 1\frac{3}{60}\text{ m}^3 = 1\frac{1}{20}\text{ m}^3$$

Total volume $=$ volume of back $+$ volume of front

Total volume $= 2\text{ m}^3 + 1\frac{1}{20}\text{ m}^3$

Total volume $= 3\frac{1}{20}\text{ m}^3$

▪   What do you notice about the volumes determined in each method?

□   *The volume calculated with each method is the same. It does not matter how we break up the shape. We still get the same volume.*

Exercises (20 minutes)

Students work in pairs. When working with composite figures, have one student solve the problem using one method and the other solve it another way so they can compare answers.

Exercises

2.

a.   The volume of the rectangular prism is $\frac{36}{15}\text{ yd}^3$. Determine the missing measurement using a one-step equation.

$$V = bh$$

$$\frac{36}{15} = \left(\frac{4}{5}\right)h$$

$$\frac{36}{15} \div \frac{12}{15} = \left(\frac{12}{15}\right)h \div \frac{12}{15}$$

$$\frac{36}{12} = h$$

$$3 = h$$

The height is 3 yd.

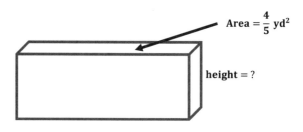

Area $= \frac{4}{5}\text{ yd}^2$

height $= ?$

EUREKA MATH™

©2015 Great Minds. eureka-math.org
G6-M5-TE-B5-1.3.1-01.2016

b.   The volume of the box is $\frac{45}{6}$ m³. Determine the area of the base using a one-step equation.

$$V = bh$$

$$\frac{45}{6} = b\left(\frac{9}{2}\right)$$

$$\frac{45}{6} \div \frac{27}{6} = b\left(\frac{27}{6}\right) \div \frac{27}{6}$$

$$\frac{45}{27} = b$$

$$\frac{5}{3} = b$$

The area of the base is $\frac{5}{3}$ *m².*

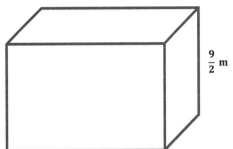

$\frac{9}{2}$ m

3.   Marissa's fish tank needs to be filled with more water.

a.   **Determine how much water the tank can hold.**

Volume of entire tank $= l\ w\ h$

$$V = \left(\frac{3}{4}\text{ m}\right)\left(\frac{1}{4}\text{ m}\right)\left(\frac{3}{5}\text{ m}\right)$$

$$V = \frac{9}{80}\text{ m}^3$$

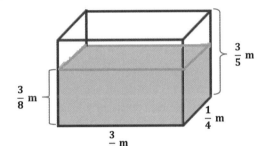

$\frac{3}{5}$ m

$\frac{3}{8}$ m

$\frac{1}{4}$ m

$\frac{3}{4}$ m

b.   **Determine how much water is already in the tank.**

Volume of water in the tank $= l\ w\ h$

$$V = \left(\frac{3}{4}\text{ m}\right)\left(\frac{1}{4}\text{ m}\right)\left(\frac{3}{8}\text{ m}\right)$$

$$V = \frac{9}{128}\text{ m}^3$$

c.   **How much more water is needed to fill the tank?**

Height of empty part of tank:

$$h = \frac{3}{5}\text{ m} - \frac{3}{8}\text{ m} = \frac{24}{40}\text{ m} - \frac{15}{40}\text{ m} = \frac{9}{40}\text{ m}$$

Volume needed to fill $= l\ w\ h$

$$V = \left(\frac{3}{4}\text{ m}\right)\left(\frac{1}{4}\text{ m}\right)\left(\frac{9}{40}\text{ m}\right)$$

$$V = \frac{27}{640}\text{ m}^3$$

4. Determine the volume of the composite figures.

a.

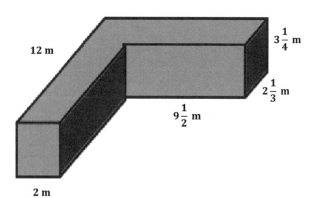

Volume of left piece = $l\,w\,h$

$V = (2 \text{ m})(12 \text{ m})\left(3\frac{1}{4} \text{ m}\right)$

$V = (2 \text{ m})(12 \text{ m})\left(\frac{13}{4} \text{ m}\right)$

$V = 78 \text{ m}^3$

Volume of back right = $l\,w\,h$

$V = \left(9\frac{1}{2} \text{ m}\right)\left(2\frac{1}{3} \text{ m}\right)\left(3\frac{1}{4} \text{ m}\right)$

$V = \left(\frac{19}{2} \text{ m}\right)\left(\frac{7}{3} \text{ m}\right)\left(\frac{13}{4} \text{ m}\right)$

$V = \frac{1{,}729}{24} \text{ m}^3 = 72\frac{1}{24} \text{ m}^3$

Total volume = $78 \text{ m}^3 + 72\frac{1}{24} \text{ m}^3 = 150\frac{1}{24} \text{ m}^3$

b.

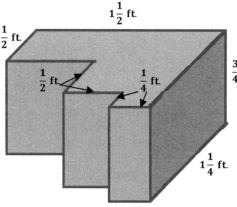

Volume of long back piece = $l\,w\,h$

$V = \left(1\frac{1}{2} \text{ ft.}\right)\left(\frac{1}{2} \text{ ft.}\right)\left(\frac{3}{4} \text{ ft.}\right)$

$V = \left(\frac{3}{2} \text{ ft.}\right)\left(\frac{1}{2} \text{ ft.}\right)\left(\frac{3}{4} \text{ ft.}\right)$

$V = \frac{9}{16} \text{ ft}^3$

Volume of middle piece = $l\,w\,h$

$V = \left(\frac{3}{4} \text{ ft.}\right)\left(\frac{1}{2} \text{ ft.}\right)\left(\frac{3}{4} \text{ ft.}\right)$

$V = \frac{9}{32} \text{ ft}^3$

Volume of front piece = $l\,w\,h$

$V = \left(\frac{1}{4} \text{ ft.}\right)\left(\frac{1}{4} \text{ ft.}\right)\left(\frac{3}{4} \text{ ft.}\right)$

$V = \frac{3}{64} \text{ ft}^3$

Total volume = sum of the three volumes

Total volume = $\frac{9}{16} \text{ ft}^3 + \frac{9}{32} \text{ ft}^3 + \frac{3}{64} \text{ ft}^3$

Total volume = $\frac{36}{64} \text{ ft}^3 + \frac{18}{64} \text{ ft}^3 + \frac{3}{64} \text{ ft}^3$

Total volume = $\frac{57}{64} \text{ ft}^3$

EUREKA
MATH™

Another possible solution:

$$V = \left(1\frac{1}{2} \text{ ft.}\right)\left(\frac{1}{2} \text{ ft.}\right)\left(\frac{3}{4} \text{ ft.}\right) + \left(\frac{3}{4} \text{ ft.}\right)\left(\frac{1}{2} \text{ ft.}\right)\left(\frac{3}{4} \text{ ft.}\right) + \left(\frac{1}{4} \text{ ft.}\right)\left(\frac{1}{4} \text{ ft.}\right)\left(\frac{3}{4} \text{ ft.}\right)$$

$$V = \frac{9}{16} \text{ ft}^3 + \frac{9}{32} \text{ ft}^3 + \frac{3}{64} \text{ ft}^3$$

$$V = \frac{36}{64} \text{ ft}^3 + \frac{18}{64} \text{ ft}^3 + \frac{3}{64} \text{ ft}^3$$

$$V = \frac{57}{64} \text{ ft}^3$$

Closing (5 minutes)

Students take time to share their solutions with the class. Discuss the differences between the types of problems and how working with volume and the many formulas or methods for solving can help in determining how to get to a solution.

Exit Ticket (8 minutes)

Name _____   Date _____

Lesson 14: Volume in the Real World

Exit Ticket

1. Determine the volume of the water that would be needed to fill the rest of the tank.

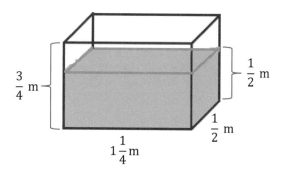

2. Determine the volume of the composite figure.

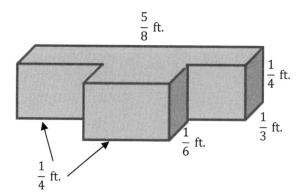

EUREKA MATH™

Exit Ticket Sample Solutions

1. Determine the volume of the water that would be needed to fill the rest of the tank.

   Volume of tank $= l\,w\,h$

   Volume of tank $= \left(1\frac{1}{4}\text{ m}\right)\left(\frac{1}{2}\text{ m}\right)\left(\frac{3}{4}\text{ m}\right)$

   Volume of tank $= \frac{15}{32}\text{ m}^3$

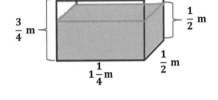

   Volume of water $= l\,w\,h$

   Volume of water $= \left(1\frac{1}{4}\text{ m}\right)\left(\frac{1}{2}\text{ m}\right)\left(\frac{1}{2}\text{ m}\right)$

   Volume of water $= \frac{5}{16}\text{ m}^3 = \frac{10}{32}\text{ m}^3$

   Remaining water needed $= \frac{15}{32}\text{ m}^3 - \frac{10}{32}\text{ m}^3 = \frac{5}{32}\text{ m}^3$

2. Determine the volume of the composite figure.

   Volume of back piece $= l\,w\,h$

   Volume of back piece $= \left(\frac{5}{8}\text{ ft.}\right)\left(\frac{1}{3}\text{ ft.}\right)\left(\frac{1}{4}\text{ ft.}\right)$

   Volume of back piece $= \frac{5}{96}\text{ ft}^3$

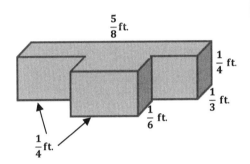

   Volume of front piece $= l\,w\,h$

   Volume of front piece $= \left(\frac{1}{4}\text{ ft.}\right)\left(\frac{1}{6}\text{ ft.}\right)\left(\frac{1}{4}\text{ ft.}\right)$

   Volume of front piece $= \frac{1}{96}\text{ ft}^3$

   Total volume $= \frac{5}{96}\text{ ft}^3 + \frac{1}{96}\text{ ft}^3 = \frac{6}{96}\text{ ft}^3 = \frac{2}{32}\text{ ft}^3$

Problem Set Sample Solutions

1. The volume of a rectangular prism is $\frac{21}{12}\text{ ft}^3$, and the height of the prism is $\frac{3}{4}$ ft. Determine the area of the base.

   $$V = bh$$

   $$\frac{21}{12} = b\left(\frac{3}{4}\right)$$

   $$\frac{21}{12} \div \frac{9}{12} = b\left(\frac{9}{12}\right) \div \frac{9}{12}$$

   $$\frac{21}{9} = b$$

   The area of the base is $\frac{21}{9}\text{ ft}^2$ OR $\frac{7}{3}\text{ ft}^2$.

Lesson 14:   Volume in the Real World

2.   The volume of a rectangular prism is $\frac{10}{21}$ ft³. The area of the base is $\frac{2}{3}$ ft². Determine the height of the rectangular prism.

Height = Volume ÷ Area of the base

Height = $\frac{10}{21}$ ft³ ÷ $\frac{2}{3}$ ft²

Height = $\frac{10}{21}$ ft³ ÷ $\frac{14}{21}$ ft²

Height = $\frac{10}{14}$ ft. OR $\frac{5}{7}$ ft.

3.   Determine the volume of the space in the tank that still needs to be filled with water if the water is $\frac{1}{3}$ ft. deep.

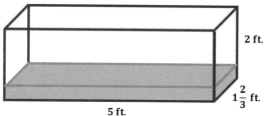

Volume of tank = $l\,w\,h$ Volume of water = $l\,w\,h$

Volume of tank = (5 ft.) $\left(1\frac{2}{3}\text{ ft.}\right)$ (2 ft.)   Volume of water = (5 ft.) $\left(1\frac{2}{3}\text{ ft.}\right)\left(\frac{1}{3}\text{ ft.}\right)$

Volume of tank = $\frac{50}{3}$ ft³   Volume of water = $\frac{25}{9}$ ft³

Volume to be filled = $\frac{50}{3}$ ft³ − $\frac{25}{9}$ ft³

Volume to be filled = $\frac{150}{9}$ ft³ − $\frac{25}{9}$ ft³

Volume to be filled = $\frac{125}{9}$ ft³

4.   Determine the volume of the composite figure.

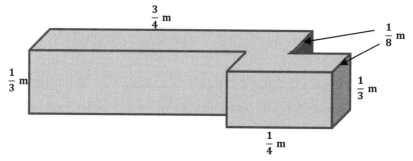

Volume of back piece = $l\,w\,h$ Volume of front piece = $l\,w\,h$

Volume of back piece = $\left(\frac{3}{4}\text{ m}\right)\left(\frac{1}{8}\text{ m}\right)\left(\frac{1}{3}\text{ m}\right)$ Volume of front piece = $\left(\frac{1}{4}\text{ m}\right)\left(\frac{1}{8}\text{ m}\right)\left(\frac{1}{3}\text{ m}\right)$

Volume of back piece = $\frac{3}{96}$ m³   Volume of front piece = $\frac{1}{96}$ m³

Total volume = $\frac{3}{96}$ m³ + $\frac{1}{96}$ m³ = $\frac{4}{96}$ m³ OR $\frac{1}{24}$ m³

EUREKA MATH™

5. Determine the volume of the composite figure.

$$V = (1 \text{ in.})\left(1\frac{1}{2} \text{ in.}\right)\left(1\frac{1}{4} \text{ in.}\right) + (3 \text{ in.})\left(2\frac{1}{2} \text{ in.}\right)\left(\frac{1}{4} \text{ in.}\right)$$

$$V = (1 \text{ in.})\left(\frac{3}{2} \text{ in.}\right)\left(\frac{5}{4} \text{ in.}\right) + (3 \text{ in.})\left(\frac{5}{2} \text{ in.}\right)\left(\frac{1}{4} \text{ in.}\right)$$

$$V = \frac{15}{8} \text{ in}^3 + \frac{15}{8} \text{ in}^3$$

$$V = \frac{30}{8} \text{ in}^3 = 3\frac{6}{8} \text{ in}^3 \text{ OR } 3\frac{3}{4} \text{ in}^3$$

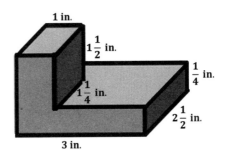

6.

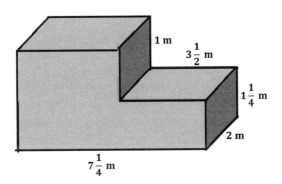

a. Write an equation to represent the volume of the composite figure.

$$V = \left(3\frac{1}{2} \text{ m} \times 2 \text{ m} \times 1\frac{1}{4} \text{ m}\right) + \left(3\frac{3}{4} \text{ m} \times 2 \text{ m} \times 2\frac{1}{4} \text{ m}\right)$$

b. Use your equation to calculate the volume of the composite figure.

$$V = \left(3\frac{1}{2} \text{ m} \times 2 \text{ m} \times 1\frac{1}{4} \text{ m}\right) + \left(3\frac{3}{4} \text{ m} \times 2 \text{ m} \times 2\frac{1}{4} \text{ m}\right)$$

$$V = \left(\frac{7}{2} \text{ m} \times \frac{2}{1} \text{ m} \times \frac{5}{4} \text{ m}\right) + \left(\frac{15}{4} \text{ m} \times \frac{2}{1} \text{ m} \times \frac{9}{4} \text{ m}\right)$$

$$V = \frac{70}{8} \text{ m}^3 + \frac{270}{16} \text{ m}^3$$

$$V = \frac{70}{8} \text{ m}^3 + \frac{135}{8} \text{ m}^3$$

$$V = \frac{205}{8} \text{ m}^3$$

$$V = 25\frac{5}{8} \text{ m}^3$$

©2015 Great Minds. eureka-math.org
G6-M5-TE-B5-1.3.1-01.2016

Mathematics Curriculum

Topic D

Nets and Surface Area

6.G.A.2, 6.G.A.4

Focus Standards:	6.G.A.2	Find the volume of a right rectangular prism with fractional edge lengths by packing it with unit cubes of the appropriate unit fraction edge lengths, and show that the volume is the same as would be found by multiplying the edge lengths of the prism. Apply the formulas $V = lwh$ and $V = bh$ to find volumes of right rectangular prisms with fractional edge lengths in the context of solving real-world and mathematical problems.
	6.G.A.4	Represent three-dimensional figures using nets made up of rectangles and triangles, and use the nets to find the surface area of these figures. Apply these techniques in the context of solving real-world and mathematical problems.
Instructional Days:	5	
	Lesson 15:	Representing Three-Dimensional Figures Using Nets (M)[1]
	Lesson 16:	Constructing Nets (E)
	Lesson 17:	From Nets to Surface Area (P)
	Lesson 18:	Determining Surface Area of Three-Dimensional Figures (P)
	Lesson 19:	Surface Area and Volume in the Real World (P)
	Lesson 19a:	Addendum Lesson for Modeling—Applying Surface Area and Volume to Aquariums (Optional) (M)

Topic D begins with students constructing three-dimensional figures through the use of nets in Lesson 15. They determine which nets make specific solid figures and also determine if nets can or cannot make a solid figure. Students use physical models and manipulatives to do actual constructions of three-dimensional figures with the nets. Then, in Lesson 16, students move to constructing nets of three-dimensional objects using the measurements of a solid's edges. Using this information, students move from nets to determining the surface area of three-dimensional figures in Lesson 17.

---

[1]Lesson Structure Key: **P**-Problem Set Lesson, **M**-Modeling Cycle Lesson, **E**-Exploration Lesson, **S**-Socratic Lesson

In Lesson 18, students determine that a right rectangular prism has six faces: top and bottom, front and back, and two sides. They determine that surface area is obtained by adding the areas of all the faces and develop the formula $SA = 2lw + 2lh + 2wh$. They develop and apply the formula for the surface area of a cube as $SA = 6s^2$.

For example:

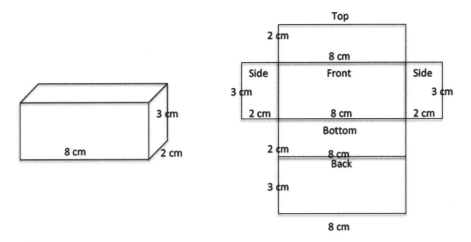

Top	Bottom	Front	Back	Side	Side
$l \times w$	$l \times w$	$l \times h$	$l \times h$	$w \times h$	$w \times h$
$8\,cm \cdot 2cm$	$8\,cm \cdot 2\,cm$	$8\,cm \cdot 3\,cm$	$8\,cm \cdot 3\,cm$	$2\,cm \cdot 3\,cm$	$2\,cm \cdot 3\,cm$
$16\,cm^2$	$16\,cm^2$	$24\,cm^2$	$24cm^2$	$6\,cm^2$	$6\,cm^2$

$$SA = 16\,cm^2 + 16\,cm^2 + 24cm^2 + 24\,cm^2 + 6\,cm^2 + 6\,cm^2 = 92\,cm^2$$

$l \times w$	$l \times w$	$l \times h$	$l \times h$	$w \times h$	$w \times h$
$2lw$		$2lh$		$2wh$	

$$SA = 2lw + 2lh + 2wh$$

Topic D concludes with Lesson 19, in which students determine the surface area of three-dimensional figures in real-world contexts. To develop skills related to application, students are exposed to contexts that involve both surface area and volume. Students are required to make sense of each context and apply concepts appropriately.

©2015 Great Minds. eureka-math.org
G6-M5-TE-B5-1.3.1-01.2016

Lesson 15: Representing Three-Dimensional Figures Using Nets

Student Outcomes

- Students construct three-dimensional figures through the use of nets. They determine which nets make specific solid figures and determine if nets can or cannot make a solid figure.

Lesson Notes

Using geometric nets is a topic that has layers of sequential understanding as students progress through the years. For Grade 6, specifically in this lesson, the working description of a net is this: If the surface of a three-dimensional solid can be cut along enough edges so that the faces can be placed in one plane to form a connected figure, then the resulting system of faces is called a net of the solid.

A more student-friendly description used for this lesson is the following: Nets are two-dimensional figures that can be folded to create three-dimensional solids.

Solid figures and the nets that represent them are necessary for this lesson. These three-dimensional figures include a cube, a right rectangular prism, a triangular prism, a tetrahedron, a triangular pyramid (equilateral base and isosceles triangular sides), and a square pyramid.

There are reproducible copies of these nets included with this lesson. The nets of the cube and right rectangular prism are sized to wrap around solid figures made from wooden or plastic cubes with 2 cm edges. Assemble these two solids prior to the lesson in enough quantities to allow students to work in pairs. If possible, the nets should be reproduced on card stock and precut and pre-folded before the lesson. One folded and taped example of each should also be assembled before the lesson.

The triangular prism has a length of 6 cm and has isosceles right triangular bases with identical legs that are 2 cm in length. Two of these triangular prisms can be arranged to form a rectangular prism.

The rectangular prism measures 4 cm × 6 cm × 8 cm, and its net can wrap around a Unifix cube solid that has dimensions of 2 × 3 × 4 cubes.

The tetrahedron has an edge length of 6 cm. The triangular pyramid has a base edge length of 6 cm and isosceles sides with a height of 4 cm.

The square pyramid has a base length 6 cm and triangular faces that have a height of 4 cm.

Also included is a reproducible sheet that contains 20 unique arrangements of six squares. Eleven of these can be folded to a cube, while nine cannot. These should also be prepared before the lesson, as indicated above. Make enough sets of nets to accommodate the number of groups of students.

Prior to the lesson, cut a large cereal box into its net, which is used for the Opening Exercise. Tape the top flaps thoroughly so this net can last through several lessons. If possible, get two identical boxes and cut two different nets like the graphic patterns of the cube nets on the next page. Add a third uncut box to serve as a right rectangular solid model.

Classwork

Mathematical Modeling Exercise (10 minutes)

Display the net of the cereal box with the unprinted side out. (Consider displaying the net with magnets on a white board.) Display the nets shown below as well (images or physical nets).

- What can you say about this cardboard (the cereal box)?
  - *Accept all correct answers, such as it is irregularly shaped; it has three sets of identical rectangles; all vertices are right angles; it has fold lines; it looks like it can be folded into a three-dimensional shape (box), etc.*

- How do you think it was made?
  - *Accept all plausible answers, including the correct one.*

- Compare the cereal box net to these others that are made of squares.
  - *Similarities: There are 6 sections in each; they can be folded to make a three-dimensional shape; etc.*
  - *Differences: One is made of rectangles; others are made of squares; there is a size difference; etc.*

Turn over the cereal box to demonstrate how it was cut. Reassemble it to resemble the intact box. Then, direct attention to the six-square arrangements.

- What do you think the six-square shapes fold up into?
  - *Cubes*
- If that were true, how many faces would it have?
  - *Six*

Fold each into a cube.

- Consider this six-square arrangement:

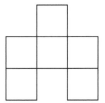

- Do you think it will fold into a cube?

Encourage a short discussion, inviting all views. As students make claims, ask for supporting evidence of their position. Use the cut-out version to demonstrate that this arrangement does not fold into a cube. Then, define the term *net*.

- Today we will work with some two-dimensional figures that can be folded to create three-dimensional solids. These are called geometric nets, or nets.

Ask students if they are able to visualize folding the nets without touching them. Expect a wide variety of spatial visualization abilities necessary to do this. Those that cannot readily see the outcome of folding will need additional time to handle and actually fold the models.

Lesson 15:   Representing Three-Dimensional Figures Using Nets

©2015 Great Minds. eureka-math.org
G6-M5-TE-B5-1.3.1-01.2016

Exercise (10 minutes): Cube

Use the previously cut-out six-square arrangements. Each pair or triad of students needs a set of 20 with which to experiment. These are sized to wrap around a cube with side lengths of 4 cm, which can be made from eight Unifix cubes. Each group needs one of these cubes.

- There are some six-square arrangements on your student page. Sort each of the six-square arrangements into one of two piles, those that are nets of a cube (can be folded into a cube) and those that are not.

Exercise: Cube

1. Nets are two-dimensional figures that can be folded into three-dimensional solids. Some of the drawings below are nets of a cube. Others are not cube nets; they can be folded, but not into a cube.

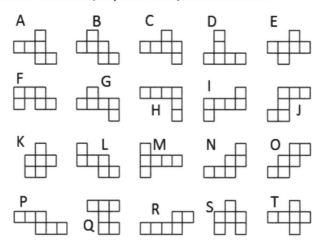

a. Experiment with the larger cut-out patterns provided. Shade in each of the figures above that can fold into a cube.

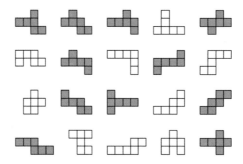

b. Write the letters of the figures that can be folded into a cube.

A, B, C, E, G, I, L, M, O, P, and T

c. Write the letters of the figures that cannot be folded into a cube.

D, F, H, J, K, N, Q, R, and S

©2015 Great Minds. eureka-math.org
G6-M5-TE-B5-1.3.1-01.2016

Example 1 (10 minutes): Other Solid Figures

Provide student pairs with a set of nets for each of the following: right rectangular prism, triangular prism, tetrahedron, triangular pyramid (equilateral base and isosceles triangular sides), and square pyramid.

Display one of each solid figure. Assemble them so the grid lines are hidden (inside).

Allow time to explore the nets folding around the solids.

- Why are the faces of the pyramid triangles?
    - *The base of the triangle matches the edge of the base of the pyramid. The top vertex of the lateral face is at the apex of the pyramid. Further, each face has two vertices that are the endpoints of one edge of the pyramid's base, and the third vertex is the apex of the pyramid.*
- Why are the faces of the prism parallelograms?
    - *The two bases are identical polygons on parallel planes. The lateral faces are created by connecting each vertex of one base with the corresponding vertex of the other base, thus forming parallelograms.*
- How are these parallelograms related to the shape and size of the base?
    - *The lengths of the base edges match one set of sides of the parallelogram. The shape of the base polygon determines the number of lateral faces the prism has.*
- If the bases are hexagons, does this mean the prism must have six faces?
    - *No, there are six sides on the prism, plus two bases, for a total of eight faces.*
- What is the relationship between the number of sides on the polygonal base and the number of faces on the prism?
    - *The total number of faces would be two more than the number of sides on the polygonal bases.*
- What additional information do you know about a prism if its base is a regular polygon?
    - *All the lateral faces of the prism are identical.*

Example 2 (8 minutes): Tracing Nets

If time allows, or as an extension, ask students to trace the faces of various solid objects (e.g., wooden or plastic geometric solids, paperback books, packs of sticky notes, or boxes of playing cards). After tracing a face, the object should be carefully rolled so one edge of the solid matches one side of the polygon that has just been traced. If this is difficult for students because they lose track of which face is which as they are rolling, the faces can be numbered or colored differently to make this easier. These drawings should be labeled "Net of a [Name of Solid]." Challenge students to make as many different nets of each solid as they can.

Closing (3 minutes)

- What kind of information can be obtained from a net of a prism about the solid it creates?
  - *We can identify the shape of the bases and the number and shape of the lateral faces (sides). The surface area can be more easily obtained since we can see all faces at once.*

- When looking at a net of a pyramid, how can you determine which faces are the bases?
  - *If the net is a pyramid, there are multiple, identical triangles that would form the lateral faces of the pyramid, while the remaining face is the base (and should identify the type of pyramid it is). Examples are triangular, square, pentagonal, and hexagonal pyramids.*

- How do the nets of a prism differ from the nets of a pyramid?
  - *If the pyramid is not a triangular pyramid, the base is the only polygon that is not a triangle. All other faces are triangles. Pyramids have one base and triangular lateral faces, while prisms have two identical bases, which could be any type of polygon, and lateral faces that are parallelograms.*

- Constructing solid figures from their nets helps us see the "suit" that fits around it. We can use this in our next lesson to find the surface area of these solid figures as we wrap them.

Lesson Summary

NET: If the surface of a 3-dimensional solid can be cut along sufficiently many edges so that the faces can be placed in one plane to form a connected figure, then the resulting system of faces is called a *net of the solid*.

Exit Ticket (4 minutes)

©2015 Great Minds. eureka-math.org
G6-M5-TE-B5-1.3.1-01.2016

Name _____   Date _____

Lesson 15: Representing Three-Dimensional Figures Using Nets

Exit Ticket

1. What is a net? Describe it in your own words.

2. Which of the following can fold to make a cube? Explain how you know.

Exit Ticket Sample Solutions

1. What is a net? Describe it in your own words.

Answers will vary but should capture the essence of the definition used in this lesson. A net is a two-dimensional figure that can be folded to create a three-dimensional solid.

2. Which of the following can fold to make a cube? Explain how you know.

Evidence for claims will vary.

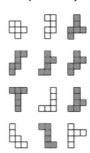

Problem Set Sample Solutions

1. Match the following nets to the picture of its solid. Then, write the name of the solid.

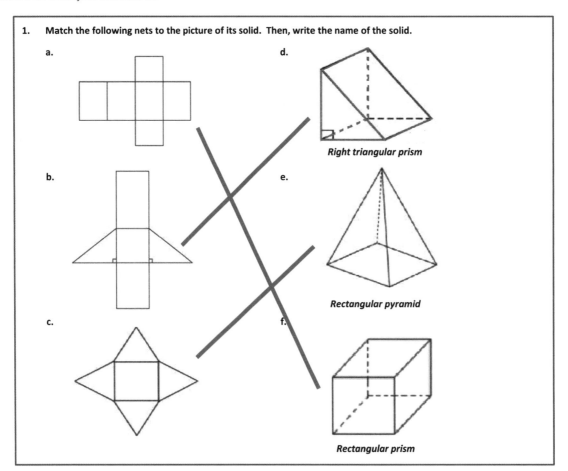

a.

b.

c.

d. *Right triangular prism*

e. *Rectangular pyramid*

f. *Rectangular prism*

EUREKA MATH

2. Sketch a net that can fold into a cube.

    Sketches will vary but should match one of the shaded ones from earlier in the lesson.

    Here are the 11 possible nets for a cube.

3. Below are the nets for a variety of prisms and pyramids. Classify the solids as prisms or pyramids, and identify the shape of the base(s). Then, write the name of the solid.

    a.

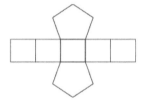

    Prism, the bases are pentagons.
    Pentagonal Prism

    b.

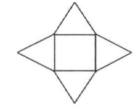

    Pyramid, the base is a rectangle.
    Rectangular Pyramid

    c.

    Pyramid, the base is a triangle.
    Triangular Pyramid

    d.

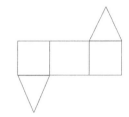

    Prism, the bases are triangles.
    Triangular Prism

    e.

    Pyramid, the base is a hexagon.
    Hexagonal Pyramid

    f.

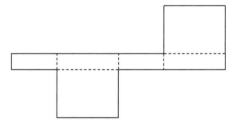

    Prism, the bases are rectangles.
    Rectangular Prism

On the following pages are graphics needed for this lesson. The graphics should be printed at 100% scale to preserve the intended size of figures for accurate measurements. Adjust your copier or printer settings to actual size, and set page scale to *none*.

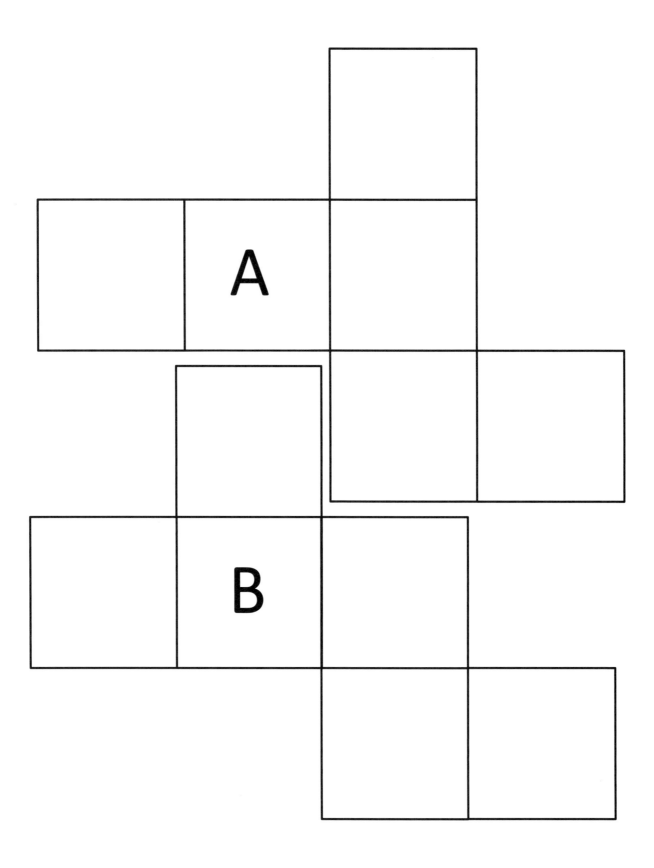

Lesson 15:   Representing Three-Dimensional Figures Using Nets

EUREKA
MATH

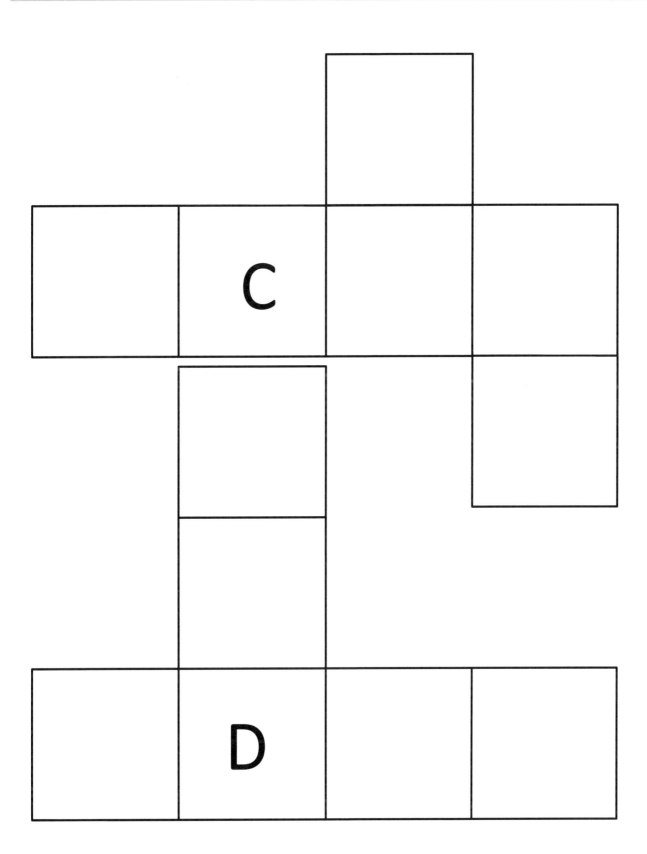

E

F

EUREKA
MATH™

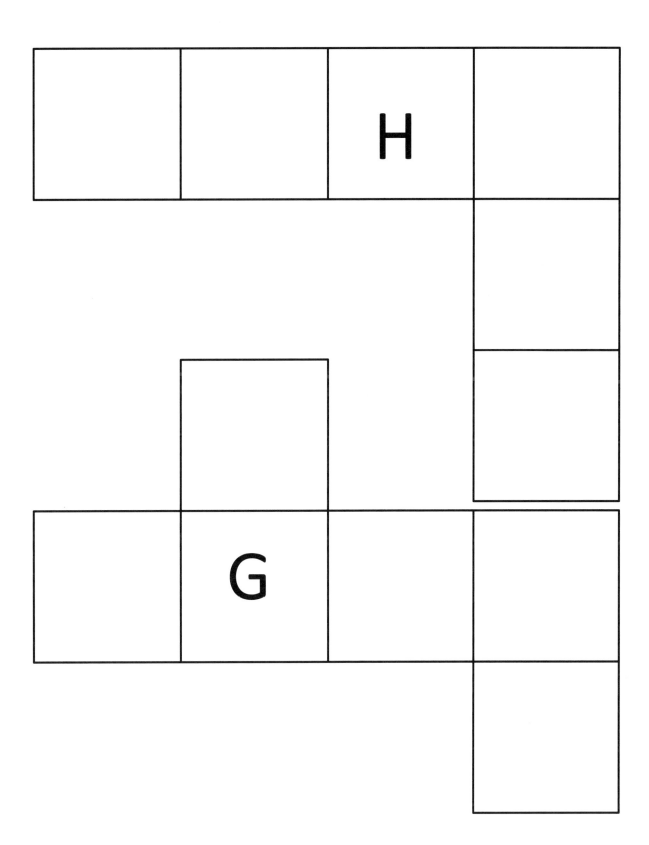

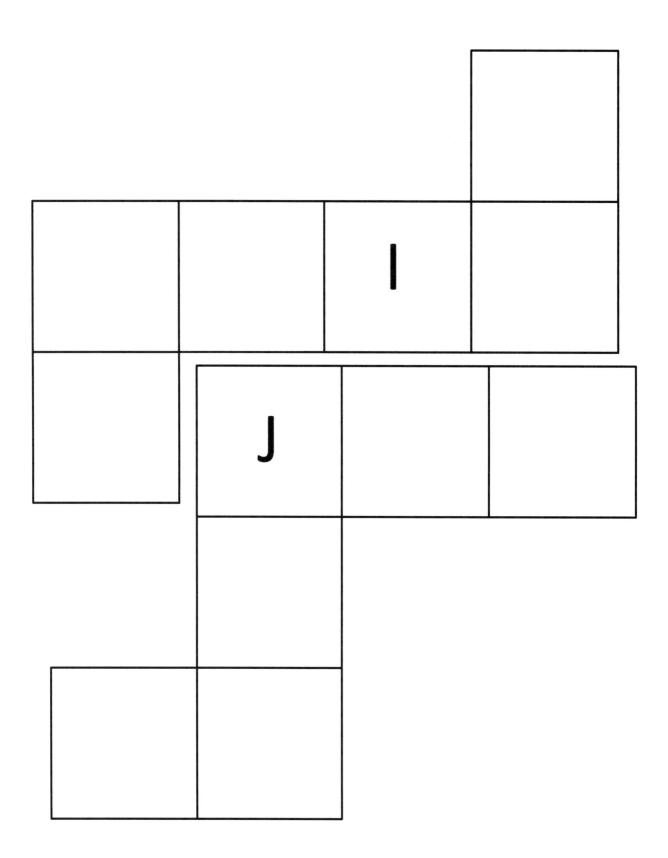

       Representing Three-Dimensional Figures Using Nets

EUREKA
MATH™

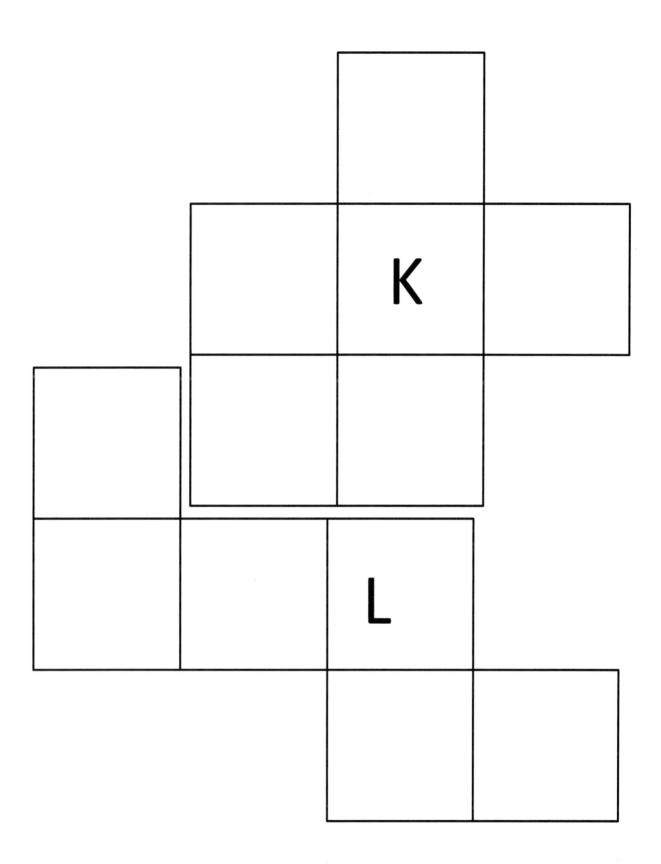

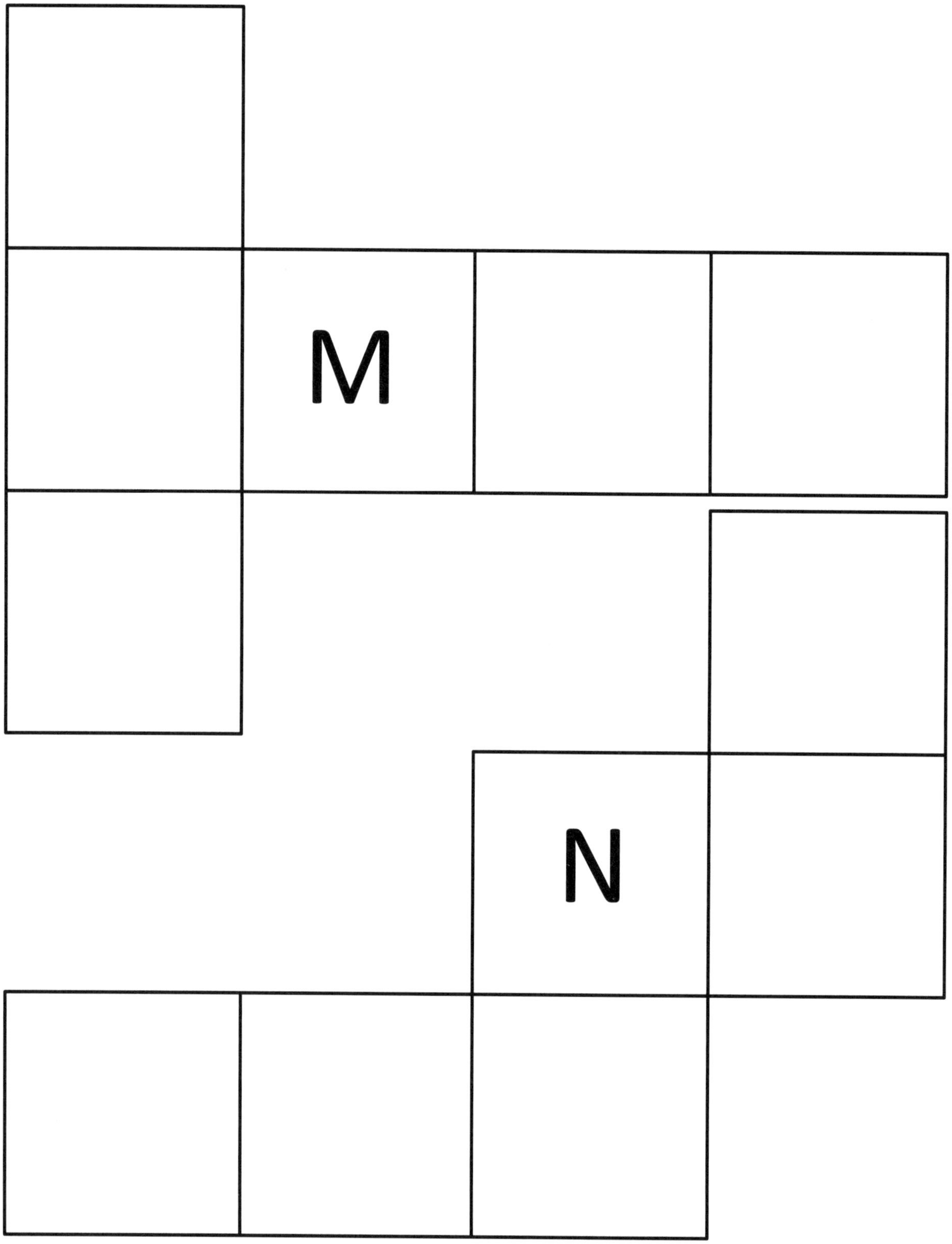

M

N

Representing Three-Dimensional Figures Using Nets

EUREKA MATH

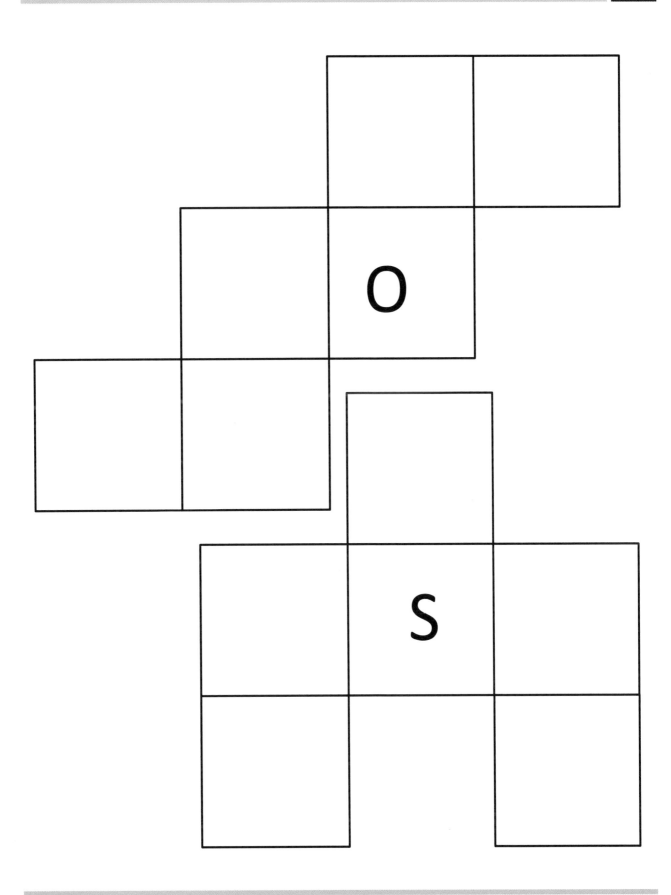

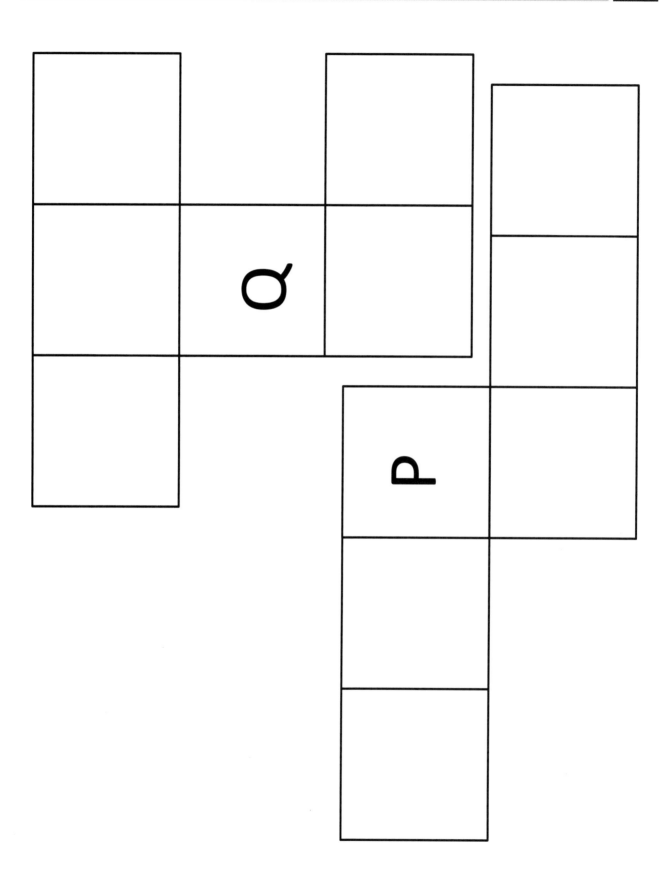

EUREKA
MATH™

©2015 Great Minds. eureka-math.org
G6-M5-TE-B5-1.3.1-01.2016

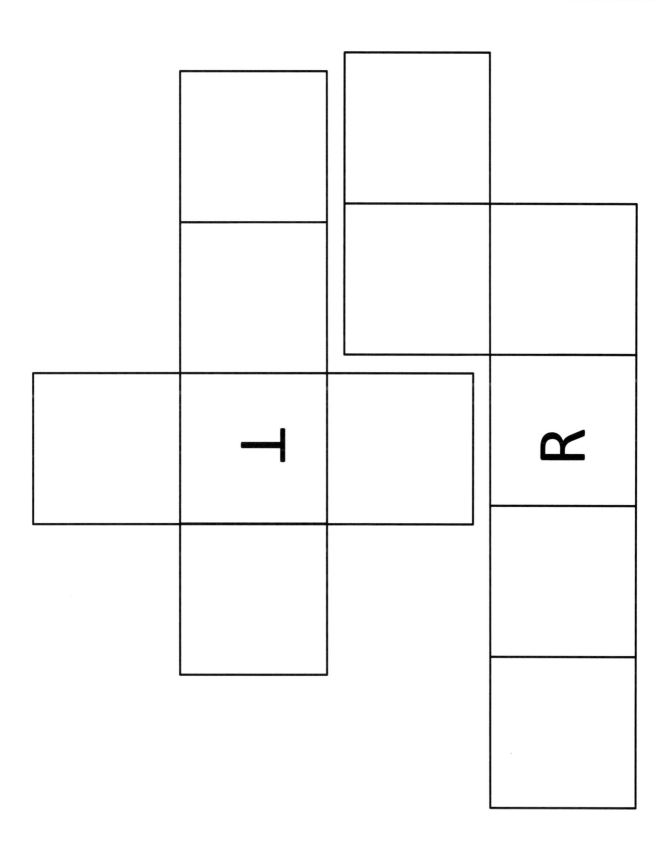

Part 1 of 2

Lesson 15:   Representing Three-Dimensional Figures Using Nets

EUREKA
MATH™

Part 2 of 2

Part 1 of 2

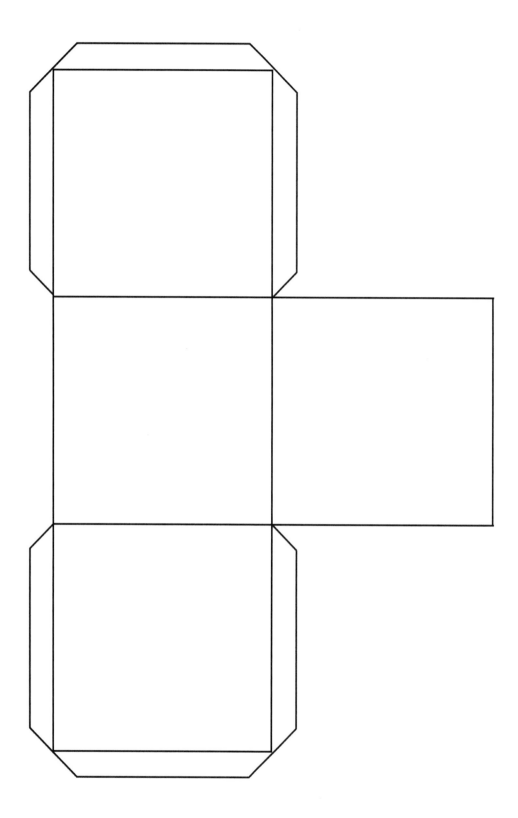

Lesson 15:   Representing Three-Dimensional Figures Using Nets

EUREKA MATH

©2015 Great Minds. eureka-math.org
G6-M5-TE-B5-1.3.1-01.2016

Part 2 of 2

Part 1 of 2

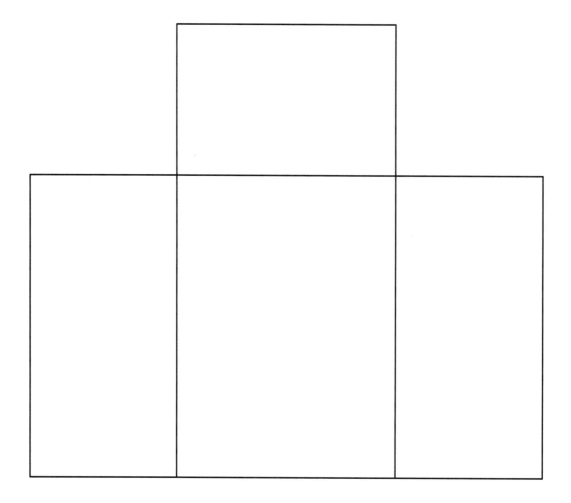

Lesson 15:   Representing Three-Dimensional Figures Using Nets

EUREKA
MATH™

Part 2 of 2

©2015 Great Minds. eureka-math.org
G6-M5-TE-B5-1.3.1-01.2016

Part 1 of 2

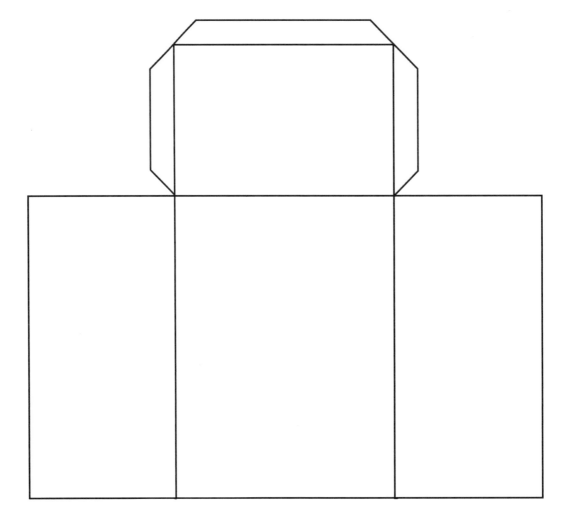

Lesson 15:   Representing Three-Dimensional Figures Using Nets

EUREKA
MATH

Part 2 of 2

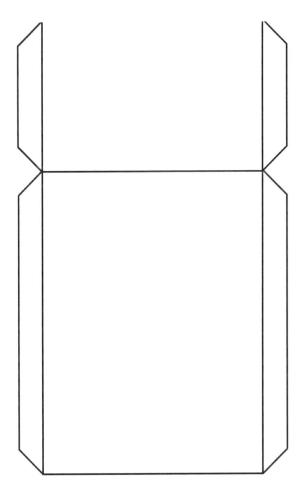

©2015 Great Minds. eureka-math.org
G6-M5-TE-B5-1.3.1-01.2016

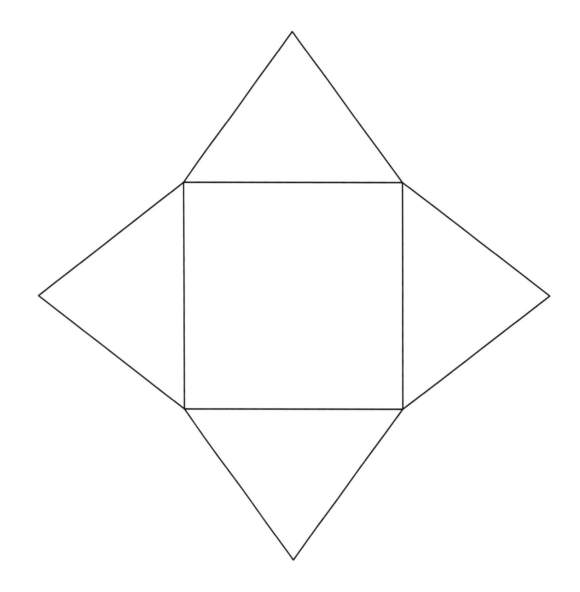

EUREKA
MATH™

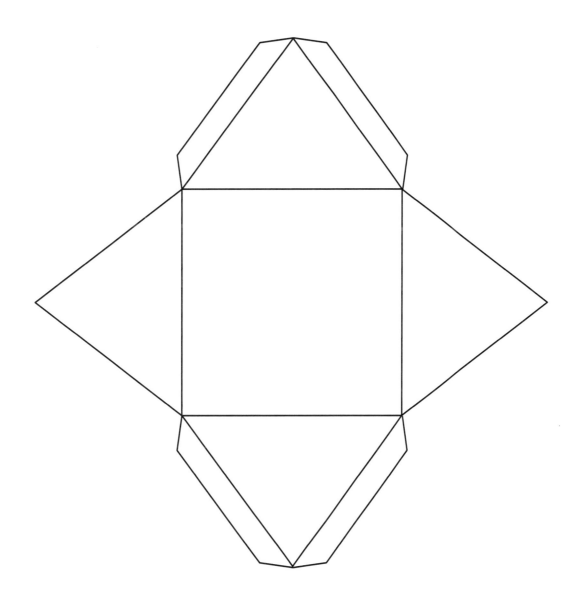

©2015 Great Minds. eureka-math.org
G6-M5-TE-B5-1.3.1-01.2016

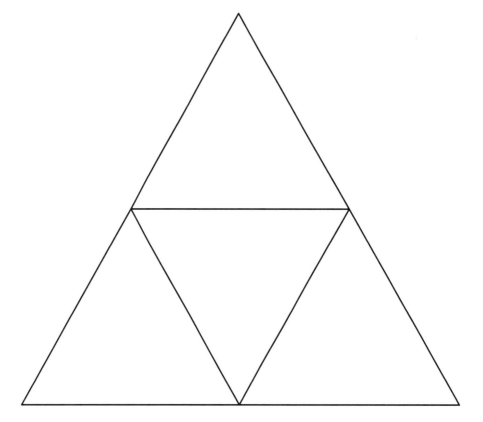

Lesson 15:   Representing Three-Dimensional Figures Using Nets

EUREKA
MATH

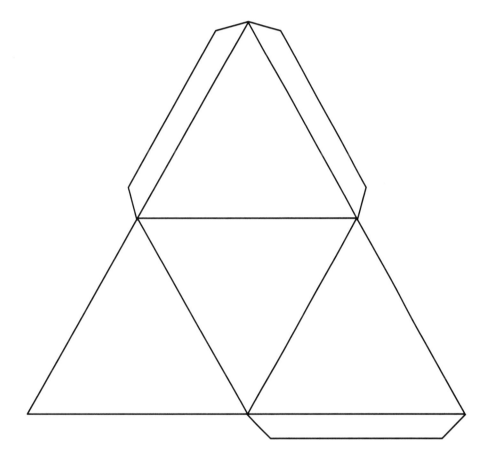

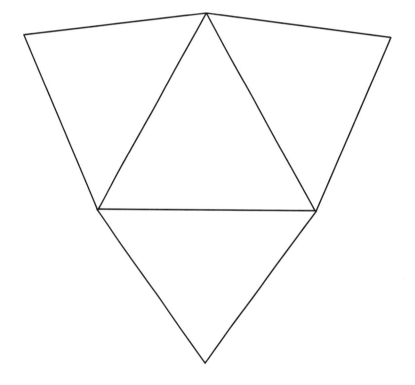

Lesson 15:   Representing Three-Dimensional Figures Using Nets

EUREKA
MATH™

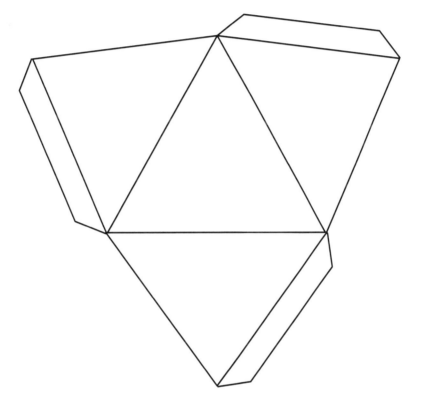

©2015 Great Minds. eureka-math.org
G6-M5-TE-B5-1.3.1-01.2016

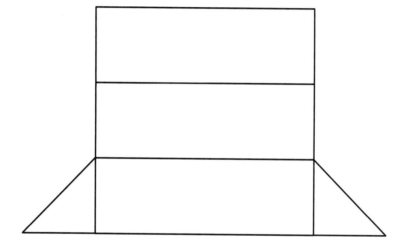

Lesson 15:   Representing Three-Dimensional Figures Using Nets

EUREKA
MATH™

©2015 Great Minds. eureka-math.org
G6-M5-TE-B5-1.3.1-01.2016

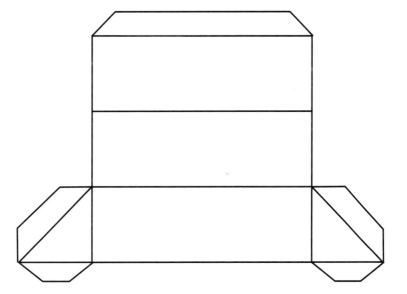

©2015 Great Minds. eureka-math.org
G6-M5-TE-B5-1.3.1-01.2016

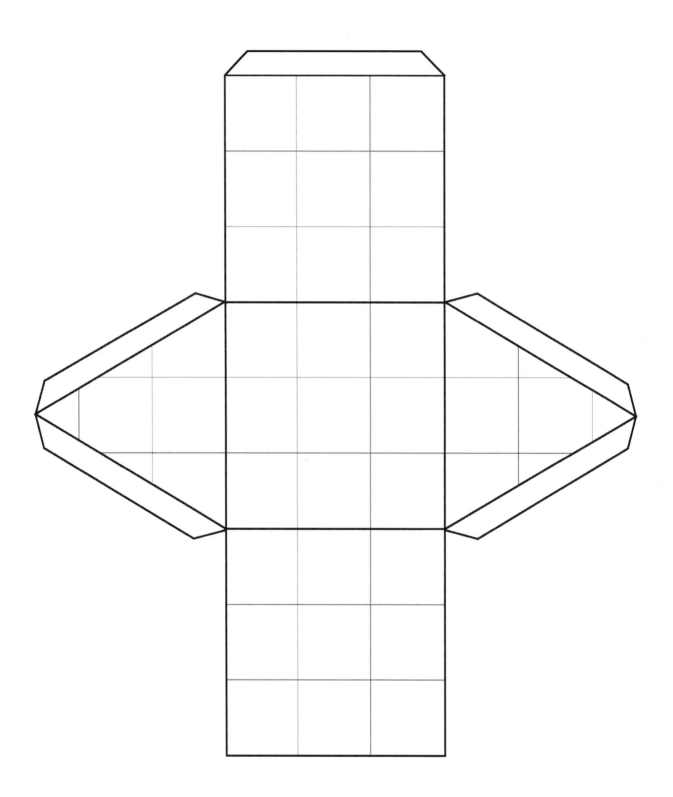

EUREKA
MATH™

Lesson 16: Constructing Nets

Student Outcomes

- Students construct nets of three-dimensional objects using the measurements of a solid's edges.

Lesson Notes

In the previous lesson, a cereal box was cut down to one of its nets. On the unprinted side, the fold lines should be highlighted with a thick marker to make all six faces easily seen. These rectangles should be labeled *Front*, *Back*, *Top*, *Bottom*, *Left Side*, and *Right Side*. Measure each rectangle to the nearest inch, and record the dimensions on each.

During this lesson, students are given the length, width, and height of a right rectangular solid. They cut out six rectangles (three pairs), arrange them into a net, tape them, and fold them up to check the arrangement to ensure the net makes the solid. Triangular pieces are also used in constructing the nets of pyramids and triangular prisms.

When students construct the nets of rectangular prisms, if no two dimensions—length, width, or height—are equal, then no two adjacent rectangular faces are identical.

The nets that were used in Lesson 15 should be available so that students have the general pattern layout of the nets.

Two-centimeter graph paper works well with this lesson. Prior to the lesson, cut enough polygons for Example 1. Cutting all the nets used in this lesson should save time as well but removes the opportunity for students to do the work.

Classwork

Opening (2 minutes)

Display the cereal box net from the previous lesson. Fold and unfold it so students can recall the outcome of the lesson.

> *Scaffolding:*
> Some students may need more opportunities than others to manipulate the nets in this lesson.

- How has this net changed since the previous lesson?
    - *It now has labels and dimensions.*
- What can you say about the angles in each rectangle?
    - *They are 90 degrees, or right angles.*
- What can you say about the angles between the faces when it is folded up?
    - *The two faces also form a right angle.*
- What can you say about the vertices where 3 faces come together?
    - *Again, they form right angles.*
- The following refolded box is an example of a right rectangular prism. It is named for the angles formed at each vertex.

Opening Exercise (3 minutes)

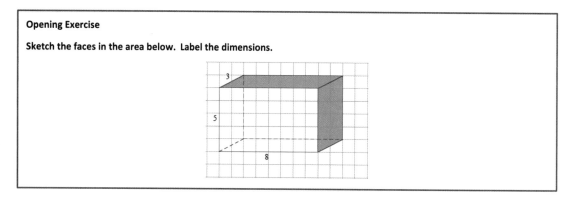

Opening Exercise

Sketch the faces in the area below. Label the dimensions.

Display this graphic using a document camera or other device.

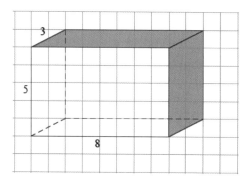

MP.1

- How could you create a net for this solid? Discuss this with a partner.

Allow a short time for discussion with a partner about this before having a whole-class discussion.

Example 1 (10 minutes): Right Rectangular Prism

- How can we use the dimensions of a rectangular solid to figure out the dimensions of the polygons that make up its net?
  - *The length, width, and height measurements of the solid will be paired to become the length and width of the rectangles.*
- How many faces does the rectangular prism have?
  - 6
- What are the dimensions of the top of this prism?
  - $8 \text{ cm} \times 3 \text{ cm}$
- What are the dimensions of the bottom?
  - $8 \text{ cm} \times 3 \text{ cm}$
- What are the dimensions of the right side?
  - $3 \text{ cm} \times 5 \text{ cm}$

©2015 Great Minds. eureka-math.org
G6-M5-TE-B5-1.3.1-01.2016

- ▪ What are the dimensions of the left side?
  - ▫ 3 cm × 5 cm
- ▪ What are the dimensions of the front?
  - ▫ 8 cm × 5 cm
- ▪ What are the dimensions of the back?
  - ▫ 8 cm × 5 cm
- ▪ The 6 faces of this rectangular solid are all rectangles that make up the net. Are there any faces that are identical to any others? Note that all measurements are in centimeters
  - ▫ *There are three different rectangles, but two copies of each are needed to make the solid. The top is identical to the bottom, the left and right sides are identical, and the front and back faces are also identical.*

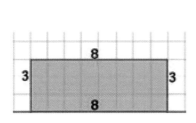 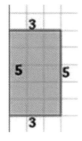 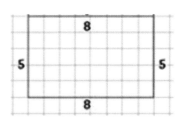

Make sure each student can visualize the rectangles depicted on the graphic of the solid and can make three different pairs of rectangle dimensions (length × width, length × height, and width × height).

Display the previously cut six rectangles from this example on either an interactive white board or on a magnetic surface. Discuss the arrangement of these rectangles. Identical sides must match.

Working in pairs, ask students to rearrange the rectangles into the shape below and to use tape to attach them. Having a second copy of these already taped saves time during the lesson.

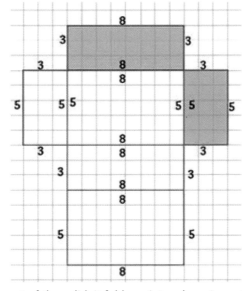

> **Scaffolding:**
> - ▪ Some students may benefit from using precut rectangles and triangles. Using cardstock or lamination makes more durable polygons.
> - ▪ Other students benefit from tracing the faces of actual solids onto paper and then cutting and arranging them.

- ▪ If this is truly a net of the solid, it folds up into a box. In mathematical language, it is known as a right rectangular prism.

Lesson 16:   Constructing Nets

251

©2015 Great Minds. eureka-math.org
G6-M5-TE-B5-1.3.1-01.2016

Students should fold the net into the solid to prove that it is indeed a net. Be prepared for questions about other arrangements of these rectangles that are also nets of the right rectangular prism. There are many possible arrangements.

Exploratory Challenge 1 (9 minutes): Rectangular Prisms

Students make nets from given measurements. Rectangles should be cut from graph paper and taped. Ask students to have their rectangle arrangements checked before taping. After taping, the net can be folded to check its fidelity.

Exploratory Challenge 1: Rectangular Prisms

a. Use the measurements from the solid figures to cut and arrange the faces into a net. (Note: All measurements are in centimeters.)

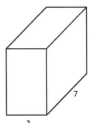

One possible configuration of rectangles is shown here:

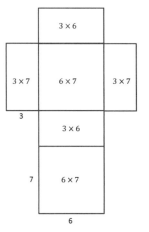

b. A juice box measures 4 inches high, 3 inches long, and 2 inches wide. Cut and arrange all 6 faces into a net. (Note: All measurements are in inches.)

One possible configuration of faces is shown here:

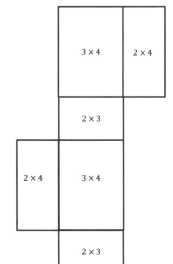

c.   Challenge: Write a numerical expression for the total area of the net for part (b). Explain each term in your expression.

Possible answer: $2(2\text{ in.} \times 3\text{ in.}) + 2(2\text{ in.} \times 4\text{ in.}) + 2(3\text{ in.} \times 4\text{ in.})$. *There are two sides that have dimensions* 2 *in. by* 3 *in., two sides that are* 2 *in. by* 4 *in., and two sides that are* 3 *in. by* 4 *in.*

Exploratory Challenge 2 (7 minutes): Triangular Prisms

Cutting these prior to the lesson saves time during the lesson.

Exploratory Challenge 2: Triangular Prisms

Use the measurements from the triangular prism to cut and arrange the faces into a net. (Note: All measurements are in inches.)

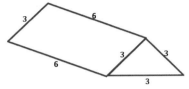

One possible configuration of rectangles and triangles is shown here:

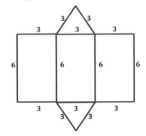

Exploratory Challenge 3 (9 minutes): Pyramids

Exploratory Challenge 3: Pyramids

Pyramids are named for the shape of the base.

a.   Use the measurements from this square pyramid to cut and arrange the faces into a net. Test your net to be sure it folds into a square pyramid.

One possible configuration of square and triangles is shown below. (Note: all measurements are in centimeters.)

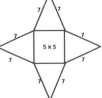

©2015 Great Minds. eureka-math.org
G6-M5-TE-B5-1.3.1-01.2016

b.   A triangular pyramid that has equilateral triangles for faces is called a tetrahedron. Use the measurements from this tetrahedron to cut and arrange the faces into a net.

All edges are 4 in. in length.

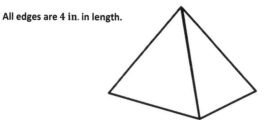

One possible configuration of triangles is shown below. (Note: All measurements are in inches.)

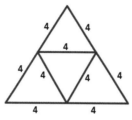

Closing (2 minutes)

- What are the most important considerations when making nets of solid figures?

  - *Each face must be taken into account.*

- After all faces are made into polygons (either real or drawings), what can you say about the arrangement of those polygons?

  - *Edges must match like on the solid.*

- Describe the similarities between the nets of right rectangular prisms.

  - *All faces are rectangles. Opposite faces are identical rectangles. If the base is a square, the lateral faces are identical rectangles. If the prism is a cube, all of the faces are identical.*

- Describe the similarities between the nets of pyramids.

  - *All of the faces that are not the base are triangles. The number of these faces is equal to the number of sides the base contains. If the base is a regular polygon, the faces are identical triangles. If all of the faces of a triangular pyramid are identical, then the solid is a tetrahedron.*

- How can you test your net to be sure that it is really a true net of the solid?

  - *Make a physical model and fold it up.*

Exit Ticket (3 minutes)

©2015 Great Minds. eureka-math.org
G6-M5-TE-B5-1.3.1-01.2016

Name _____   Date _____

Lesson 16: Constructing Nets

Exit Ticket

Sketch and label a net of this pizza box. It has a square top that measures 16 inches on a side, and the height is 2 inches. Treat the box as a prism, without counting the interior flaps that a pizza box usually has.

Exit Ticket Sample Solutions

Sketch and label a net of this pizza box. It has a square top that measures 16 inches on a side, and the height is 2 inches. Treat the box as a prism, without counting the interior flaps that a pizza box usually has.

One possible configuration of faces is shown below. (Note: all measurements are in inches.)

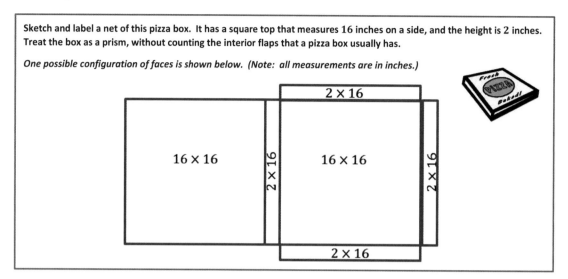

Problem Set Sample Solutions

1. Sketch and label the net of the following solid figures, and label the edge lengths.

    a. A cereal box that measures 13 inches high, 7 inches long, and 2 inches wide

        One possible configuration of faces is shown below. (Note: all measurements are in inches.)

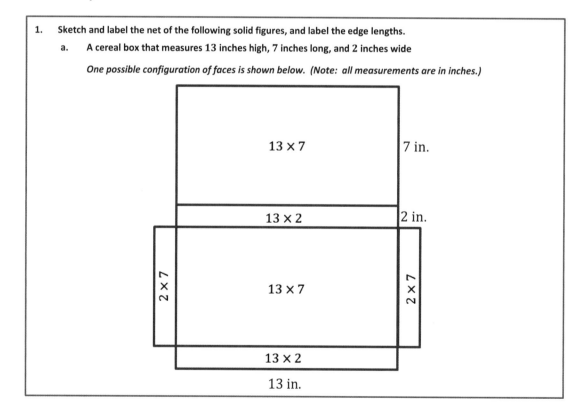

EUREKA MATH™

b.   A cubic gift box that measures 8 cm on each edge

One possible configuration of faces is shown here:

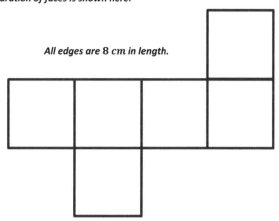

All edges are 8 cm in length.

c.   Challenge: Write a numerical expression for the total area of the net in part (b). Tell what each of the terms in your expression means.

$6(8 \text{ cm} \times 8 \text{ cm})$ *or*

$(8 \text{ cm} \times 8 \text{ cm}) + (8 \text{ cm} \times 8 \text{ cm}) + (8 \text{ cm} \times 8 \text{ cm}) + (8 \text{ cm} \times 8 \text{ cm}) + (8 \text{ cm} \times 8 \text{ cm}) + (8 \text{ cm} \times 8 \text{ cm})$

There are 6 faces in the cube, and each has dimensions 8 cm by 8 cm.

2.   This tent is shaped like a triangular prism. It has equilateral bases that measure 5 feet on each side. The tent is 8 feet long. Sketch the net of the tent, and label the edge lengths.

Possible net:

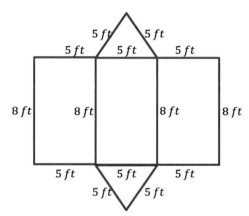
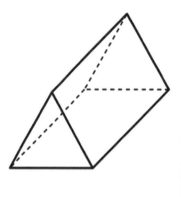

EUREKA
MATH™

Lesson 16:   Constructing Nets

257

©2015 Great Minds. eureka-math.org
G6-M5-TE-B5-1.3.1-01.2016

3. The base of a table is shaped like a square pyramid. The pyramid has equilateral faces that measure 25 inches on each side. The base is 25 inches long. Sketch the net of the table base, and label the edge lengths.

Possible net:

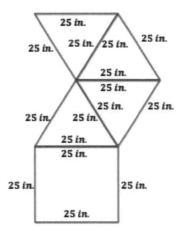

4. The roof of a shed is in the shape of a triangular prism. It has equilateral bases that measure 3 feet on each side. The length of the roof is 10 feet. Sketch the net of the roof, and label the edge lengths.

Possible net:

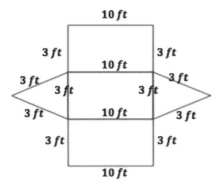

Lesson 16:   Constructing Nets

EUREKA
MATH

Rectangles for Opening Exercise

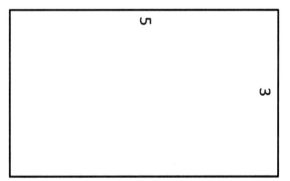

©2015 Great Minds. eureka-math.org
G6-M5-TE-B5-1.3.1-01.2016

Rectangles for Exercise 1, part (a)

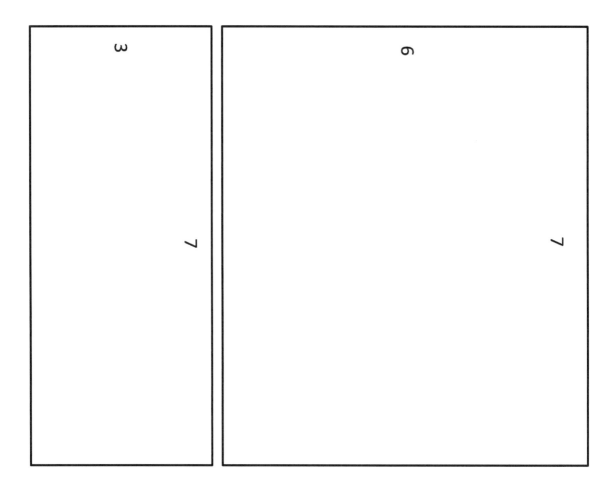

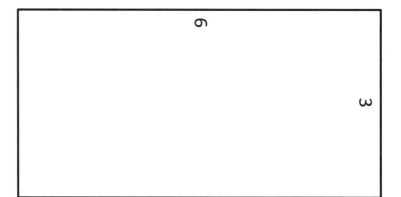

EUREKA
MATH

Rectangles for Exercise 1, part (b)

4 in.

3 in.

4 in.

2 in.

3 in.

2 in.

©2015 Great Minds. eureka-math.org
G6-M5-TE-B5-1.3.1-01.2016

Polygons for Exercise 2

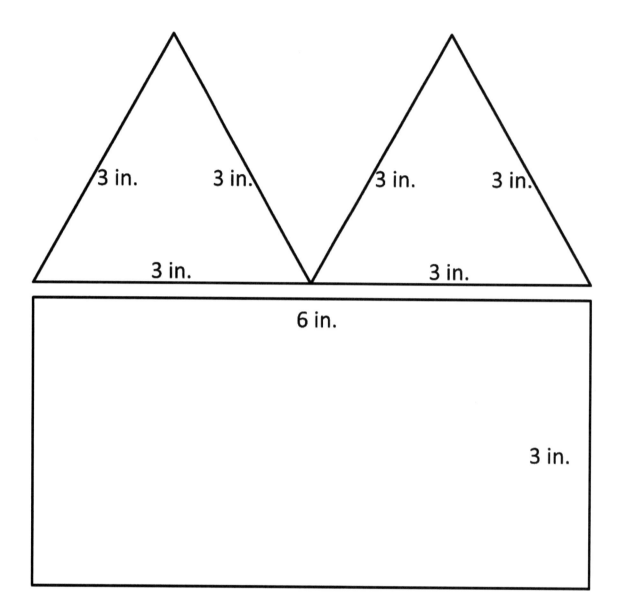

Polygons for Exercise 3, part (a)

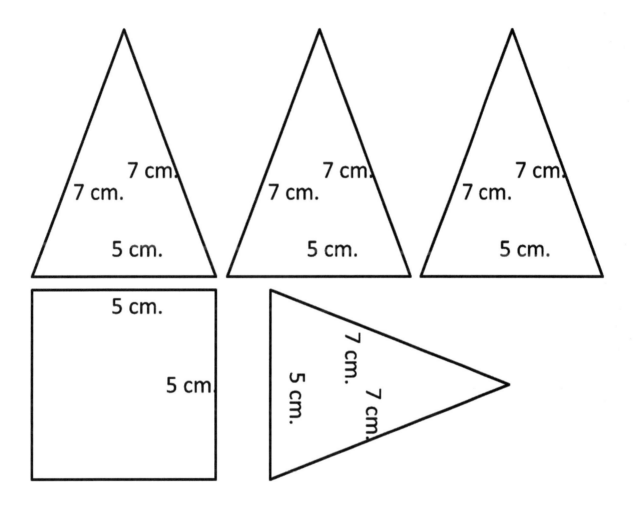

Triangles for Exercise 3, part (b)

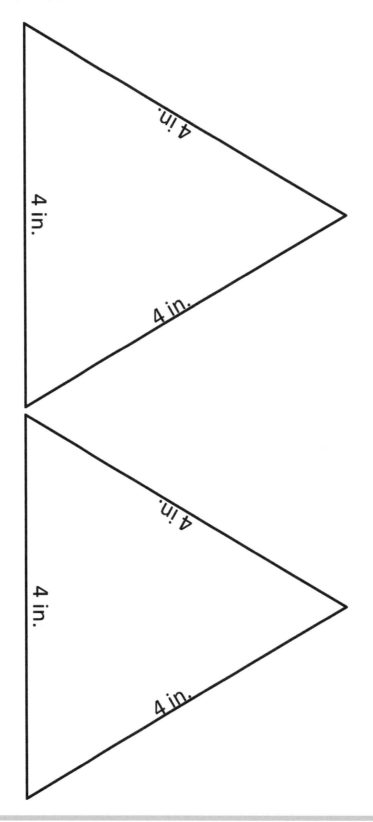

EUREKA
MATH™

Lesson 17: From Nets to Surface Area

Student Outcomes

▪ Students use nets to determine the surface area of three-dimensional figures.

Classwork

Fluency Exercise (5 minutes): Addition and Subtraction Equations

Sprint: Refer to the Sprints and the Sprint Delivery Script sections of the Module 4 Module Overview for directions on how to administer a Sprint.

Opening Exercise (4 minutes)

Students work independently to calculate the area of the shapes below.

Opening Exercise

a. Write a numerical equation for the area of the figure below. Explain and identify different parts of the figure.

i.

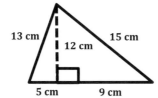

$$A = \frac{1}{2}(14 \text{ cm})(12 \text{ cm}) = 84 \text{ cm}^2$$

14 cm *represents the base of the figure because* **5 cm + 9 cm = 14 cm**, *and* **12 cm** *represents the altitude of the figure because it forms a right angle with the base.*

ii. How would you write an equation that shows the area of a triangle with base b and height h?

$$A = \frac{1}{2}bh$$

b. Write a numerical equation for the area of the figure below. Explain and identify different parts of the figure.

i.

18 ft.

28 ft.

$$A = (28 \text{ ft.})(18 \text{ ft.}) = 504 \text{ ft}^2$$

28 ft. *represents the base of the rectangle, and* **18 ft.** *represents the height of the rectangle.*

ii. How would you write an equation that shows the area of a rectangle with base b and height h?

$$A = bh$$

Discussion (5 minutes)

English language learners may not recognize the word *surface*; take this time to explain what *surface area* means. Demonstrate that *surface* is the upper or outer part of something, like the top of a desk. Therefore, *surface area* is the area of all the faces, including the bases of a three-dimensional figure.

Use the diagram below to discuss nets and surface area.

- Examine the net on the left and the three-dimensional figure on the right. What do you notice about the two diagrams?
    - *The two diagrams represent the same rectangular prism.*

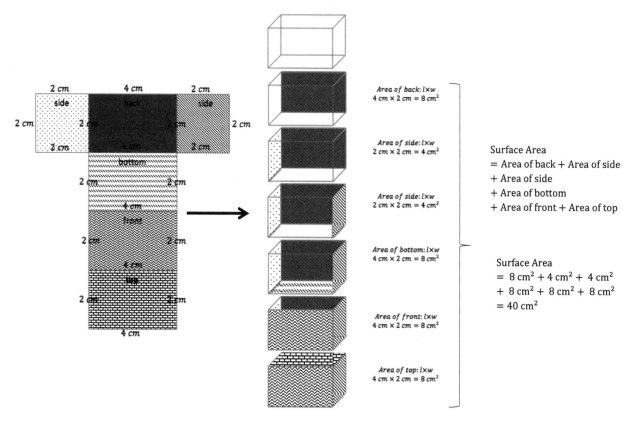

- Examine the second rectangular prism in the center column. The one shaded face is the back of the figure, which matches the face labeled back on the net. What do you notice about those two faces?
    - *The faces are identical and have the same area.*

Continue the discussion by talking about one rectangular prism pictured at a time, connecting the newly shaded face with the identical face on the net.

- Will the surface area of the net be the same as the surface area of the rectangular prism? Why or why not?
    - *The surface area for the net and the rectangular prism are the same because all the matching faces are identical, which means their areas are also the same.*

EUREKA MATH™

Example 1 (4 minutes)

Lead students through the problem.

> **Example 1**
>
> Use the net to calculate the surface area of the figure. (Note: all measurements are in centimeters.)

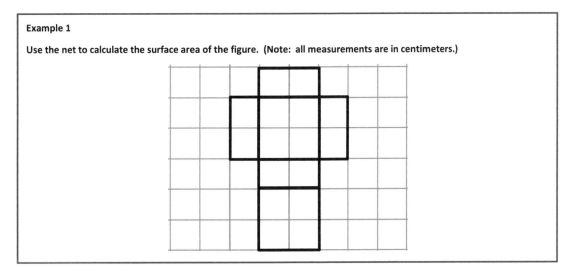

- When you are calculating the area of a figure, what are you finding?
  - *The area of a figure is the amount of space inside a two-dimensional figure.*
- Surface area is similar to area, but surface area is used to describe three-dimensional figures. What do you think is meant by the surface area of a solid?
  - *The surface area of a three-dimensional figure is the area of each face added together.*
- What type of figure does the net create? How do you know?
  - *It creates a rectangular prism because there are six rectangular faces.*
- If the boxes on the grid paper represent a 1 cm × 1 cm box, label the dimensions of the net.

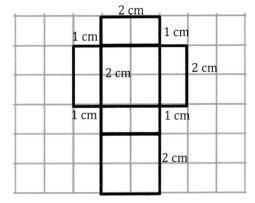

- The surface area of a figure is the sum of the areas of all faces. Calculate the area of each face, and record this value inside the corresponding rectangle.

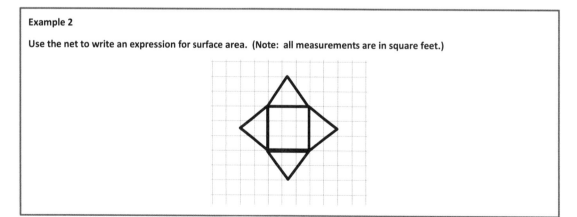

- In order to calculate the surface area, we have to find the sum of the areas we calculated since they represent the area of each face. There are two faces that have an area of 4 cm^2 and four faces that have an area of 2 cm^2. How can we use these areas to write a numerical expression to show how to calculate the surface area of the net?

MP.2
&
MP.7

  - *The numerical expression to calculate the surface area of the net would be*
    $(1 \text{ cm} \times 2 \text{ cm}) + (1 \text{ cm} \times 2 \text{ cm}) + (1 \text{ cm} \times 2 \text{ cm}) + (1 \text{ cm} \times 2 \text{ cm}) + (2 \text{ cm} \times 2 \text{ cm}) + (2 \text{ cm} \times 2 \text{ cm})$.

- Write the expression more compactly, and explain what each part represents on the net.
  - $4(1 \text{ cm} \times 2 \text{ cm}) + 2(2 \text{ cm} \times 2 \text{ cm})$
  - *The expression means there are 4 rectangles that have dimensions* $1 \text{ cm} \times 2 \text{ cm}$ *on the net and 2 rectangles that have dimensions* $2 \text{ cm} \times 2 \text{ cm}$ *on the net.*

- What is the surface area of the net?
  - *The surface area of the net is* 16 cm^2.

Example 2 (4 minutes)

Lead students through the problem.

Example 2

Use the net to write an expression for surface area. (Note: all measurements are in square feet.)

EUREKA
MATH

- What type of figure does the net create? How do you know?

    □ *It creates a square pyramid because one face is a square and the other four faces are triangles.*

- If the boxes on the grid paper represent a 1 ft. × 1 ft. square, label the dimensions of the net.

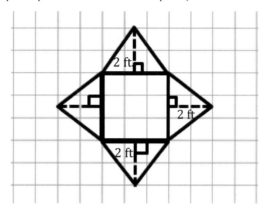

- How many faces does the rectangular pyramid have?

    □ 5

- Knowing the figure has 5 faces, use the knowledge you gained in Example 1 to calculate the surface area of the rectangular pyramid.

    □ *Area of Base:* 3 ft. × 3 ft. = 9 ft²

    Area of Triangles: $\frac{1}{2}$ × 3 ft. × 2 ft. = 3 ft²

    Surface Area: 9 ft² + 3 ft² + 3 ft² + 3 ft² + 3 ft² = 21 ft²

Exercises (13 minutes)

Students work individually to calculate the surface area of the figures below.

MP.1

Exercises

Name the solid the net would create, and then write an expression for the surface area. Use the expression to determine the surface area. Assume that each box on the grid paper represents a 1 cm × 1 cm square. Explain how the expression represents the figure.

1.

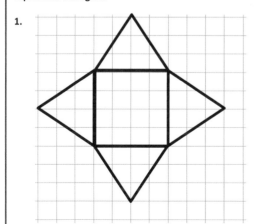

Name of Shape: Rectangular Pyramid, but more specifically a Square Pyramid

Surface Area: 4 cm × 4 cm + 4 $\left(\frac{1}{2} \times 4 \text{ cm} \times 3 \text{ cm}\right)$

Work: 16 cm² + 4(6 cm²) = 40 cm²

The surface area is 40 cm². The figure is made up of a square base that measures 4 cm × 4 cm and four triangles, each with a base of 4 cm and a height of 3 cm.

MP.1

2.

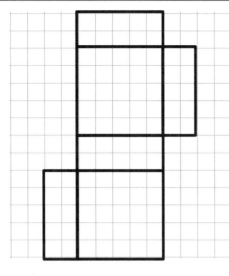

Name of Shape: Rectangular Prism

Surface Area: $2(5 \text{ cm} \times 5 \text{ cm}) + 4(5 \text{ cm} \times 2 \text{ cm})$

Work: $2(25 \text{ cm}^2) + 4(10 \text{ cm}^2) = 90 \text{ cm}^2$

The surface area is 90 cm^2. The figure has 2 square faces, each of which measures $5 \text{ cm} \times 5 \text{ cm}$ and 4 rectangular faces, each of which measures $5 \text{ cm} \times 2 \text{ cm}$.

3.

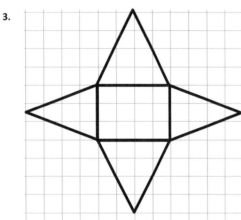

Name of Shape: Rectangular Pyramid

Surface Area: $3 \text{ cm} \times 4 \text{ cm} + 2\left(\frac{1}{2} \times 4 \text{ cm} \times 4 \text{ cm}\right) + 2\left(\frac{1}{2} \times 4 \text{ cm} \times 3 \text{ cm}\right)$

Work: $12 \text{ cm}^2 + 2(8 \text{ cm}^2) + 2(6 \text{ cm}^2) = 40 \text{ cm}^2$

The surface area is 40 cm^2. The figure has 1 rectangular base that measures $3 \text{ cm} \times 4 \text{ cm}$, 2 triangular faces, each with a base of 4 cm and a height of 4 cm, and 2 other triangular faces, each with a base of 3 cm and a height of 4 cm.

4.

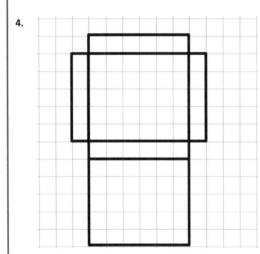

Name of Shape: Rectangular Prism

Surface Area: $2(6 \text{ cm} \times 5 \text{ cm}) + 2(5 \text{ cm} \times 1 \text{ cm}) + 2(6 \text{ cm} \times 1 \text{ cm})$

Work: $2(30 \text{ cm}^2) + 2(5 \text{ cm}^2) + 2(6 \text{ cm}^2) = 82 \text{ cm}^2$

The surface area is 82 cm^2. The figure has two $6 \text{ cm} \times 5 \text{ cm}$ rectangular faces, two $5 \text{ cm} \times 1 \text{ cm}$ rectangular faces, and two $6 \text{ cm} \times 1 \text{ cm}$ rectangular faces.

EUREKA
MATH™

Closing (5 minutes)

- Why is a net helpful when calculating the surface area of pyramids and prisms?
  - *Answers will vary. The nets are helpful when calculating surface area because it is easier to find the areas of all the faces.*
- What type of pyramids and/or prisms requires the fewest calculations when finding surface area?
  - *Regular pyramids or prisms require the fewest calculations because the lateral faces are identical, so the faces have equal areas.*

Exit Ticket (5 minutes)

Name _____   Date _____

Lesson 17: From Nets to Surface Area

Exit Ticket

Name the shape, and then calculate the surface area of the figure. Assume each box on the grid paper represents a 1 in. × 1 in. square.

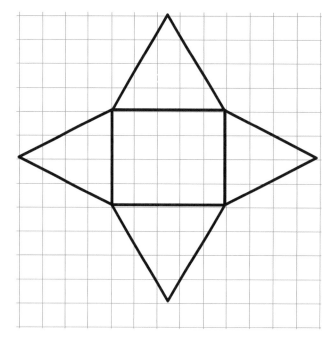

Exit Ticket Sample Solutions

Name the shape, and then calculate the surface area of the figure. Assume each box on the grid paper represents a 1 in. × 1 in. square.

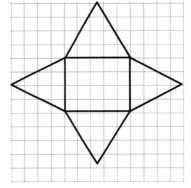

Name of Shape: Rectangular Pyramid

Area of Base: 5 in. × 4 in. = 20 in^2

Area of Triangles: $\frac{1}{2}$ × 4 in. × 4 in. = 8 in^2, $\frac{1}{2}$ × 5 in. × 4 in. = 10 in^2

Surface Area: 20 in^2 + 8 in^2 + 8 in^2 + 10 in^2 + 10 in^2 = 56 in^2

Problem Set Sample Solutions

Name the shape, and write an expression for surface area. Calculate the surface area of the figure. Assume each box on the grid paper represents a 1 ft. × 1 ft. square.

1.

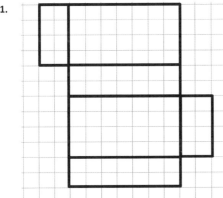

Name of Shape: Rectangular Prism

Surface Area: (2 ft. × 4 ft.) + (2 ft. × 4 ft.) + (4 ft. × 7 ft.) + (4 ft. × 7 ft.) + (7 ft. × 2 ft.) + (7 ft. × 2 ft.)

Work: 2(2 ft. × 4 ft.) + 2(4 ft. × 7 ft.) + 2(7 ft. × 2 ft.)
= 16 ft^2 + 56 ft^2 + 28 ft^2 = 100 ft^2

2.

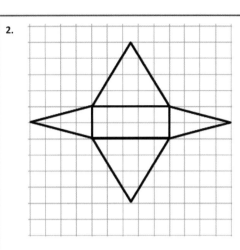

Name of Shape: Rectangular Pyramid

Surface Area: $(2 \text{ ft.} \times 5 \text{ ft.}) + \left(\frac{1}{2} \times 2 \text{ ft.} \times 4 \text{ ft.}\right) + \left(\frac{1}{2} \times 2 \text{ ft.} \times 4 \text{ ft.}\right) + \left(\frac{1}{2} \times 5 \text{ ft.} \times 4 \text{ ft.}\right) + \left(\frac{1}{2} \times 5 \text{ ft.} \times 4 \text{ ft.}\right)$

Work: $2 \text{ ft.} \times 5 \text{ ft.} + 2\left(\frac{1}{2} \times 2 \text{ ft.} \times 4 \text{ ft.}\right) + 2\left(\frac{1}{2} \times 5 \text{ ft.} \times 4 \text{ ft.}\right) = 10 \text{ ft}^2 + 8 \text{ ft}^2 + 20 \text{ ft}^2 = 38 \text{ ft}^2$

Explain the error in each problem below. Assume each box on the grid paper represents a $1 \text{ m} \times 1 \text{ m}$ square.

3.

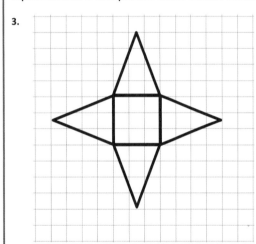

Name of Shape: Rectangular Pyramid, but more specifically a Square Pyramid

Area of Base: $3 \text{ m} \times 3 \text{ m} = 9 \text{ m}^2$

Area of Triangles: $3 \text{ m} \times 4 \text{ m} = 12 \text{ m}^2$

Surface Area: $9 \text{ m}^2 + 12 \text{ m}^2 + 12 \text{ m}^2 + 12 \text{ m}^2 + 12 \text{ m}^2 = 57 \text{ m}^2$

The error in the solution is the area of the triangles. In order to calculate the correct area of the triangles, you must use the correct formula $A = \frac{1}{2} bh$. Therefore, the area of each triangle would be 6 m^2 and not 12 m^2.

4.

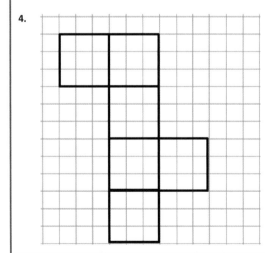

Name of Shape: Rectangular Prism or, more specifically, a Cube

Area of Faces: $3 \text{ m} \times 3 \text{ m} = 9 \text{ m}^2$

Surface Area: $9 \text{ m}^2 + 9 \text{ m}^2 + 9 \text{ m}^2 + 9 \text{ m}^2 + 9 \text{ m}^2 = 45 \text{ m}^2$

The surface area is incorrect because the student did not find the sum of all 6 faces. The solution shown above only calculates the sum of 5 faces. Therefore, the correct surface area should be $9 \text{ m}^2 + 9 \text{ m}^2 + 9 \text{ m}^2 + 9 \text{ m}^2 + 9 \text{ m}^2 + 9 \text{ m}^2 = 54 \text{ m}^2$ and not 45 m^2.

EUREKA
MATH™

5. Sofia and Ella are both writing expressions to calculate the surface area of a rectangular prism. However, they wrote different expressions.

a. Examine the expressions below, and determine if they represent the same value. Explain why or why not.

Sofia's Expression:

$$(3 \text{ cm} \times 4 \text{ cm}) + (3 \text{ cm} \times 4 \text{ cm}) + (3 \text{ cm} \times 5 \text{ cm}) + (3 \text{ cm} \times 5 \text{ cm}) + (4 \text{ cm} \times 5 \text{ cm}) + (4 \text{ cm} \times 5 \text{ cm})$$

Ella's Expression:

$$2(3 \text{ cm} \times 4 \text{ cm}) + 2(3 \text{ cm} \times 5 \text{ cm}) + 2(4 \text{ cm} \times 5 \text{ cm})$$

Sofia's and Ella's expressions are the same, but Ella used the distributive property to make her expression more compact than Sofia's.

b. What fact about the surface area of a rectangular prism does Ella's expression show more clearly than Sofia's?

A rectangular prism is composed of three pairs of sides with identical areas.

©2015 Great Minds. eureka-math.org
G6-M5-TE-B5-1.3.1-01.2016

Number Correct: _____

Addition and Subtraction Equations—Round 1

Directions: Find the value of m in each equation.

1.	$m + 4 = 11$	
2.	$m + 2 = 5$	
3.	$m + 5 = 8$	
4.	$m - 7 = 10$	
5.	$m - 8 = 1$	
6.	$m - 4 = 2$	
7.	$m + 12 = 34$	
8.	$m + 25 = 45$	
9.	$m + 43 = 89$	
10.	$m - 20 = 31$	
11.	$m - 13 = 34$	
12.	$m - 45 = 68$	
13.	$m + 34 = 41$	
14.	$m + 29 = 52$	
15.	$m + 37 = 61$	
16.	$m - 43 = 63$	
17.	$m - 21 = 40$	

18.	$m - 54 = 37$	
19.	$4 + m = 9$	
20.	$6 + m = 13$	
21.	$2 + m = 31$	
22.	$15 = m + 11$	
23.	$24 = m + 13$	
24.	$32 = m + 28$	
25.	$4 = m - 7$	
26.	$3 = m - 5$	
27.	$12 = m - 14$	
28.	$23.6 = m - 7.1$	
29.	$14.2 = m - 33.8$	
30.	$2.5 = m - 41.8$	
31.	$64.9 = m + 23.4$	
32.	$72.2 = m + 38.7$	
33.	$1.81 = m - 15.13$	
34.	$24.68 = m - 56.82$	

Lesson 17:   From Nets to Surface Area

EUREKA
MATH™

©2015 Great Minds. eureka-math.org
G6-M5-TE-B5-1.3.1-01.2016

Addition and Subtraction Equations—Round 1 [KEY]

Directions: Find the value of m in each equation.

1.	$m + 4 = 11$	$m = 7$
2.	$m + 2 = 5$	$m = 3$
3.	$m + 5 = 8$	$m = 3$
4.	$m - 7 = 10$	$m = 17$
5.	$m - 8 = 1$	$m = 9$
6.	$m - 4 = 2$	$m = 6$
7.	$m + 12 = 34$	$m = 22$
8.	$m + 25 = 45$	$m = 20$
9.	$m + 43 = 89$	$m = 46$
10.	$m - 20 = 31$	$m = 51$
11.	$m - 13 = 34$	$m = 47$
12.	$m - 45 = 68$	$m = 113$
13.	$m + 34 = 41$	$m = 7$
14.	$m + 29 = 52$	$m = 23$
15.	$m + 37 = 61$	$m = 24$
16.	$m - 43 = 63$	$m = 106$
17.	$m - 21 = 40$	$m = 61$

18.	$m - 54 = 37$	$m = 91$
19.	$4 + m = 9$	$m = 5$
20.	$6 + m = 13$	$m = 7$
21.	$2 + m = 31$	$m = 29$
22.	$15 = m + 11$	$m = 4$
23.	$24 = m + 13$	$m = 11$
24.	$32 = m + 28$	$m = 4$
25.	$4 = m - 7$	$m = 11$
26.	$3 = m - 5$	$m = 8$
27.	$12 = m - 14$	$m = 26$
28.	$23.6 = m - 7.1$	$m = 30.7$
29.	$14.2 = m - 33.8$	$m = 48$
30.	$2.5 = m - 41.8$	$m = 44.3$
31.	$64.9 = m + 23.4$	$m = 41.5$
32.	$72.2 = m + 38.7$	$m = 33.5$
33.	$1.81 = m - 15.13$	$m = 16.94$
34.	$24.68 = m - 56.82$	$m = 81.5$

EUREKA
MATH™

Lesson 17:   From Nets to Surface Area

277

©2015 Great Minds. eureka-math.org
G6-M5-TE-B5-1.3.1-01.2016

Number Correct: _____

Improvement: _____

Addition and Subtraction Equations—Round 2

Directions: Find the value of m in each equation.

1.	$m + 2 = 7$	
2.	$m + 4 = 10$	
3.	$m + 8 = 15$	
4.	$m + 7 = 23$	
5.	$m + 12 = 16$	
6.	$m - 5 = 2$	
7.	$m - 3 = 8$	
8.	$m - 4 = 12$	
9.	$m - 14 = 45$	
10.	$m + 23 = 40$	
11.	$m + 13 = 31$	
12.	$m + 23 = 48$	
13.	$m + 38 = 52$	
14.	$m - 14 = 27$	
15.	$m - 23 = 35$	
16.	$m - 17 = 18$	
17.	$m - 64 = 1$	

18.	$6 = m + 3$	
19.	$12 = m + 7$	
20.	$24 = m + 16$	
21.	$13 = m + 9$	
22.	$32 = m - 3$	
23.	$22 = m - 12$	
24.	$34 = m - 10$	
25.	$48 = m + 29$	
26.	$21 = m + 17$	
27.	$52 = m + 37$	
28.	$\dfrac{6}{7} = m + \dfrac{4}{7}$	
29.	$\dfrac{2}{3} = m - \dfrac{5}{3}$	
30.	$\dfrac{1}{4} = m - \dfrac{8}{3}$	
31.	$\dfrac{5}{6} = m - \dfrac{7}{12}$	
32.	$\dfrac{7}{8} = m - \dfrac{5}{12}$	
33.	$\dfrac{7}{6} + m = \dfrac{16}{3}$	
34.	$\dfrac{1}{3} + m = \dfrac{13}{15}$	

EUREKA
MATH™

Addition and Subtraction Equations—Round 2 [KEY]

Directions: Find the value of m in each equation.

1.	$m + 2 = 7$	$m = 5$	18.	$6 = m + 3$	$m = 3$
2.	$m + 4 = 10$	$m = 6$	19.	$12 = m + 7$	$m = 5$
3.	$m + 8 = 15$	$m = 7$	20.	$24 = m + 16$	$m = 8$
4.	$m + 7 = 23$	$m = 16$	21.	$13 = m + 9$	$m = 4$
5.	$m + 12 = 16$	$m = 4$	22.	$32 = m - 3$	$m = 35$
6.	$m - 5 = 2$	$m = 7$	23.	$22 = m - 12$	$m = 34$
7.	$m - 3 = 8$	$m = 11$	24.	$34 = m - 10$	$m = 44$
8.	$m - 4 = 12$	$m = 16$	25.	$48 = m + 29$	$m = 19$
9.	$m - 14 = 45$	$m = 59$	26.	$21 = m + 17$	$m = 4$
10.	$m + 23 = 40$	$m = 17$	27.	$52 = m + 37$	$m = 15$
11.	$m + 13 = 31$	$m = 18$	28.	$\frac{6}{7} = m + \frac{4}{7}$	$m = \frac{2}{7}$
12.	$m + 23 = 48$	$m = 25$	29.	$\frac{2}{3} = m - \frac{5}{3}$	$m = \frac{7}{3}$
13.	$m + 38 = 52$	$m = 14$	30.	$\frac{1}{4} = m - \frac{8}{3}$	$m = \frac{35}{12}$
14.	$m - 14 = 27$	$m = 41$	31.	$\frac{5}{6} = m - \frac{7}{12}$	$m = \frac{17}{12}$
15.	$m - 23 = 35$	$m = 58$	32.	$\frac{7}{8} = m - \frac{5}{12}$	$m = \frac{31}{24}$
16.	$m - 17 = 18$	$m = 35$	33.	$\frac{7}{6} + m = \frac{16}{3}$	$m = \frac{25}{6}$
17.	$m - 64 = 1$	$m = 65$	34.	$\frac{1}{3} + m = \frac{13}{15}$	$m = \frac{8}{15}$

©2015 Great Minds. eureka-math.org
G6-M5-TE-B5-1.3.1-01.2016

Lesson 18: Determining Surface Area of Three-Dimensional Figures

Student Outcomes

- Students determine that a right rectangular prism has six faces: top and bottom, front and back, and two sides. They determine that surface area is obtained by adding the areas of all the faces and develop the formula $SA = 2lw + 2lh + 2wh$.
- Students develop and apply the formula for the surface area of a cube as $SA = 6s^2$.

Lesson Notes

In order to complete this lesson, each student needs a ruler and the shape template that is attached to the lesson. To save time, teachers should have the shape template cut out for students.

Classwork

Opening Exercise (5 minutes)

In order to complete the Opening Exercise, each student needs a copy of the shape template that is already cut out.

Opening Exercise

a. What three-dimensional figure does the net create?

   Rectangular Prism

b. Measure (in inches) and label each side of the figure.

<table>
<tr><td></td><td></td><td>4 in.</td><td></td><td></td></tr>
<tr><td></td><td>1 in.</td><td>4 in.</td><td>1 in.</td><td></td></tr>
<tr><td>2 in.</td><td></td><td></td><td></td><td>2 in.</td></tr>
<tr><td></td><td></td><td>4 in.</td><td></td><td></td></tr>
<tr><td></td><td>1 in.</td><td>4 in.</td><td>1 in.</td><td></td></tr>
<tr><td></td><td>2 in.</td><td></td><td>2 in.</td><td></td></tr>
<tr><td></td><td></td><td>4 in.</td><td></td><td></td></tr>
</table>

EUREKA
MATH™

c.   Calculate the area of each face, and record this value inside the corresponding rectangle.

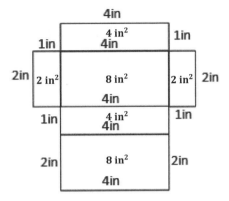

d.   How did we compute the surface area of solid figures in previous lessons?

To determine surface area, we found the area of each of the faces and then added those areas.

e.   Write an expression to show how we can calculate the surface area of the figure above.

$(4 \text{ in.} \times 1 \text{ in.}) + (4 \text{ in.} \times 2 \text{ in.}) + (4 \text{ in.} \times 1 \text{ in.}) + (4 \text{ in.} \times 2 \text{ in.}) + (2 \text{ in.} \times 1 \text{ in.}) + (2 \text{ in.} \times 1 \text{ in.})$

OR

$2(4 \text{ in.} \times 1 \text{ in.}) + 2(4 \text{ in.} \times 2 \text{ in.}) + 2(2 \text{ in.} \times 1 \text{ in.})$

f.   What does each part of the expression represent?

Each part of the expression represents an area of one face of the given figure. We were able to write a more compacted form because there are three pairs of two faces that are identical.

g.   What is the surface area of the figure?

$(4 \text{ in.} \times 1 \text{ in.}) + (4 \text{ in.} \times 2 \text{ in.}) + (4 \text{ in.} \times 1 \text{ in.}) + (4 \text{ in.} \times 2 \text{ in.}) + (2 \text{ in.} \times 1 \text{ in.}) + (2 \text{ in.} \times 1 \text{ in.})$

$2(4 \text{ in.} \times 1 \text{ in.}) + 2(4 \text{ in.} \times 2 \text{ in.}) + 2(2 \text{ in.} \times 1 \text{ in.})$

28 in^2

Example 1 (8 minutes)

■ Fold the net used in the Opening Exercise to make a rectangular prism. Have the two faces with the largest area be the bases of the prism.

■ Fill in the first row of the table below.

Example 1

Fold the net used in the Opening Exercise to make a rectangular prism. Have the two faces with the largest area be the bases of the prism. Fill in the first row of the table below.

Area of Top (base)	Area of Bottom (base)	Area of Front	Area of Back	Area of Left Side	Area of Right Side
8 in^2	8 in^2	4 in^2	4 in^2	2 in^2	2 in^2

©2015 Great Minds. eureka-math.org
G6-M5-TE-B5-1.3.1-01.2016

- What do you notice about the areas of the faces?
    - *Pairs of faces have equal areas.*
- What is the relationship between the faces having equal area?
    - *The faces that have the same area are across from each other. The bottom and top have the same area, the front and the back have the same area, and the two sides have the same area.*
- How do we calculate the area of the two bases of the prism?
    - length × width
- How do we calculate the area of the front and back faces of the prism?
    - length × height
- How do we calculate the area of the right and left faces of the prism?
    - width × height
- Using the name of the dimensions, fill in the third row of the table.

Area of Top (base)	Area of Bottom (base)	Area of Front	Area of Back	Area of Left Side	Area of Right Side
4 in. × 2 in.	4 in. × 2 in.	2 in. × 2 in.	2 in. × 2 in.	1 in. × 2 in.	1 in. × 2 in.
8 in²	8 in²	4 in²	4 in²	2 in²	2 in²
$l \times w$	$l \times w$	$l \times h$	$l \times h$	$w \times h$	$w \times h$

- Examine the rectangular prism below. Complete the table.

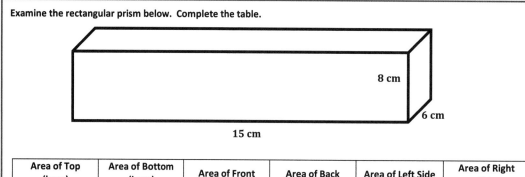

Examine the rectangular prism below. Complete the table.

8 cm

6 cm

15 cm

Area of Top (base)	Area of Bottom (base)	Area of Front	Area of Back	Area of Left Side	Area of Right Side
15 cm × 6 cm	15 cm × 6 cm	15 cm × 8 cm	15 cm × 8 cm	8 cm × 6 cm	8 cm × 6 cm
90 cm²	90 cm²	120 cm²	120 cm²	48 cm²	48 cm²
$l \times w$	$l \times w$	$l \times h$	$l \times h$	$w \times h$	$w \times h$

MP.8

- When comparing the methods to finding surface area of the two rectangular prisms, can you develop a general formula?
    - $SA = l \times w + l \times w + l \times h + l \times h + w \times h + w \times h$
- Since we use the same expression to calculate the area of pairs of faces, we can use the distributive property to write an equivalent expression for the surface area of the figure that uses half as many terms.

Scaffolding:

Students may benefit from a poster or handout highlighting the length, width, and height of a three-dimensional figure. This poster may also include that l = length, w = width, and h = height.

MP.8

- We have determined that there are two $l \times w$ dimensions. Let's record that as 2 times l times w, or simply $2(l \times w)$. How can we use this knowledge to alter other parts of the formula?
  - *We also have two $l \times h$, so we can write that as $2(l \times h)$, and we can write the two $w \times h$ as $2(w \times h)$.*
- Writing each pair in a simpler way, what is the formula to calculate the surface area of a rectangular prism?
  - $SA = 2(l \times w) + 2(l \times h) + 2(w \times h)$
- Knowing the formula to calculate surface area makes it possible to calculate the surface area without a net.

Example 2 (5 minutes)

Work with students to calculate the surface area of the given rectangular prism.

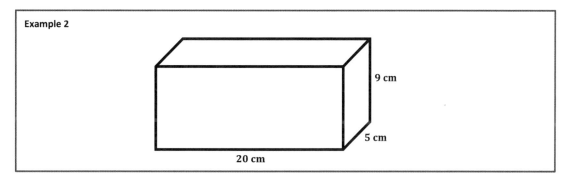

Example 2

9 cm

5 cm

20 cm

- What are the dimensions of the rectangular prism?
  - *The length is 20 cm, the width is 5 cm, and the height is 9 cm.*
- We use substitution in order to calculate the area. Substitute the given dimensions into the surface area formula.
  - $SA = 2(20 \text{ cm})(5 \text{ cm}) + 2(20 \text{ cm})(9 \text{ cm}) + 2(5 \text{ cm})(9 \text{ cm})$
- Solve the equation. Remember to use order of operations.
  - $SA = 200 \text{ cm}^2 + 360 \text{ cm}^2 + 90 \text{ cm}^2$
  - $SA = 650 \text{ cm}^2$

Exercises 1–3 (17 minutes)

Students work individually to answer the following questions.

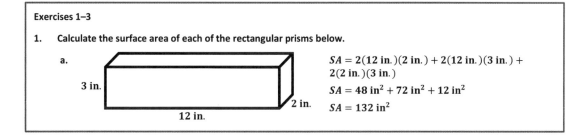

Exercises 1–3

1. Calculate the surface area of each of the rectangular prisms below.

   a.

   3 in.

   12 in.

   2 in.

   $SA = 2(12 \text{ in.})(2 \text{ in.}) + 2(12 \text{ in.})(3 \text{ in.}) + 2(2 \text{ in.})(3 \text{ in.})$

   $SA = 48 \text{ in}^2 + 72 \text{ in}^2 + 12 \text{ in}^2$

   $SA = 132 \text{ in}^2$

b.

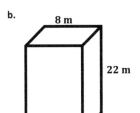

$$SA = 2(8\text{ m})(6\text{ m}) + 2(8\text{ m})(22\text{ m}) + 2(6\text{ m})(22\text{ m})$$
$$SA = 96\text{ m}^2 + 352\text{ m}^2 + 264\text{ m}^2$$
$$SA = 712\text{ m}^2$$

c.

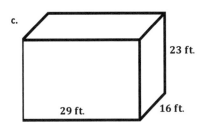

$$SA = 2(29\text{ ft.})(16\text{ ft.}) + 2(29\text{ ft.})(23\text{ ft.}) + 2(16\text{ ft.})(23\text{ ft.})$$
$$SA = 928\text{ ft}^2 + 1{,}334\text{ ft}^2 + 736\text{ ft}^2$$
$$SA = 2{,}998\text{ ft}^2$$

d.

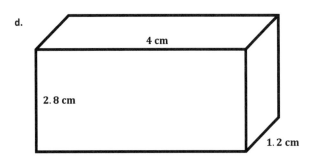

$$SA = 2(4\text{ cm})(1.2\text{ cm}) + 2(4\text{ cm})(2.8\text{ cm}) + 2(1.2\text{ cm})(2.8\text{ cm})$$
$$SA = 9.6\text{ cm}^2 + 22.4\text{ cm}^2 + 6.72\text{ cm}^2$$
$$SA = 38.72\text{ cm}^2$$

2. Calculate the surface area of the cube.

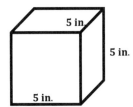

$$SA = 2(5\text{ in.})(5\text{ in.}) + 2(5\text{ in.})(5\text{ in.}) + 2(5\text{ in.})(5\text{ in.})$$
$$SA = 50\text{ in}^2 + 50\text{ in}^2 + 50\text{ in}^2$$
$$SA = 150\text{ in}^2$$

©2015 Great Minds. eureka-math.org
G6-M5-TE-B5-1.3.1-01.2016

EUREKA
MATH™

MP.3

3. All the edges of a cube have the same length. Tony claims that the formula $SA = 6s^2$, where s is the length of each side of the cube, can be used to calculate the surface area of a cube.

    a. Use the dimensions from the cube in Problem 2 to determine if Tony's formula is correct.

    Tony's formula is correct because $SA = 6(5 \text{ km})^2 = 150 \text{ km}^2$, which is the same surface area when we use the surface area formula for rectangular prisms.

    b. Why does this formula work for cubes?

    Each face is a square, and to find the area of a square, you multiply the side lengths together. However, since the side lengths are the same, you can just square the side length. Also, a cube has 6 identical faces, so after calculating the area of one face, we can just multiply this area by 6 to determine the total surface area of the cube.

    c. Becca does not want to try to remember two formulas for surface area, so she is only going to remember the formula for a cube. Is this a good idea? Why or why not?

    Becca's idea is not a good idea. The surface area formula for cubes only works for cubes because rectangular prisms do not have 6 identical faces. Therefore, Becca also needs to know the surface area formula for rectangular prisms.

Closing (5 minutes)

- Use two different ways to calculate the surface area of a cube with side lengths of 8 cm.
    - $SA = 2(8 \text{ cm} \times 8 \text{ cm}) + 2(8 \text{ cm} \times 8 \text{ cm}) + 2(8 \text{ cm} \times 8 \text{ cm})$
      $SA = 128 \text{ cm}^2 + 128 \text{ cm}^2 + 128 \text{ cm}^2$
      $SA = 384 \text{ cm}^2$
    - $SA = 6s^2$
      $SA = 6(8 \text{ cm})^2$
      $SA = 384 \text{ cm}^2$

- If you had to calculate the surface area of 20 different-sized cubes, which method would you prefer to use, and why?
    - *Answers may vary, but most likely students will choose the formula for surface area of a cube because it is a shorter formula, so it would take less time.*

Lesson Summary

Surface Area Formula for a Rectangular Prism: $SA = 2lw + 2lh + 2wh$

Surface Area Formula for a Cube: $SA = 6s^2$

Exit Ticket (5 minutes)

©2015 Great Minds. eureka-math.org
G6-M5-TE-B5-1.3.1-01.2016

Name _____ Date _____

Lesson 18: Determining Surface Area of Three-Dimensional Figures

Exit Ticket

Calculate the surface area of each figure below. Figures are not drawn to scale.

1.

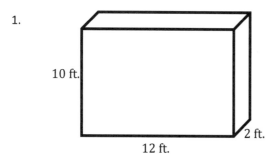

2.

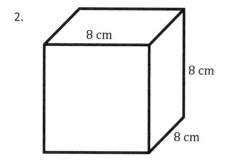

EUREKA
MATH™

Exit Ticket Sample Solutions

Calculate the surface area of each figure below. Figures are not drawn to scale.

1.

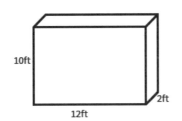

$SA = 2lw + 2lh + 2wh$

$SA = 2(12 \text{ ft.})(2 \text{ ft.}) + 2(12 \text{ ft.})(10 \text{ ft.}) + 2(2 \text{ ft.})(10 \text{ ft.})$

$SA = 48 \text{ ft}^2 + 240 \text{ ft}^2 + 40 \text{ ft}^2$

$SA = 328 \text{ ft}^2$

2.

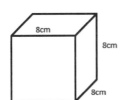

$SA = 6s^2$

$SA = 6(8 \text{ cm})^2$

$SA = 6(64 \text{ cm}^2)$

$SA = 384 \text{ cm}^2$

Problem Set Sample Solutions

Calculate the surface area of each figure below. Figures are not drawn to scale.

1.

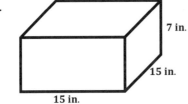

$SA = 2(15 \text{ in.})(15 \text{ in.}) + 2(15 \text{ in.})(7 \text{ in.}) + 2(15 \text{ in.})(7 \text{ in.})$

$SA = 450 \text{ in}^2 + 210 \text{ in}^2 + 210 \text{ in}^2$

$SA = 870 \text{ in}^2$

2.

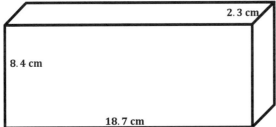

$SA = 2(18.7 \text{ cm})(2.3 \text{ cm}) + 2(18.7 \text{ cm})(8.4 \text{ cm}) + 2(2.3 \text{ cm})(8.4 \text{ cm})$

$SA = 86.02 \text{ cm}^2 + 314.16 \text{ cm}^2 + 38.64 \text{ cm}^2$

$SA = 438.82 \text{ cm}^2$

3.

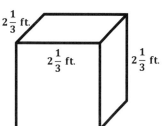

$$SA = 6\left(2\frac{1}{3} \text{ ft.}\right)^2$$

$$SA = 6\left(\frac{7}{3} \text{ ft.}\right)^2$$

$$SA = 6\left(\frac{49}{9} \text{ ft}^2\right)$$

$$SA = \frac{294}{9} \text{ ft}^2 = 32\frac{2}{3} \text{ ft}^2$$

4.

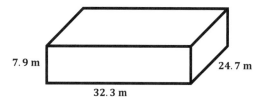

$$SA = 2(32.3 \text{ m})(24.7 \text{ m}) + 2(32.3 \text{ m})(7.9 \text{ m}) + 2(24.7 \text{ m})(7.9 \text{ m})$$

$$SA = 1,595.62 \text{ m}^2 + 510.34 \text{ m}^2 + 390.26 \text{ m}^2$$

$$SA = 2,496.22 \text{ m}^2$$

5. Write a numerical expression to show how to calculate the surface area of the rectangular prism. Explain each part of the expression.

$$2(12 \text{ ft.} \times 3 \text{ ft.}) + 2(12 \text{ ft.} \times 7 \text{ ft.}) + 2(7 \text{ ft.} \times 3 \text{ ft.})$$

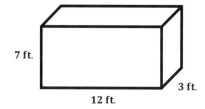

The first part of the expression shows the area of the top and bottom of the rectangular prism. The second part of the expression shows the area of the front and back of the rectangular prism. The third part of the expression shows the area of the two sides of the rectangular prism.

The surface area of the figure is 282 ft².

6. When Louie was calculating the surface area for Problem 4, he identified the following:

length = 24.7 m, width = 32.3 m, and height = 7.9 m.

However, when Rocko was calculating the surface area for the same problem, he identified the following:

length = 32.3 m, width = 24.7 m, and height = 7.9 m.

Would Louie and Rocko get the same answer? Why or why not?

Louie and Rocko would get the same answer because they are still finding the correct area of all six faces of the rectangular prism.

©2015 Great Minds. eureka-math.org
G6-M5-TE-B5-1.3.1-01.2016

7. Examine the figure below.

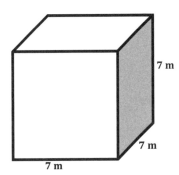

7 m

7 m

7 m

a. What is the most specific name of the three-dimensional shape?

Cube

b. Write two different expressions for the surface area.

$(7 \text{ m} \times 7 \text{ m}) + (7 \text{ m} \times 7 \text{ m}) + (7 \text{ m} \times 7 \text{ m}) + (7 \text{ m} \times 7 \text{ m}) + (7 \text{ m} \times 7 \text{ m}) + (7 \text{ m} \times 7 \text{ m})$

OR

$6 \times (7 \text{ m})^2$

c. Explain how these two expressions are equivalent.

The two expressions are equivalent because the first expression shows $7 \text{ m} \times 7 \text{ m}$, which is equivalent to $(7 \text{ m})^2$. Also, the 6 represents the number of times the product $7 \text{ m} \times 7 \text{ m}$ is added together.

©2015 Great Minds. eureka-math.org
G6-M5-TE-B5-1.3.1-01.2016

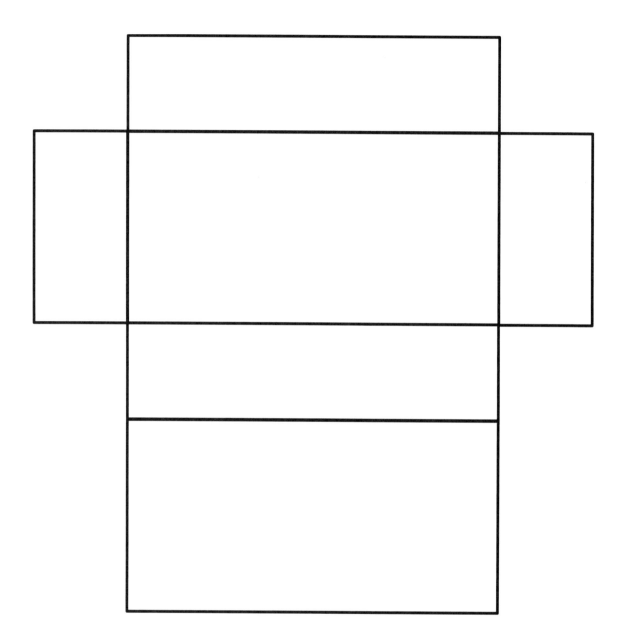

Lesson 18:   Determining Surface Area of Three-Dimensional Figures

Lesson 19: Surface Area and Volume in the Real World

Student Outcomes

- Students determine the surface area of three-dimensional figures in real-world contexts.
- Students choose appropriate formulas to solve real-life volume and surface area problems.

Classwork

Fluency Exercise (5 minutes): Area of Shapes

RWBE: Refer to the Rapid White Board Exchange section in the Module 4 Module Overview for directions on how to administer an RWBE.

Opening Exercise (4 minutes)

MP.1

Opening Exercise

A box needs to be painted. How many square inches need to be painted to cover the entire surface of the box?

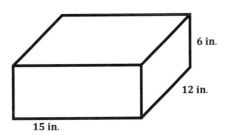

$SA = 2(15 \text{ in.})(12 \text{ in.}) + 2(15 \text{ in.})(6 \text{ in.}) + 2(12 \text{ in.})(6 \text{ in.})$

$SA = 360 \text{ in}^2 + 180 \text{ in}^2 + 144 \text{ in}^2$

$SA = 684 \text{ in}^2$

A juice box is 4 in. tall, 1 in. wide, and 2 in. long. How much juice fits inside the juice box?

$V = 1 \text{ in.} \times 2 \text{ in.} \times 4 \text{ in.} = 8 \text{ in}^3$

How did you decide how to solve each problem?

I chose to use surface area to solve the first problem because you would need to know how much area the paint would need to cover. I chose to use volume to solve the second problem because you would need to know how much space is inside the juice box to determine how much juice it can hold.

If students struggle deciding whether to calculate volume or surface area, use the Venn diagram on the next page to help them make the correct decision.

Discussion (5 minutes)

Students need to be able to recognize the difference between volume and surface area. As a class, complete the Venn diagram below so students have a reference when completing the application problems.

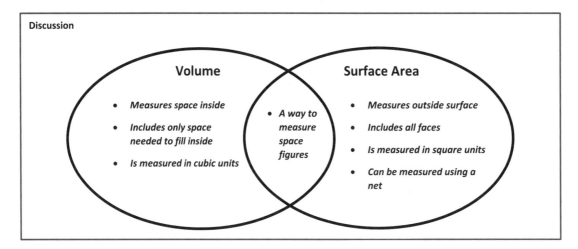

Example 1 (5 minutes)

Work through the word problem below with students. Students should be leading the discussion in order for them to be prepared to complete the exercises.

Example 1

Vincent put logs in the shape of a rectangular prism outside his house. However, it is supposed to snow, and Vincent wants to buy a cover so the logs stay dry. If the pile of logs creates a rectangular prism with these measurements:

33 cm long, 12 cm wide, and 48 cm high,

what is the minimum amount of material needed to cover the pile of logs?

- ▪ Where do we start?
  - □ *We need to find the size of the cover for the logs, so we need to calculate the surface area. In order to find the surface area, we need to know the dimensions of the pile of logs.*
- ▪ Why do we need to find the surface area and not the volume?
  - □ *We want to know the size of the cover Vincent wants to buy. If we calculated volume, we would not have the information Vincent needs when he goes shopping for a cover.*
- ▪ What are the dimensions of the pile of logs?
  - □ *The length is 33 cm, the width is 12 cm, and the height is 48 cm.*

Scaffolding:
- ▪ Add to the poster or handout made in the previous lesson showing that *long* represents length, *wide* represents width, and *high* represents height.
- ▪ Later, students have to recognize that *deep* also represents height. Therefore, this vocabulary word should also be added to the poster.

©2015 Great Minds. eureka-math.org
G6-M5-TE-B5-1.3.1-01.2016

- How do we calculate the surface area to determine the size of the cover?
    - *We can use the surface area formula for a rectangular prism.*

$$SA = 2(33 \text{ cm})(12 \text{ cm}) + 2(33 \text{ cm})(48 \text{ cm}) + 2(12 \text{ cm})(48 \text{ cm})$$
$$SA = 792 \text{ cm}^2 + 3{,}168 \text{ cm}^2 + 1{,}152 \text{ cm}^2$$
$$SA = 5{,}112 \text{ cm}^2$$

- What is different about this problem from other surface area problems of rectangular prisms you have encountered? How does this change the answer?
    - *If Vincent just wants to cover the wood to keep it dry, he does not need to cover the bottom of the pile of logs. Therefore, the cover can be smaller.*

- How can we change our answer to find the exact size of the cover Vincent needs?
    - *We know the area of the bottom of the pile of logs has the dimensions* 33 cm *and* 12 cm. *We can calculate the area and subtract this area from the total surface area.*
    - *The area of the bottom of the pile of logs is* 396 cm²; *therefore, the total surface area of the cover would need to be* 5,112 cm² − 396 cm² = 4,716 cm².

Exercises (17 minutes)

Students complete the volume and surface area problems in small groups.

Exercises

Use your knowledge of volume and surface area to answer each problem.

1. Quincy Place wants to add a pool to the neighborhood. When determining the budget, Quincy Place determined that it would also be able to install a baby pool that requires less than 15 cubic feet of water. Quincy Place has three different models of a baby pool to choose from.

    Choice One: 5 ft. × 5 ft. × 1 ft.

    Choice Two: 4 ft. × 3 ft. × 1 ft.

    Choice Three: 4 ft. × 2 ft. × 2 ft.

    Which of these choices is best for the baby pool? Why are the others not good choices?

    Choice One Volume: 5 ft. × 5 ft. × 1 ft. = 25 ft³

    Choice Two Volume: 4 ft. × 3 ft. × 1 ft. = 12 ft³

    Choice Three Volume: 4 ft. × 2 ft. × 2 ft. = 16 ft³

    Choice Two is within the budget because it holds less than 15 *cubic feet of water. The other two choices do not work because they require too much water, and Quincy Place will not be able to afford the amount of water it takes to fill the baby pool.*

2. A packaging firm has been hired to create a box for baby blocks. The firm was hired because it could save money by creating a box using the least amount of material. The packaging firm knows that the volume of the box must be 18 cm³.
    a. What are possible dimensions for the box if the volume must be exactly 18 cm³?

        Choice 1: 1 cm × 1 cm × 18 cm

        Choice 2: 1 cm × 2 cm × 9 cm

        Choice 3: 1 cm × 3 cm × 6 cm

        Choice 4: 2 cm × 3 cm × 3 cm

MP.1

©2015 Great Minds. eureka-math.org
G6-M5-TE-B5-1.3.1-01.2016

b. Which set of dimensions should the packaging firm choose in order to use the least amount of material? Explain.

Choice 1: $SA = 2(1\text{ cm})(1\text{ cm}) + 2(1\text{ cm})(18\text{ cm}) + 2(1\text{ cm})(18\text{ cm}) = 74\text{ cm}^2$

Choice 2: $SA = 2(1\text{ cm})(2\text{ cm}) + 2(1\text{ cm})(9\text{ cm}) + 2(2\text{ cm})(9\text{ cm}) = 58\text{ cm}^2$

Choice 3: $SA = 2(1\text{ cm})(3\text{ cm}) + 2(1\text{ cm})(6\text{ cm}) + 2(3\text{ cm})(6\text{ cm}) = 54\text{ cm}^2$

Choice 4: $SA = 2(2\text{ cm})(3\text{ cm}) + 2(2\text{ cm})(3\text{ cm}) + 2(3\text{ cm})(3\text{ cm}) = 42\text{ cm}^2$

The packaging firm should choose Choice 4 because it requires the least amount of material. In order to find the amount of material needed to create a box, the packaging firm would have to calculate the surface area of each box. The box with the smallest surface area requires the least amount of material.

3. A gift has the dimensions of 50 cm × 35 cm × 5 cm. You have wrapping paper with dimensions of 75 cm × 60 cm. Do you have enough wrapping paper to wrap the gift? Why or why not?

Surface Area of the Present: $SA = 2(50\text{ cm})(35\text{ cm}) + 2(50\text{ cm})(5\text{ cm}) + 2(35\text{ cm})(5\text{ cm}) =$
$$3,500\text{ cm}^2 + 500\text{ cm}^2 + 350\text{ cm}^2 = 4,350\text{ cm}^2$$

Area of Wrapping Paper: $A = 75\text{ cm} \times 60\text{ cm} = 4,500\text{ cm}^2$

I do have enough paper to wrap the present because the present requires 4,350 square centimeters of paper, and I have 4,500 square centimeters of wrapping paper.

MP.1

4. Tony bought a flat-rate box from the post office to send a gift to his mother for Mother's Day. The dimensions of the medium-size box are 14 inches × 12 inches × 3.5 inches. What is the volume of the largest gift he can send to his mother?

Volume of the Box: $V = 14\text{ in.} \times 12\text{ in.} \times 3.5\text{ in.} = 588\text{ in}^3$

Tony would have 588 cubic inches of space to fill with a gift for his mother.

5. A cereal company wants to change the shape of its cereal box in order to attract the attention of shoppers. The original cereal box has dimensions of 8 inches × 3 inches × 11 inches. The new box the cereal company is thinking of would have dimensions of 10 inches × 10 inches × 3 inches.

a. Which box holds more cereal?

Volume of Original Box: $V = 8\text{ in.} \times 3\text{ in.} \times 11\text{ in.} = 264\text{ in}^3$

Volume of New Box: $V = 10\text{ in.} \times 10\text{ in.} \times 3\text{ in.} = 300\text{ in}^3$

The new box holds more cereal because it has a larger volume.

b. Which box requires more material to make?

Surface Area of Original Box: $SA = 2(8\text{ in.})(3\text{ in.}) + 2(8\text{ in.})(11\text{ in.}) + 2(3\text{ in.})(11\text{ in.}) =$
$$48\text{ in}^2 + 176\text{ in}^2 + 66\text{ in}^2 = 290\text{ in}^2$$

Surface Area of New Box: $SA = 2(10\text{ in.})(10\text{ in.}) + 2(10\text{ in.})(3\text{ in.}) + 2(10\text{ in.})(3\text{ in.}) =$
$$200\text{ in}^2 + 60\text{ in}^2 + 60\text{ in}^2 = 320\text{ in}^2$$

The new box requires more material than the original box because the new box has a larger surface area.

EUREKA
MATH™

©2015 Great Minds. eureka-math.org
G6-M5-TE-B5-1.3.1-01.2016

6. Cinema theaters created a new popcorn box in the shape of a rectangular prism. The new popcorn box has a length of 6 inches, a width of 3.5 inches, and a height of 3.5 inches but does not include a lid.

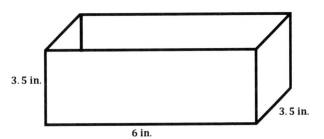

3.5 in.

3.5 in.

6 in.

Scaffolding:

English language learners may not be familiar with the term *lid*. Provide an illustration or demonstration.

MP.1

a. How much material is needed to create the box?

Surface Area of the Box: $SA = 2(6 \text{ in.})(3.5 \text{ in.}) + 2(6 \text{ in.})(3.5 \text{ in.}) + 2(3.5 \text{ in.})(3.5 \text{ in.}) =$
$42 \text{ in}^2 + 42 \text{ in}^2 + 24.5 \text{ in}^2 = 108.5 \text{ in}^2$

The box does not have a lid, so we have to subtract the area of the lid from the surface area.

Area of Lid: $6 \text{ in.} \times 3.5 \text{ in.} = 21 \text{ in}^2$

Total Surface Area: $108.5 \text{ in}^2 - 21 \text{ in}^2 = 87.5 \text{ in}^2$

87.5 square inches of material is needed to create the new popcorn box.

b. How much popcorn does the box hold?

Volume of the Box: $V = 6 \text{ in.} \times 3.5 \text{ in.} \times 3.5 \text{ in.} = 73.5 \text{ in}^3$

The box holds 73.5 in^3 of popcorn.

Closing (4 minutes)

- Is it possible for two containers having the same volume to have different surface areas? Explain.
  - *Yes, it is possible for two containers to have the same volume but different surface areas. This was the case in Exercise 2. All four boxes would hold the same amount of baby blocks (same volume) but required a different amount of material (surface area) to create the box.*

- If you want to create an open box with dimensions 3 inches × 4 inches × 5 inches, which face should be the base if you want to minimize the amount of material you use?
  - *The face with dimensions 4 inches × 5 inches should be the base because that face would have the largest area.*

If students have a hard time understanding an open box, use a shoe box to demonstrate the difference between a closed box and an open box.

Exit Ticket (5 minutes)

Lesson 19:   Surface Area and Volume in the Real World

©2015 Great Minds. eureka-math.org
G6-M5-TE-B5-1.3.1-01.2016

Name _____   Date _____

Lesson 19: Surface Area and Volume in the Real World

Exit Ticket

Solve the word problem below.

Kelly has a rectangular fish aquarium that measures 18 inches long, 8 inches wide, and 12 inches tall.

    a.   What is the maximum amount of water the aquarium can hold?

    b.   If Kelly wanted to put a protective covering on the four glass walls of the aquarium, how big does the cover have to be?

©2015 Great Minds. eureka-math.org
G6-M5-TE-B5-1.3.1-01.2016

Exit Ticket Sample Solutions

Solve the word problem below.

Kelly has a rectangular fish aquarium that measures 18 inches long, 8 inches wide, and 12 inches tall.

    a.   What is the maximum amount of water the aquarium can hold?

        Volume of the Aquarium: $V = 18 \text{ in.} \times 8 \text{ in.} \times 12 \text{ in.} = 1,728 \text{ in}^3$

        The maximum amount of water the aquarium can hold is $1,728$ *cubic inches.*

    b.   If Kelly wanted to put a protective covering on the four glass walls of the aquarium, how big does the cover have to be?

        Surface Area of the Aquarium: $SA = 2(18 \text{ in.})(8 \text{ in.}) + 2(18 \text{ in.})(12 \text{ in.}) + 2(8 \text{ in.})(12 \text{ in.}) =$
$$288 \text{ in}^2 + 432 \text{ in}^2 + 192 \text{ in}^2 = 912 \text{ in}^2$$

        We only need to cover the four glass walls, so we can subtract the area of both the top and bottom of the aquarium.

        Area of Top: $A = 18 \text{ in.} \times 8 \text{ in.} = 144 \text{ in}^2$

        Area of Bottom: $A = 18 \text{ in.} \times 8 \text{ in.} = 144 \text{ in}^2$

        Surface Area of the Four Walls: $SA = 912 \text{ in}^2 - 144 \text{ in}^2 - 144 \text{ in}^2 = 624 \text{ in}^2$

        Kelly would need 624 in^2 *to cover the four walls of the aquarium.*

Problem Set Sample Solutions

Solve each problem below.

1.   Dante built a wooden, cubic toy box for his son. Each side of the box measures 2 feet.

    a.   How many square feet of wood did he use to build the box?

        Surface Area of the Box: $SA = 6(2 \text{ ft})^2 = 6(4 \text{ ft}^2) = 24 \text{ ft}^2$

        Dante used 24 *square feet of wood to build the box.*

    b.   How many cubic feet of toys will the box hold?

        Volume of the Box: $V = 2 \text{ ft.} \times 2 \text{ ft.} \times 2 \text{ ft.} = 8 \text{ ft}^3$

        The toy box would hold 8 *cubic feet of toys.*

2.   A company that manufactures gift boxes wants to know how many different-sized boxes having a volume of 50 cubic centimeters it can make if the dimensions must be whole centimeters.

    a.   List all the possible whole number dimensions for the box.

        Choice One: $1 \text{ cm} \times 1 \text{ cm} \times 50 \text{ cm}$

        Choice Two: $1 \text{ cm} \times 2 \text{ cm} \times 25 \text{ cm}$

        Choice Three: $1 \text{ cm} \times 5 \text{ cm} \times 10 \text{ cm}$

        Choice Four: $2 \text{ cm} \times 5 \text{ cm} \times 5 \text{ cm}$

b.   Which possibility requires the least amount of material to make?

Choice One: $SA = 2(1 \text{ cm})(1 \text{ cm}) + 2(1 \text{ cm})(50 \text{ cm}) + 2(1 \text{ cm})(50 \text{ cm}) = 2 \text{ cm}^2 + 100 \text{ cm}^2 + 100 \text{ cm}^2 = 202 \text{ cm}^2$

Choice Two: $SA = 2(1 \text{ cm})(2 \text{ cm}) + 2(1 \text{ cm})(25 \text{ cm}) + 2(2 \text{ cm})(25 \text{ cm}) = 4 \text{ cm}^2 + 50 \text{ cm}^2 + 100 \text{ cm}^2 = 154 \text{ cm}^2$

Choice Three: $SA = 2(1 \text{ cm})(5 \text{ cm}) + 2(1 \text{ cm})(10 \text{ cm}) + 2(5 \text{ cm})(10 \text{ cm}) = 10 \text{ cm}^2 + 20 \text{ cm}^2 + 100 \text{ cm}^2 = 130 \text{ cm}^2$

Choice Four: $SA = 2(2 \text{ cm})(5 \text{ cm}) + 2(2 \text{ cm})(5 \text{ cm}) + 2(5 \text{ cm})(5 \text{ cm}) = 20 \text{ cm}^2 + 20 \text{ cm}^2 + 50 \text{ cm}^2 = 90 \text{ cm}^2$

Choice Four requires the least amount of material because it has the smallest surface area.

c.   Which box would you recommend the company use? Why?

I would recommend the company use the box with dimensions of $2 \text{ cm} \times 5 \text{ cm} \times 5 \text{ cm}$ (Choice Four) because it requires the least amount of material to make, so it would cost the company the least amount of money to make.

3.   A rectangular box of rice is shown below. What is the greatest amount of rice, in cubic inches, that the box can hold?

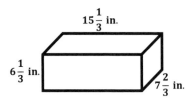

Volume of the Rice Box: $V = 15\frac{1}{3} \text{ in.} \times 7\frac{2}{3} \text{ in.} \times 6\frac{1}{3} \text{ in.} = \frac{20,102}{27} \text{ in}^3 = 744\frac{14}{27} \text{ in}^3$

4.   The Mars Cereal Company has two different cereal boxes for Mars Cereal. The large box is 8 inches wide, 11 inches high, and 3 inches deep. The small box is 6 inches wide, 10 inches high, and 2.5 inches deep.

a.   How much more cardboard is needed to make the large box than the small box?

Surface Area of the Large Box: $SA = 2(8 \text{ in.})(11 \text{ in.}) + 2(8 \text{ in.})(3 \text{ in.}) + 2(11 \text{ in.})(3 \text{ in.}) = 176 \text{ in}^2 + 48 \text{ in}^2 + 66 \text{ in}^2 = 290 \text{ in}^2$

Surface Area of the Small Box: $SA = 2(6 \text{ in.})(10 \text{ in.}) + 2(6 \text{ in.})(2.5 \text{ in.}) + 2(10 \text{ in.})(2.5 \text{ in.}) = 120 \text{ in}^2 + 30 \text{ in}^2 + 50 \text{ in}^2 = 200 \text{ in}^2$

Difference: $290 \text{ in}^2 - 200 \text{ in}^2 = 90 \text{ in}^2$

The large box requires 90 square inches more cardboard than the small box.

b.   How much more cereal does the large box hold than the small box?

Volume of the Large Box: $V = 8 \text{ in.} \times 11 \text{ in.} \times 3 \text{ in.} = 264 \text{ in}^3$

Volume of the Small Box: $V = 6 \text{ in.} \times 10 \text{ in.} \times 2.5 \text{ in.} = 150 \text{ in}^3$

Difference: $264 \text{ in}^3 - 150 \text{ in}^3 = 114 \text{ in}^3$

The large box holds 114 cubic inches more cereal than the small box.

EUREKA MATH

5. A swimming pool is 8 meters long, 6 meters wide, and 2 meters deep. The water-resistant paint needed for the pool costs $6 per square meter. How much will it cost to paint the pool?

   a. How many faces of the pool do you have to paint?

   You have to point 5 faces.

   b. How much paint (in square meters) do you need to paint the pool?

   $SA = 2(8 \text{ m} \times 6 \text{ m}) + 2(8 \text{ m} \times 2 \text{ m}) + 2(6 \text{ m} \times 2 \text{ m}) = 96 \text{ m}^2 + 32 \text{ m}^2 + 24 \text{ m}^2 = 152 \text{ m}^2$

   Area of Top of Pool: $8 \text{ m} \times 6 \text{ m} = 48 \text{ m}^2$

   Total Paint Needed: $152 \text{ m}^2 - 48 \text{ m}^2 = 104 \text{ m}^2$

   c. How much will it cost to paint the pool?

   $104 \text{ m}^2 \times \$6/\text{m}^2 = \$624$

   It will cost $\$624$ *to paint the pool.*

6. Sam is in charge of filling a rectangular hole with cement. The hole is 9 feet long, 3 feet wide, and 2 feet deep. How much cement will Sam need?

   $V = 9 \text{ ft.} \times 3 \text{ ft.} \times 2 \text{ ft.} = 54 \text{ ft}^3$

   Sam will need 54 *cubic feet of cement to fill the hole.*

7. The volume of Box D subtracted from the volume of Box C is 23.14 cubic centimeters. Box D has a volume of 10.115 cubic centimeters.

   a. Let C be the volume of Box C in cubic centimeters. Write an equation that could be used to determine the volume of Box C.

   $C - 10.115 \text{ cm}^3 = 23.14 \text{ cm}^3$

   b. Solve the equation to determine the volume of Box C.

   $C - 10.115 \text{ cm}^3 + 10.115 \text{ cm}^3 = 23.14 \text{ cm}^3 + 10.115 \text{ cm}^3$
   $$C = 33.255 \text{ cm}^3$$

   c. The volume of Box C is one-tenth the volume of another box, Box E. Let E represent the volume of Box E in cubic centimeters. Write an equation that could be used to determine the volume of Box E, using the result from part (b).

   $33.255 \text{ cm}^3 = \dfrac{1}{10}E$

   d. Solve the equation to determine the volume of Box E.

   $33.255 \text{ cm}^3 \div \dfrac{1}{10} = \dfrac{1}{10}E \div \dfrac{1}{10}$
   $$332.55 \text{ cm}^3 = E$$

Area of Shapes

1.

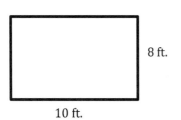

$A = 80 \text{ ft}^2$

2.

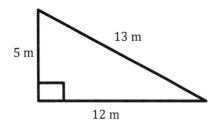

$A = 30 \text{ m}^2$

3.

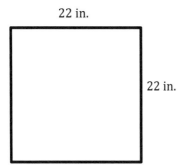

$A = 484 \text{ in}^2$

4.

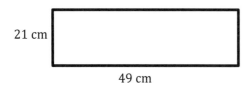

$A = 1,029 \text{ cm}^2$

5.

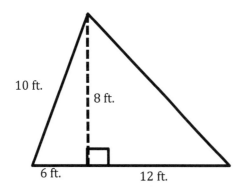

$A = 72 \text{ ft}^2$

Lesson 19:   Surface Area and Volume in the Real World

EUREKA
MATH™

©2015 Great Minds. eureka-math.org
G6-M5-TE-B5-1.3.1-01.2016

6.

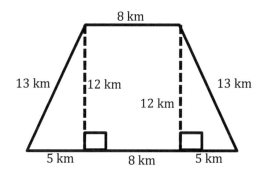

$A = 156 \text{ km}^2$

7.

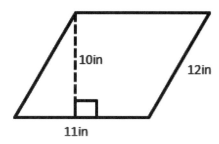

$A = 110 \text{ in}^2$

8.

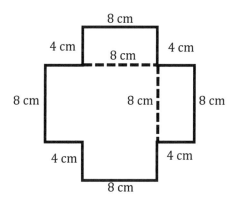

$A = 192 \text{ cm}^2$

9.

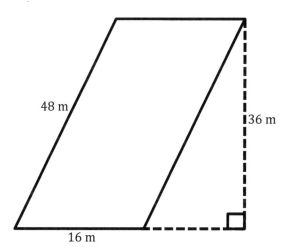

$A = 576 \text{ m}^2$

10.

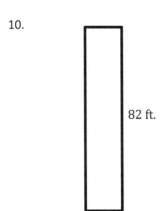

82 ft.

18 ft.

$A = 1,476 \text{ ft}^2$

EUREKA
MATH

©2015 Great Minds. eureka-math.org
G6-M5-TE-B5-1.3.1-01.2016

Lesson 19a: Applying Surface Area and Volume to Aquariums

Student Outcomes

- Students apply the formulas for surface area and volume to determine missing dimensions of aquariums and water level.

Lesson Notes

The purpose of this lesson is to demonstrate an abridged version of the modeling cycle in preparation for shortened modeling cycles in Grades 7 and 8 and, finally, in preparation for the complete modeling cycle in Grade 9. The modeling cycle is described and detailed in the New York State P–12 Common Core Standards for Mathematics, pages 61 and 62. Although the modeling cycle is addressed in detail in high school, the goal of instruction in Grades 6–8 is to prepare students for this kind of thinking. The graphic below is a brief summation of the modeling cycle in which students:

- Identify variables in a situation and select those that represent essential figures.

- Formulate a model by creating and selecting geometric, graphical, tabular, algebraic, or statistical representations between variables.

- Analyze and perform operations on these relationships to draw conclusions.

- Interpret results of the mathematics in terms of the original situation.

- Validate conclusions by comparing them with the situation, and then either improve the model or determine if it is acceptable.

- Report on the conclusions and the reasoning behind them.

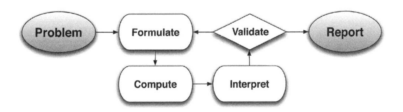

This lesson affords students the opportunity to apply their knowledge of surface area and volume in the real-life context of aquariums. Students also utilize their knowledge of rates and ratios, as well as apply arithmetic operations and their knowledge of expressions and equations from Module 4 to determine missing aquarium dimensions. On the next page is an outline of the CCSS-M addressed in this lesson.

©2015 Great Minds. eureka-math.org
G6-M5-TE-B5-1.3.1-01.2016

Module	Other Related Modules	Standards
Module 5: Area, Surface Area, and Volume Problems 6.EE.A.2c, 6.EE.B.5, 6.EE.B.6, 6.EE.B.7, 6.G.A.2, 6.G.A.4	Module 1: Ratios and Rates Module 2: Arithmetic Operations Including Dividing by a Fraction Module 4: Expressions and Equations	6.RP.A.1, 6.RP.A.2, 6.RP.A.3a, 6.RP.A.3b 6.NS.B.2, 6.NS.B.3, 6.NS.C.5 6.EE.A.2c, 6.EE.B.7, 6.EE.B.8

Students model with mathematics, demonstrating CCSS Mathematical Practice Standard 4 throughout this lesson. They use proportional reasoning to plan, approximate, and execute problem solving and calculations in this contextual platform.

The activities in this lesson are based on the standard dimensions of a 10-gallon aquarium. Because real-life materials may not be accessible in all classrooms, problems are presented in two ways. Students use proportional reasoning to determine a course of action to calculate volume, surface area, and missing dimensions, and/or students experience a hands-on, tangible experience through optional exercises that are offered for those classrooms that have access to real-life materials. Teacher preparation includes finding aquariums with the dimensions noted in the lesson or adjusting the measurements throughout the lesson to match the aquariums actually used in the lesson. Teachers need to prepare stations with liter measuring tools, gallon measuring tools, water, aquariums, and rulers. The exercises found in this teacher lesson are reproduced for the students in their student materials.

Classwork

Opening Exercise (2 minutes)

Display the following figure.

Most standard tanks and aquariums have a length of 20 inches, a width of 10 inches, and a height of 12 inches.

- Using the formula for volume, determine the volume of this aquarium in cubic inches.

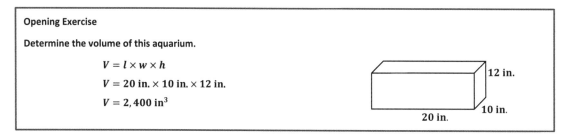

Opening Exercise

Determine the volume of this aquarium.

$$V = l \times w \times h$$
$$V = 20 \text{ in.} \times 10 \text{ in.} \times 12 \text{ in.}$$
$$V = 2,400 \text{ in}^3$$

12 in.
10 in.
20 in.

Mathematical Modeling Exercise (10 minutes): Using Ratios and Unit Rate to Determine Volume

- On the next page is a table of values that indicates the relationship between gallons of water and cubic inches.

- Use the table to determine how many cubic inches are in one gallon of water or, more specifically, the unit rate of gallons/cubic inches.

Mathematical Modeling Exercise: Using Ratios and Unit Rate to Determine Volume

For his environmental science project, Jamie is creating habitats for various wildlife including fish, aquatic turtles, and aquatic frogs. For each of these habitats, he uses a standard aquarium with length, width, and height dimensions measured in inches, identical to the aquarium mentioned in the Opening Exercise. To begin his project, Jamie needs to determine the volume, or cubic inches, of water that can fill the aquarium.

Use the table below to determine the unit rate of gallons/cubic inches.

Gallons	Cubic Inches
1	231
2	462
3	693
4	924
5	1,155

There are 231 cubic inches for every 1 gallon of water. So, the unit rate is 231.

- Since we determined that for every gallon of water, there are 231 cubic inches, determine how many cubic inches are in the 10 gallons of water that Jamie needs for the fish.

- How can we determine how many cubic inches are in 10 gallons of water?

  □ *We could use a tape diagram or a double number line, or we could find equivalent ratios.*

- Using either of these representations, determine the volume of the aquarium.

Determine the volume of the aquarium.

Answers will vary depending on student choice. An example of a tape diagram is below.

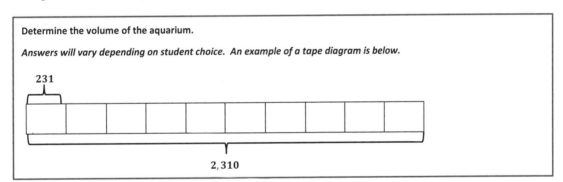

231

2,310

- We determined the volume of this tank is 2,310 in^3. This is not the same volume we calculated earlier in the Opening Exercise. Why do you think the volumes are different?

  □ *Answers will vary but should include discussion that there needs to be room for a lid; also, the water level cannot go all the way to the top so that there is room for heaters, filters, and fish, etc., without the water spilling over.*

- Generally, it is suggested that the highest level of water in this tank should be approximately 11.55 inches. Calculate the volume of the aquarium using this new dimension.

  □ $V = l \times w \times h$; $V = 20$ in. $\times 10$ in. $\times 11.55$ in.; $V = 2,310$ in^3

- What do you notice about this volume?

  □ *This volume is the same as the volume we determined when we found the volume using ratio and unit rates.*

- Let's use the dimensions 20 in. $\times$ 10 in. $\times$ 11.55 in. for our exploration.

Optional Exercise 1

- We have determined that the volume for the 10-gallon aquarium with dimensions 20 in. × 10 in. × 11.55 in. is 2,310 in³.

- Suppose Jamie needs to fill the aquarium to the top in order to prepare the tank for fish. According to our calculations, if Jamie pours 10 gallons of water into the tank, the height of the water is approximately 11.55 in.

- Let's test it. Begin pouring water into the aquarium 1 gallon at a time. Be sure to keep track of the number of gallons. Use a tally system.

Tally the Number of Gallons	Number of Gallons
ⵉⵀⵀ ⵀⵀⵉ	10

- Measure the height of the water with your ruler.
- What did you find about our height calculation?
  - *Our calculation was correct. The height is approximately* 11.55 *in.*

Exercise 1 (10 minutes)

- Next, suppose Jamie needs to prepare another aquarium for aquatic frogs. He contacted the local pet store, and the employee recommended that Jamie only partially fill the tank in order for the frogs to have room to jump from the water to a lily pad or designated resting place. The employee suggested that the tank hold 7 gallons of water. Considering that the length and the width of the tank remain the same (20 in. × 10 in.), use what you know about volume to determine the height of the water that is appropriate for the frogs in the tank.

- To determine the missing dimension of height, we need the volume formula $V = l \cdot w \cdot h$.

Exercise 1

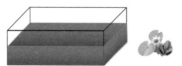

a. **Determine the volume of the tank when filled with 7 gallons of water.**

$$231 \frac{\text{cubic inches}}{\text{gallon}} \cdot 7 \text{ gallons} = 1,617 \text{ in}^3$$

The volume for 7 gallons of water is 1, 617 *in³.*

EUREKA MATH

b. Work with your group to determine the height of the water when Jamie places 7 gallons of water in the aquarium.

$$1{,}617 \text{ in}^3 = (20 \text{ in.})(10 \text{ in.})h$$

$$\frac{1{,}617 \text{in}^3}{200 \text{ in}^2} = \frac{200 \text{ in}^2}{200 \text{ in}^2}h$$

$$8.085 \text{ in.} = h$$

The tank should have a water height of 8.085 *inches.*

Optional Exercise 2

- Let's test it. Begin by pouring water into the aquarium 1 gallon at a time.
- Be sure to keep track of the number of gallons poured. Use a tally system.

Or, have students mark the height of the water using a wax marker or a dry erase marker on the outside of the tank after each gallon is poured in. Then, students measure the intervals (distance between the marks). Students should notice that the intervals are equal.

- Test the height at 7 gallons, and record the height measurement.
    - ▫

Tally the Number of Gallons	Number of Gallons
₦₦ ‖	7

- What did you find about our calculation?
    - ▫ *Our calculation was correct. The height is about* 8 *inches.*

Exercise 2 (5 minutes)

- According to the local pet store, turtles need very little water in an aquarium. The suggested amount of water in the aquarium for a turtle is 3 gallons. Determine the height of the water in another aquarium of the same size that is housing a turtle when the amount of water Jamie pours into the tank is 3 gallons.
- Describe how you would estimate the height level?
    - ▫ *First, determine the volume of the water. Then, to determine the missing dimension of height, we need the volume formula* $V = l \cdot w \cdot h$.

Exercise 2

a. Use the table from Example 1 to determine the volume of the aquarium when Jamie pours 3 gallons of water into the tank.

The volume of the tank is $231 \text{ in}^3 \times 3 = 693 \text{ in}^3$.

---

b. Use the volume formula to determine the missing height dimension.

$$693 \text{ in}^3 = 20 \text{ in.} \, (10 \text{ in.}) h$$

$$\frac{693 \text{ in}^3}{200 \text{ in}^2} = \frac{200 \text{ in}^2}{200 \text{ in}^2} h$$

$$3.465 \text{ in.} = h$$

The tank should have a water height of 3.465 in.

Optional Exercise 3

- Let's test it. Begin by pouring water into the aquarium 1 gallon at a time.

- Be sure to keep track of the number of gallons poured. Use a tally system.

- Test the height at 3 gallons, and record the height measurement.

  □

Tally the Number of Gallons	Number of Gallons
				3

- What did you find about our calculation?

  □ *Our calculation was correct. The height is about* $3 \frac{1}{2}$ *inches.*

Exercise 3 (5 minutes)

- Let's say that when Jamie sets up these aquariums of the same size at home, he does not have any tools that measure gallons. What he does have at home is a few leftover one-liter soft drink bottles. How could Jamie calculate the volume of the aquarium?

  □ *Answers will vary but should include that gallons need to be converted to liters.*

- Using the table of values, determine the unit rate for liters to gallons.

- What is the unit rate?

  □ *The unit rate is* 3.785.

- What does this mean?

  □ *Answers will vary. For every gallon of water, there are* 3.785 *liters of water.*

- If this conversion is accurate, determine the number of liters Jamie needs to fill a 10-gallon tank.

  □ $3.785 \dfrac{\text{liters}}{\text{gallon}} \times 10 \text{ gallons} = 37.85 \text{ liters}$

- It is not advantageous to combine liters and inches. Liters and centimeters are both in the metric system of measurement. The ratio of the number of centimeters to the number of inches is 2.54: 1. What does this mean?

  □ *Answers will vary. For every inch, there are* 2.54 *centimeters.*

- What is the unit rate?

  □ *The unit rate is* 2.54.

- Use the conversion to determine the length, the width, and the height of the aquariums in centimeters.

Exercise 3

a. Using the table of values below, determine the unit rate of liters to gallon.

Gallons	Liters
1	3.785
2	7.57
4	15.14

The unit rate is 3.785.

b. Using this conversion, determine the number of liters needed to fill the 10-gallon tank.

$$3.785 \frac{\text{liters}}{\text{gallon}} \times 10 \text{ gallons} = 37.85 \text{ liters}$$

c. The ratio of the number of centimeters to the number of inches is 2.54: 1. What is the unit rate?

2.54

d. Using this information, complete the table to convert the heights of the water in inches to the heights of the water in centimeters Jamie will need for his project at home.

Height (in inches)	Convert to Centimeters	Height (in centimeters)
1	$2.54 \dfrac{\text{centimeters}}{\text{inch}} \times 1 \text{ inch}$	2.54
3.465	$2.54 \dfrac{\text{centimeters}}{\text{inch}} \times 3.465 \text{ inches}$	8.8011
8.085	$2.54 \dfrac{\text{centimeters}}{\text{inch}} \times 8.085 \text{ inches}$	20.5359
11.55	$2.54 \dfrac{\text{centimeters}}{\text{inch}} \times 11.55 \text{ inches}$	29.337

Exercise 4 (5 minutes)

- Jamie had the tanks he used at home shipped from the manufacturer. Typically, the manufacturer sends aquariums already assembled; however, they use plastic film to cover the glass in order to protect it during shipping.

- Determine the amount of plastic film the manufacturer uses to cover the aquarium faces. Draw a sketch of the aquarium to assist in your calculations. Remember that the actual height of the aquarium is 12 inches.

Exercise 4

a. Determine the amount of plastic film the manufacturer uses to cover the aquarium faces. Draw a sketch of the aquarium to assist in your calculations. Remember that the actual height of the aquarium is inches.

$$SA = (2lw) + (2lh) + (2wh)$$

$$SA = (2 \cdot 20 \text{ in.} \cdot 10 \text{ in.}) + (2 \cdot 20 \text{ in.} \cdot 12 \text{ in.}) + (2 \cdot 10 \text{ in.} \cdot 12 \text{ in.})$$

$$SA = 400 \text{ in}^2 + 480 \text{ in}^2 + 240 \text{ in}^2$$

$$SA = 1,120 \text{ in}^2$$

- We do not include the measurement of the top of the aquarium since it is open without glass. It does not need to be covered with film.

---

b. **We do not include the measurement of the top of the aquarium since it is open without glass and does not need to be covered with film. Determine the area of the top of the aquarium, and find the amount of film the manufacturer uses to cover only the sides, front, back, and bottom.**

Area of the top of the aquarium $= l \cdot w$

Area of the top of the aquarium $= 20$ in. $\cdot 10$ in.

Area of the top of the aquarium $= 200$ in^2

SA of aquarium without the top $= 1,120$ in$^2 - 200$ in$^2 = 920$ in^2

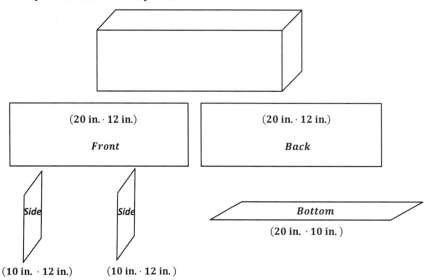

| (20 in. · 12 in.) | (20 in. · 12 in.) |
| *Front* | *Back* |

Side   *Side*   *Bottom*
                                                         (20 in. · 10 in.)

(10 in. · 12 in.)   (10 in. · 12 in.)

c. **Since Jamie needs three aquariums, determine the total surface area of the three aquariums.**

920 in$^2 + 920$ in$^2 + 920$ in$^2 = 2,760$ in^2 *or* $3 \cdot 920$ in$^2 = 2,760$ in^2

Closing/Challenge Exercises (5 minutes)

1. An internet company that sells aquariums charges $300 per aquarium. Jamie is considering building the aquariums at home and buying the parts from a different company that sells glass for $0.11 per square inch. Which option, buying the aquariums already built from the first company or buying the glass and building at home, is a better deal?

Sample Solution:

$2,760$ in$^2 \cdot 0.11 \dfrac{\text{dollars}}{\text{in}^2} = 303.6$ *dollars or* $303.60. *It would be a better deal for Jamie to purchase the aquariums from the company that ships the aquariums because for one aquarium* $303.60 > $300. *For three aquariums, the comparison is* $910.80 > $900.

EUREKA MATH

2. If Jamie wanted to increase the length of the aquarium by 20%, how would that affect the surface area? How would it affect the volume of water the tank could contain?

Sample Solution:

20 in. $\cdot\ 0.20 = 4$ in. *The length of the aquarium would increase by 4 inches.*

20 in. $+4$ in. $= 24$ in. *The new length of the aquarium would be* 24 in.

$SA = 2(24$ in. $\cdot\ 12$ in.$) + 2(24$ in. $\cdot\ 10$ in.$) + 2(10$ in. $\cdot\ 12$ in.$)$

$SA = 576$ in$^2 + 480$ in$^2 + \ 240$ in^2

$SA = 1{,}296$ in^2

The new surface area without the top is $1{,}296$ in$^2 - 288$ in^2, *or* $1{,}008$ in^2.

The new surface area of $1{,}008$ in^2 *is* 88 in^2 *more than the original surface area of* 920 in^2.

$V = l \cdot w \cdot h$

$V = 24$ in. $\cdot\ 12$ in. $\cdot\ 10$ in.

$V = 2{,}880$ in^3

The new volume of $2{,}880$ in^3 *is* 480 in^3 *more than the original volume of* $2{,}400$ in^3.

Exit Ticket (3 minutes)

Lesson 19a: Applying Surface Area and Volume to Aquariums   **311**

©2015 Great Minds. eureka-math.org
G6-M5-TE-B5-1.3.1-01.2016

Name _____   Date _____

Lesson 19a: Applying Surface Area and Volume to Aquariums

Exit Ticket

What did you learn today? Describe at least one situation in real life that would draw on the skills you used today.

Exit Ticket Sample Solution

What did you learn today? Describe at least one situation in real life that would draw on the skills you used today.

Answers will vary.

Problem Set Sample Solutions

This Problem Set is a culmination of skills learned in this module. Note that the figures are not drawn to scale.

1. Calculate the area of the figure below.

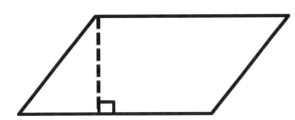

$A = bh$
$A = (40 \text{ ft.})(20 \text{ ft.})$
$A = 800 \text{ ft}^2$

2. Calculate the area of the figure below.

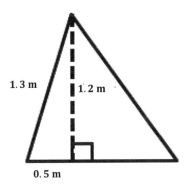

1.3 m

1.2 m

0.5 m

$A = \frac{1}{2}bh$
$A = \frac{1}{2}(1.3 \text{ m})(1.2 \text{ m})$
$A = 0.78 \text{ m}^2$

3. Calculate the area of the figure below.

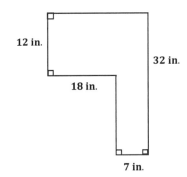

12 in.

32 in.

18 in.

7 in.

Area of top rectangle:
$A = lw$
$A = (25 \text{ in.})(12 \text{ in.})$
$A = 300 \text{ in}^2$

Area of bottom rectangle:
$A = lw$
$A = (7 \text{ in.})(20 \text{ in.})$
$A = 140 \text{ in}^2$

Total Area $= 300 \text{ in}^2 + 140 \text{ in}^2 = 440 \text{ in}^2$

©2015 Great Minds. eureka-math.org
G6-M5-TE-B5-1.3.1-01.2016

4. Complete the table using the diagram on the coordinate plane.

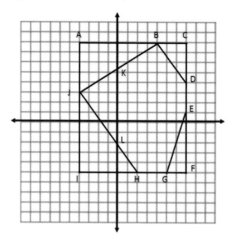

Line Segment	Point	Point	Distance	Proof
$\overline{AB}$	$(-4, 8)$	$(4, 8)$	8	$|-4| + |4| = 8$
$\overline{CE}$	$(7, 8)$	$(7, 1)$	7	$|8| - |1| = 7$
$\overline{GI}$	$(5, -5)$	$(-4, -5)$	9	$|5| + |-4| = 9$
$\overline{HI}$	$(2, -5)$	$(-4, -5)$	6	$|2| + |-4| = 6$
$\overline{IJ}$	$(-4, -5)$	$(-4, 3)$	8	$|-5| + |3| = 8$
$\overline{AI}$	$(-4, 8)$	$(-4, -5)$	13	$|8| + |-5| = 13$
$\overline{AJ}$	$(-4, 8)$	$(-4, 3)$	5	$|8| - |3| = 5$

5. Plot the points below, and draw the shape. Then, determine the area of the polygon.

$A(-3, 5), B(4, 3), C(0, -5)$

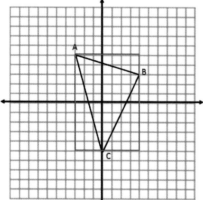

Area of Rectangle:

$$\text{Area} = lw$$
$$\text{Area} = (7 \text{ units})(10 \text{ units})$$
$$\text{Area} = 70 \text{ units}^2$$

Area of Triangle on Left:

$$\text{Area} = \frac{1}{2}bh$$
$$\text{Area} = \frac{1}{2}(3 \text{ units})(10 \text{ units})$$
$$\text{Area} = 15 \text{ units}^2$$

Area of Triangle on Top:

$$\text{Area on top} = \frac{1}{2}bh$$
$$\text{Area} = \frac{1}{2}(7 \text{ units})(2 \text{ units})$$
$$\text{Area} = 7 \text{ units}^2$$

Area of Triangle on Right:

$$\text{Area} = \frac{1}{2}bh$$
$$\text{Area} = \frac{1}{2}(4 \text{ units})(8 \text{ units})$$
$$\text{Area} = 16 \text{ units}^2$$

Total Area $= 70 \text{ units}^2 - 15 \text{ units}^2 - 7 \text{ units}^2 - 16 \text{ units}^2$

Total Area $= 32 \text{ units}^2$

EUREKA
MATH™

6. Determine the volume of the figure.

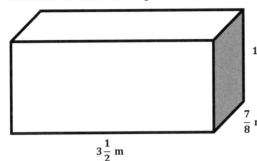

$$V = l\,w\,h$$
$$V = \left(3\frac{1}{2}\text{ m}\right)\left(\frac{7}{8}\text{ m}\right)\left(1\frac{1}{4}\text{ m}\right)$$
$$V = \frac{245}{64}\text{ m}^3$$
$$V = 3\frac{53}{64}\text{ m}^3$$

7. Give at least three more expressions that could be used to determine the volume of the figure in Problem 6.

    Answers will vary. Some examples include the following:

$$\left(\frac{35}{32}\text{ m}^2\right)\left(3\frac{1}{2}\text{ m}\right)$$
$$\left(1\frac{1}{4}\text{ m}\right)\left(\frac{7}{8}\text{ m}\right)\left(3\frac{1}{2}\text{ m}\right)$$
$$\left(\frac{49}{16}\text{ m}^2\right)\left(1\frac{1}{4}\text{ m}\right)$$

8. Determine the volume of the irregular figure.

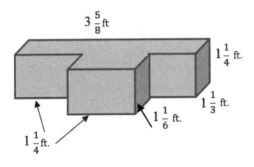

Volume of the back Rectangular Prism:
$$V = l\,w\,h$$
$$V = \left(3\frac{5}{8}\text{ ft.}\right)\left(1\frac{1}{3}\text{ ft.}\right)\left(1\frac{1}{4}\text{ ft.}\right)$$
$$V = \frac{580}{96}\text{ ft}^3$$

Volume of the front Rectangular Prism:
$$V = l\,w\,h$$
$$V = \left(1\frac{1}{4}\text{ ft.}\right)\left(1\frac{1}{6}\text{ ft.}\right)\left(1\frac{1}{4}\text{ ft.}\right)$$
$$V = \frac{175}{96}\text{ ft}^3$$

$$\text{Total Volume} = \frac{580}{96}\text{ ft}^3 + \frac{175}{96}\text{ ft}^3 = \frac{755}{96}\text{ ft}^3 = 7\frac{83}{96}\text{ ft}^3$$

9. Draw and label a net for the following figure. Then, use the net to determine the surface area of the figure.

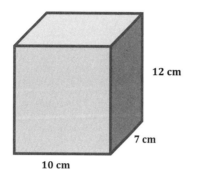

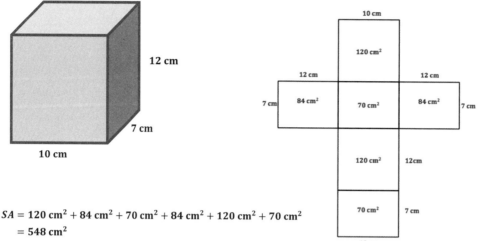

$$SA = 120 \text{ cm}^2 + 84 \text{ cm}^2 + 70 \text{ cm}^2 + 84 \text{ cm}^2 + 120 \text{ cm}^2 + 70 \text{ cm}^2$$
$$= 548 \text{ cm}^2$$

10. Determine the surface area of the figure in Problem 9 using the formula $SA = 2lw + 2lh + 2wh$. Then, compare your answer to the solution in Problem 9.

$SA = 2lw + 2lh + 2wh$

$SA = 2(10 \text{ cm})(7 \text{ cm}) + 2(10 \text{ cm})(12 \text{ cm}) + 2(7 \text{ cm})(12 \text{ cm})$

$SA = 140 \text{ cm}^2 + 240 \text{ cm}^2 + 168 \text{ cm}^2$

$SA = 548 \text{ cm}^2$

The answer in Problem 10 is the same as in Problem 9. The formula finds the areas of each pair of equal faces and adds them together, like we did with the net.

11. A parallelogram has a base of 4.5 cm and an area of 9.495 cm². Tania wrote the equation $4.5x = 9.495$ to represent this situation.

    a. Explain what x represents in the equation.

    x represents the height of the parallelogram in centimeters.

    b. Solve the equation for x and determine the height of the parallelogram.

    $$\frac{4.5x}{4.5} = \frac{9.495}{4.5}$$
    $$x = 2.11$$

    The height of the parallelogram is 2.11 cm.

12. Triangle A has an area equal to one-third the area of Triangle B. Triangle A has an area of $3\frac{1}{2}$ square meters.

    a. Gerard wrote the equation $\frac{B}{3} = 3\frac{1}{2}$. Explain what B represents in the equation.

    B represents the area of Triangle B in square meters.

    b. Determine the area of Triangle B.

    $$\frac{B}{3} \cdot 3 = 3\frac{1}{2} \cdot 3$$

    The area of Triangle B is $10\frac{1}{2}$ square meters.

Name _____   Date _____

1. The juice box pictured below is 4 inches high, 3 inches long, and 2 inches wide.

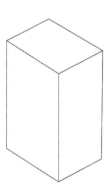 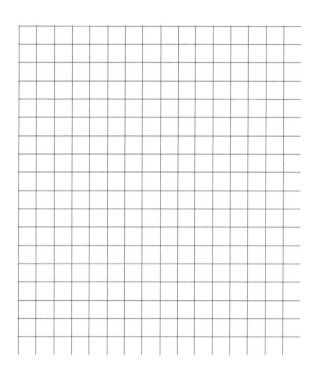

a. In the grid above, the distance between grid lines represents one inch. Use the grid paper to sketch the net of the juice box.

b. Find the surface area of the juice box. Show your work.

c. Find the volume of the juice box. Show your work.

2. The Cubic Crystal Company has a new Crystal Cube they want to sell. The packaging manager insists that the cubes be arranged to form a rectangular prism and that the package be designed to hold the Crystal Cubes exactly, with no leftover packaging. Each Crystal Cube measures 1 in. × 1 in. × 1 in. There are 24 Crystal Cubes to be sold in a box.

   a. What are the dimensions of the possible box designs in inches?

Height	Width	Length

   b. Which Crystal Cube box design will use the least amount of cardboard for packaging? Justify your answer as completely as you can.

Height	Width	Length	Surface Area

   c. Another type of cube is the Mini Crystal Cube, which has an edge length of $\frac{3}{4}$ inch. What is the volume in cubic inches of one Mini Crystal Cube? Show your work.

Module 5:   Area, Surface Area, and Volume Problems

EUREKA
MATH

©2015 Great Minds. eureka-math.org
G6-M5-TE-B5-1.3.1-01.2016

3. Which of these nets can be folded to form a cube?

A 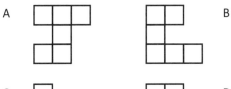   B

C 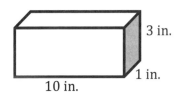   D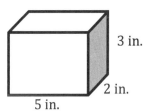

4. Which box below has the larger surface area?

3 in.
1 in.
10 in.

3 in.
2 in.
5 in.

5. a. Draw a polygon in the coordinate plane using the given coordinates.

$$(4, -4)$$
$$(6, -2)$$
$$(8, -6)$$

b. Calculate the area of the polygon.

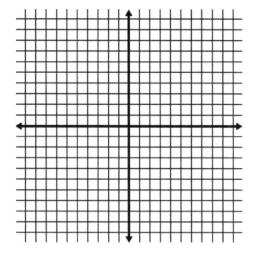

6. Eaglecrest Elementary School is creating a vegetable garden at the school.

a. What is the area of the garden?

Module 5:   Area, Surface Area, and Volume Problems

EUREKA
MATH™

b. After more discussion, Eaglecrest decided to change the location of the garden so that the vegetables can get more sunlight. Below is the new garden.

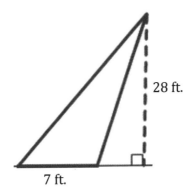

28 ft.

7 ft.

In which garden can Eaglecrest students plant more vegetables? Explain your reasoning.

A Progression Toward Mastery

Assessment Task Item		STEP 1 Missing or incorrect answer and little evidence of reasoning or application of mathematics to solve the problem	STEP 2 Missing or incorrect answer but evidence of some reasoning or application of mathematics to solve the problem	STEP 3 A correct answer with some evidence of reasoning or application of mathematics to solve the problem, OR an incorrect answer with substantial evidence of solid reasoning or application of mathematics to solve the problem	STEP 4 A correct answer supported by substantial evidence of solid reasoning or application of mathematics to solve the problem
1	a 6.G.A.4	Student sketch does not contain 6 rectangles.	Student sketch contains 6 rectangles but not 3 different sizes (two each of 2×3, 2×4, and 3×4); they are arranged in a way that will not fold into a rectangular solid.	Student sketch contains 6 rectangles of 3 different sizes (two each of 2×3, 2×4, and 3×4); however, they are arranged in a way that will not fold into a rectangular solid.	Student sketch is one of many nets of a $2 \times 3 \times 4$ rectangular solid. Here is one example: Critical performance indicators: The net must have 6 rectangles of 3 different sizes (two each of 2×3, 2×4, and 3×4), similar rectangles must not be adjacent to one another, and the net must fold to a $2 \times 3 \times 4$ rectangular solid.
	b 6.G.A.4	Student response does not include the use of a formula and is incorrect (52 in²).	Student uses a formula other than $SA = 2(l \cdot w + l \cdot h + w \cdot h)$, or equivalent, to make the calculation. Alternatively, the volume may have been calculated.	Student uses the formula $SA = 2(l \cdot w + l \cdot h + w \cdot h)$, or equivalent, to make the calculation, but an arithmetic error results in an incorrect final answer. Alternatively, the correct number is calculated, and the units (in²) are incorrect.	Student uses the formula $SA = 2(l \cdot w + l \cdot h + w \cdot h)$, or equivalent, to make the calculation, and the surface area of the box is correctly found (52 in²). Both number and units are correct.

EUREKA
MATH™

	c **6.G.A.2**	Student response does not include the use of a formula and is incorrect (24 in^3).	Student uses a formula other than $V = l \cdot w \cdot h$, or equivalent, to make the calculation. Alternatively, the surface area may have been calculated.	Student uses the formula $V = l \cdot w \cdot h$, or equivalent, to make the calculation, but an arithmetic error results in an incorrect final answer. Alternatively, the correct number is calculated, and the units (in^3) are incorrect.	Student uses the formula $V = l \cdot w \cdot h$, or equivalent, to make the calculation, and the volume of the box is correctly found (24 in^3). Both number and units are correct.
2	**a** **6.G.A.2**	Student response includes none or only one of the six possible configurations of the box.	Student response includes at least two of the six possible configurations of the box.	Student response includes at least four of the six possible configurations of the box.	Student response includes all six possible configurations of the box (all measurements in inches): $1 \times 1 \times 24$, $1 \times 2 \times 12$, $1 \times 3 \times 8$, $1 \times 4 \times 6$, $2 \times 2 \times 6$, and $2 \times 3 \times 4$. **L / W / H table:** 1 in. / 1 in. / 24 in. 1 in. / 2 in. / 12 in. 1 in. / 3 in. / 8 in. 1 in. / 4 in. / 6 in. 2 in. / 2 in. / 6 in. 2 in. / 3 in. / 4 in.
	b **6.G.A.4**	Student response does not include a calculation for the surface area of any of the box designs.	Student response includes calculations for at least two of the six possible configurations of the box. The smallest number of these calculations is chosen as the box needing the least amount of cardboard.	Student response includes calculations for at least four of the six possible configurations of the box. The smallest number of these calculations is chosen as the box needing the least amount of cardboard.	Student calculates the surface area of all six boxes correctly. **L / W / H / SA table:** 1 in. / 1 in. / 24 in. / 98 in² 1 in. / 2 in. / 12 in. / 76 in² 1 in. / 3 in. / 8 in. / 70 in² 1 in. / 4 in. / 6 in. / 68 in² 2 in. / 2 in. / 6 in. / 56 in² 2 in. / 3 in. / 4 in. / 52 in² Student concludes that the minimum surface area is found to be on the 2 in.× 3 in.× 4 in. box. That box needs the least amount of cardboard.
	c **6.G.A.2**	Student response does not include a length, width, and height of a Crystal Cube.	Student response includes length, width, and height dimensions other than $\frac{3}{4}$ in. $\times \frac{3}{4}$ in. $\times \frac{3}{4}$ in.	Student response includes $\frac{3}{4}$ in. $\times \frac{3}{4}$ in. $\times \frac{3}{4}$ in. but is calculated incorrectly.	Student correctly calculates the volume of a single Crystal Cube: $\frac{3}{4}$ in. $\times \frac{3}{4}$ in. $\times \frac{3}{4}$ in. $= \frac{27}{64}$ in^3.

©2015 Great Minds. eureka-math.org
G6-M5-TE-B5-1.3.1-01.2016

3	6.G.A.4	Student response does not include choice D.	Student response includes choice D and two or three other (incorrect) choices.	Student response includes choice D and one other (incorrect) choice.	Student response is choice D only.
4	6.G.A.4	Student is not able to calculate the surface area of either rectangular prism.	Student is able to calculate the surface area, but calculations may have mathematical errors.	Student calculates the surface area of one prism correctly but one incorrectly. OR Student calculates both surface areas correctly but does not answer the question.	Student finds the surface area of the prisms to be 86 in^2 and 62 in^2. The student also states that the prism with dimensions $10 \text{ in.} \times 1 \text{ in.} \times 3 \text{ in.}$ has the larger surface area.
5	a 6.G.A.3	Student does not plot any of the points correctly.	Student plots the points backwards. For example, student may have plotted the points $(-4, 4)$, $(-2, 6)$, and $(-6, 8)$.	Student plots two of the three points correctly.	Student plots all three points correctly.
	b 6.G.A.3	Student does not calculate the area.	Student counts the squares inside the shape by estimating the parts of squares that are part of the area.	Student uses the area of rectangles and/or triangles to calculate the area of the shape but does so incorrectly.	Student uses the area of rectangles and/or triangles to calculate the area of the shape and correctly calculates 6 square units as the area.
6	a 6.G.A.1	Student does not calculate the area.	Student calculates the area incorrectly, perhaps using the wrong dimensions.	Student calculates the area correctly but does not label the answer.	Student calculates the area correctly and labels accurately 150 ft^2.
	b 6.G.A.1	Student does not calculate the area.	Student calculates the area of the new garden but does not divide by 2.	Student calculates the area of both shapes correctly but does not answer the question.	Student calculates the area of both shapes correctly and explains that the original garden has a larger area because 150 ft^2 is larger than 98 ft^2; therefore, students can plant more vegetables in the original garden.

Name _____   Date _____

1. The juice box pictured below is 4 inches high, 3 inches long, and 2 inches wide.

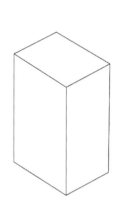

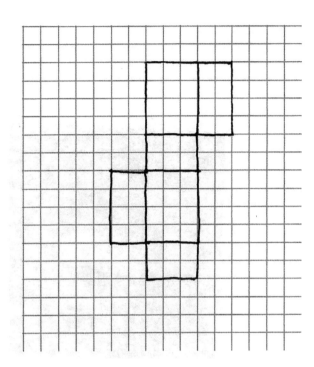

a. In the grid above, the distance between grid lines represents one inch. Use the grid paper to sketch the net of the juice box.

b. Find the surface area of the juice box. Show your work.

$$SA = 2(\ell \cdot w + \ell \cdot h + w \cdot h)$$
$$SA = 2(3in \cdot 2in. + 3in. \cdot 4in. + 2in. \cdot 4in.)$$
$$SA = 2(6in.^2 + 12in.^2 + 8in.^2)$$
$$SA = 2(26\ in.^2)$$
$$SA = 52\ in.^2$$

c. Find the volume of the juice box. Show your work.

$$V = \ell \cdot w \cdot h$$
$$V = 3in. \cdot 2in. \cdot 4in.$$
$$V = 24\ in.^3$$

©2015 Great Minds. eureka-math.org
G6-M5-TE-B5-1.3.1-01.2016

2. The Cubic Crystal Company has a new Crystal Cube they want to sell. The packaging manager insists that the cubes be arranged to form a rectangular prism and that the package be designed to hold the Crystal Cubes exactly, with no leftover packaging. Each Crystal Cube measures 1 in. × 1 in. × 1 in. There are 24 Crystal Cubes to be sold in a box.

   a. What are the dimensions of the possible box designs in inches?

Height	Width	Length
1 in	1 in	24 in
1 in	2 in	12 in
1 in	3 in	8 in
1 in	4 in	6 in
2 in	2 in	6 in
2 in	3 in	4 in

   b. Which Crystal Cube box design will use the least amount of cardboard for packaging? Justify your answer as completely as you can.

Height	Width	Length	Surface Area
1 in	1 in	24 in	98 in²
1 in	2 in	12 in	76 in²
1 in	3 in	8 in	70 in²
1 in	4 in	6 in	68 in²
2 in	2 in	6 in	56 in²
2 in	3 in	4 in	52 in²

   The minimum surface area is found to be on the 2in × 3in × 4in box. That box needs the least amount of cardboard.

   c. Another type of cube is the Mini Crystal Cube, which has an edge length of $\frac{3}{4}$ inch. What is the volume in cubic inches of one Mini Crystal Cube? Show your work.

   $$V = l \cdot w \cdot h$$
   $$V = \frac{3}{4} \text{ in.} \cdot \frac{3}{4} \text{ in.} \cdot \frac{3}{4} \text{ in.}$$
   $$V = \frac{27}{64} \text{ in.}^3$$

EUREKA MATH

©2015 Great Minds. eureka-math.org
G6-M5-TE-B5-1.3.1-01.2016

3. Which of these nets can be folded to form a cube?

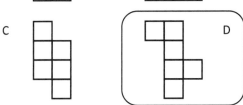

A   B

C   D

4. Which box below has the larger surface area?

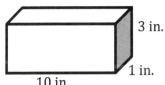

3 in.

1 in.

10 in.

3 in.

2 in.

5 in.

$SA = 2(l \cdot w + l \cdot h + w \cdot h)$
$SA = 2(10in \cdot 1in + 10in \cdot 3in + 1in \cdot 3in)$
$SA = 2(10in^2 + 30in^2 + 3in^2)$
$SA = 2(43in^2)$
$SA = 86 in^2$

This box has the larger surface area.

$SA = 2(l \cdot w + l \cdot h + w \cdot h)$
$SA = 2(5in \cdot 2in + 5in \cdot 3in + 2in \cdot 3in)$
$SA = 2(10in^2 + 15in^2 + 6in^2)$
$SA = 2(31 in^2)$
$SA = 62 in^2$

5. a. Draw a polygon in the coordinate plane using the given coordinates.

$$(4, -4)$$
$$(6, -2)$$
$$(8, -6)$$

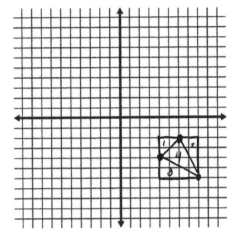

b. Calculate the area of the polygon.

Area of Square:
A = l·w or s²
A = 4u·4u or (4u)²
A = 16u²

Area of Δ1:
A = ½ b·h
A = ½ · 2u·2u
A = 2u²

Area of Δ2:
Area = ½ bh
A = ½ · 2u·4u
A = 4u²

Area of Δ3:
A = ½ bh
A = ½ · 2u·4u
A = 4u²

Area Δ4 = 16u² − 2u² − 4u² − 4u² = 6u²

6. Eaglecrest Elementary School is creating a vegetable garden at the school.

8 ft. [parallelogram diagram] 6 ft.

25 ft.

a. What is the area of the garden?

A = b·h
A = 25 ft · 6 ft
A = 150 ft²

EUREKA
MATH

b. After more discussion, Eaglecrest decided to change the location of the garden so that the vegetables can get more sunlight. Below is the new garden.

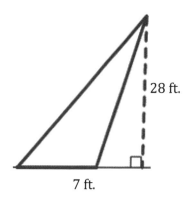

28 ft.

7 ft.

In which garden can Eaglecrest students plant more vegetables? Explain your reasoning.

$$A = \tfrac{1}{2}bh$$
$$A = \tfrac{1}{2}(7ft. \cdot 28 ft.)$$
$$A = \tfrac{1}{2}(196 ft.^2)$$
$$A = 98 ft.^2$$

The students of Eaglecrest can plant more vegetables in original garden in the shape of the parallelogram. It has a larger area than the triangular garden.

This page intentionally left blank